LISREL 8:
User's Reference Guide

LISREL® 8

User's Reference Guide

Karl G. Jöreskog and Dag Sörbom

Uppsala University

SSI SCIENTIFIC SOFTWARE INTERNATIONAL

LISREL® 8: User's Reference Guide

Copyright © 1996–2001 by Karl G. Jöreskog and Dag Sörbom.

Edited by Leo Stam

Cover by M. James Scott.

Based on an architectural detail from Frank Lloyd Wright's Robie House.

ISBN: 0–89498–040–8

4 5 6 7 8 9 0   04 03 02 01 (second edition; updated to LISREL 8)

Published by:

Scientific Software International, Inc.
7383 North Lincoln Avenue, Suite 100
Lincolnwood, IL 60712–1704, USA
Tel: (847) 675–0720
Fax: (847) 675–2140
Web: *http://www.ssicentral.com*

Note from the editor on the second edition

The LISREL 7 User's Reference Guide was first published in 1989. In 1993, SSI published a major upgrade of the program: LISREL 8.

The authors, Prof. Karl G. Jöreskog and Prof. Dag Sörbom, described the improvements that were made in a paper: *New features in LISREL 8*. SSI published this paper as an insert together with the original *LISREL 7 User's Reference Guide* as the temporary *LISREL 8 User's Reference Guide*. Meanwhile, the authors have undertaken a complete rewrite of the LISREL and PRELIS documentation.

Because this task is taking longer than anticipated, SSI sought and received permission from the authors to integrate those two separate pieces into one document, thereby creating a more accessible product for the user of the program, without making substantive changes to the text.

Chapter 2 has been updated and now describes the current state of the program. Commands, keywords and options that have become obsolete with LISREL 8 have been deleted and the new commands, keywords and options added.

The former insert now appears as Appendix A (*New features in LISREL 8*) and Appendix B (*Syntax overview*). As a result, the list of references, the subject index, and the author index are integrated for the LISREL 8 documentation.

The methodological background for the program together with the examples is still spread out over different parts: Chapter 1 has the old LISREL 7 text, while Appendix A describes the improvements and new features. The new examples can also be found in that appendix; the LISREL 7 examples — still very useful — are in Chapters 3 through 10.

At the same time, the whole documentation has been redone with the LaTeX computer typesetting system so that it now conforms with the other LISREL documentation.

Preface

This edition of the LISREL 7 manual is designed for reference use with all versions of the program: Mainframe, UNIX, MAC, and PC. In addition to digests of the main chapters of *LISREL 7: A Guide to the Program and Applications* (Jöreskog & Sörbom, 1989), it contains detailed command summaries and an overview of the program input and output. All of this material is contained in Chapter 2. Chapter 1 summarizes the LISREL model and analytical procedures. Chapters 3 through 6 present sample problem setups for the various LISREL models in the one-group case. Chapter 7 considers dichotomous, ordinal and nonnormal data, and Chapter 8 suggests methods for constraining parameters, calculating power, and discusses problems with equivalent models. Chapter 9 introduces the multiple group case. Chapter 10 discusses models with mean structures. Finally, Chapter 11 contains hints for handling hard-to-analyze models.

The present guide and the *PRELIS 2 User's Reference Guide* (Jöreskog & Sörbom, 1996) contain all the information required for successful and productive use of PRELIS and/or LISREL 7. For more extensive discussion of LISREL theory and applications, the user should consult *LISREL 7: A Guide to the Program and Applications*.

We acknowledge the support of the *Swedish Council for Research in the Humanities and the Social Sciences*, Research Program for *Multivariate Statistical Analysis*. Carina Skoog-Eriksson and Suzanne Lindman typed the original manuscript, and Peter Götlind set it in TEX. Leo Stam and Werner Wothke assisted in editing the present version, and the former produced the final TEX copy.

We also wish to thank the following persons who helped test the present version of LISREL: Alan Acock, Cheryl Adkins, Kenneth Bollen, Fritz Drasgow, William Finley, Edgar Johns, Michael Neale, Joy Newmann, Ruth O'Brien, Niels Waller, Werner Wothke, and Catherine Zimmer.

LISREL 7 versus LISREL 6

Compatibility of input

A command file prepared for LISREL 6 will run on LISREL 7 with the following exceptions.

- ☐ The default value of NO (number of cases, sample size) on the DA command has been changed from 100 to 0. When a covariance, correlation or other moment matrix is to be read, NO must be specified or the program will stop.

- ☐ If there are fixed zero elements in the diagonals of $\Phi, \Psi, \Theta_\epsilon$, or Θ_δ, AD=OFF must be set on the OU command. More generally, this must be done for all models which, by definition, prevent these matrices from being positive definite. See section *Admissibility of the estimates* on page 25.

- ☐ The default value for the *maximum number of iterations* (IT) has been changed to three times the number of free parameters in the model. In LISREL 6, this value was 250.

- ☐ LISREL 7 handles *missing values by listwise deletion only*. For pairwise deletion or any other raw data problems, the companion program PRELIS produces the relevant covariance or correlation matrix, see section *PRELIS* on page 15. LISREL 7 assumes that there is a global numeric value XM assigned to represent all missing values in the whole data matrix (keyword XM on the DA command). With PRELIS, one can have different missing value representations for different variables. The MV keyword and PP option of Mainframe LISREL 6 are no longer supported. Use PRELIS to compute polychoric and polyserial correlations.

- ☐ LISREL 7 checks that a scale has been defined for each latent variable as described in section *Instrumental variables and two-stage least squares* on page 17. If a scale for a latent variable has not been specified in this way, the program will stop unless the SO option appears on the OU command.

Compatibility of output

The output from LISREL 7 may differ in many ways from that obtained by LISREL 6. The output has been reorganized so that many sections appear in a different order. Also, many sections contain other and/or additional information. Note particularly the following.

- ☐ The options MR, RS, and EF on the OU command have slightly different meanings:

    MR produces covariances between the observed and latent variables. These covariances were previously included in tables produced by the option VA. In LISREL 6, the option MR was equivalent to VA, RS and EF. Now MR is equivalent to VA, which is now obsolete.

    RS still produces matrices of fitted and standardized residuals and a Q-plot of standardized residuals. But stemleaf plots of fitted and standardized residuals are produced *without* RS. This is convenient to avoid large matrices in the output. The fitted covariance matrix will be included in the output, when RS is specified.

    EF produces both *total* and *indirect* effects and, when used in combination with SE, it produces *standard errors* of total and indirect effects.

- ☐ Because of improvements of the iterative algorithm LISREL 7 will successfully run many problems that did not run with LISREL 6.

- ☐ New and improved methods of initial estimates (IV and TSLS) may produce different values, especially when equality constraints are imposed. Differences may also result when starting values are explicitly given for free parameters.

- ☐ The methods ULS, GLS, and ML produce the same parameter estimates in LISREL 6 and LISREL 7. GLS and ML produce the same standard errors, t-values, and χ^2 in LISREL 6 and LISREL 7. Improved methods of estimating modification indices, in particular in the context of equality constraints, may produce different results in LISREL 6 and LISREL 7.

- ☐ An error in GFI for GLS has been corrected so that GFI will differ between LISREL 6 and LISREL 7 for method GLS but not for ULS and ML. As a consequence, AGFI will also differ. See the sections *Methods of estimation* on page 17 and *Evaluation of the LISREL solution* on page 25.

- ☐ Standardized residuals (called normalized residuals in LISREL 6) may differ considerably between LISREL 6 and LISREL 7. An oversimplified formula for the asymptotic variances of the residuals was used in LISREL 6. A formula, which requires much more computations, but yields asymptotically correct variances, is used in LISREL 7. See section *Residuals* on page 30.

- ☐ The parameter plot in LISREL 6 is a plot of the *marginal* fit function against a specified parameter. By contrast, LISREL 7 plots the *concentrated* fit function. This takes much more time but gives a more useful plot.

Features included in LISREL 7 but not in LISREL 6

- ☐ A thorough check of the syntax in the LISREL command file in the same way it is done in PRELIS.

- ☐ An *admissibility check* of the model with options to stop before iterations begin or after a specified number of iterations if a non-admissible solution is produced. See section *Admissibility of the estimates* on page 25.

- ☐ Two new estimation methods, WLS and DWLS, have been added to those already available in LISREL 6 and a unified approach to estimation is now taken. WLS requires an asymptotic covariance matrix produced by PRELIS. This method produces asymptotically correct standard errors and χ^2 values under non-normality and when one or more of the observed variables are ordinal. WLS is particularly important when analyzing polychoric and/or polyserial correlations. Note that the computational requirements for WLS become demanding as the number of variables increases. A reasonable compromise between normal theory ML or GLS and non-normal WLS may be DWLS which requires only the asymptotic variances of estimated correlations (or variances and covariances). These asymptotic variances are also obtained by PRELIS.

- ☐ Standard errors, t-values, standardized residuals and χ^2 goodness-of-fit values can now be obtained for method ULS. These are correct under standard normal theory.

❏ The *Ridge Option* is a new feature in LISREL 7. This option handles covariance and correlation matrices which are not positive definite. If the covariance or correlation matrix to be analyzed is not positive definite, a constant times the diagonal is added to the diagonal before iterations begin. This *Ridge Constant* is automatically determined by the program or can be be specified by the user. See the OU command in Chapter 2.

The Ridge Option is particularly useful in econometric models containing identities and in regression models with high multicollinearity among the regressors. See Chapter 4.

The Ridge Option may also be chosen even if the covariance or correlation matrix to be analyzed is positive definite. This adds a whole new class of estimation methods. The Ridge Option may be used in combination with all the iterative methods ULS, GLS, ML, WLS, and DWLS. Methods IV and TSLS are not affected by the Ridge Option.

❏ The modification indices will now work with all iterative estimation methods and have been extended and supplied with tables of the estimated change in each parameter potentially to be relaxed. This indicates how sensitive the model is to changes in each parameter and gives information about the power of the χ^2 measure.

❏ Stemleaf plots of residuals and standardized residuals are obtained in the standard output. These are useful in the assessment of fit.

❏ Both *indirect* and total effects are given and *standard errors* of these will be obtained by requesting both SE and EF on the OU command.

❏ The LISREL model has been extended to include four new parameter matrices, see Chapter 10. Models with mean parameters (intercept terms and mean values of latent variables) can now be specified directly. This makes it much easier to analyze models with mean structures.

Karl G. Jöreskog and Dag Sörbom   January 1989

Contents

List of tables

List of figures

List of examples
(with input and data files)

This book has many examples illustrating most of the common types of models and methods used with LISREL. For beginners of LISREL it is instructive to go over these examples to learn how to set up the command file for particular models and problems. We also suggest using these examples as exercises in the following ways:

- Estimate the same model with a different method of estimation
- Estimate the same model from correlations instead of covariances or vice versa
- Request other options for the output
- Formulate and test hypotheses about the parameters of the model
- Estimate a different model for the same data
- Make deliberate mistakes in the input file and see what happens

Input and data files for these examples are included with the program on the distribution diskettes. For these files we use the following naming conventions.

The first part in the filename refers to the example in the book. Thus, EX72B means Example 7.2B. Command files have the suffix .LS8 for LISREL 8 files and .PR2 for PRELIS 2 files. The suffix after the period in the name of a data file refers to the type of data it contains:

- LAB for labels
- COV for covariance matrix
- COR for correlation matrix
- RAW for raw data

- DAT for a file containing several types of data
- PML for matrix of polychoric (and polyserial) correlations produced by PRELIS under listwise deletion
- KML for matrix of product-moment correlations (based on raw scores or normal scores) produced by PRELIS under listwise deletion
- ACP for asymptotic covariance matrix of the elements of a PML matrix produced by PRELIS
- ACK for asymptotic covariance matrix of the elements of a KML matrix produced by PRELIS

1   LISREL models and methods

The LISREL model, in its most general form, consists of two parts: the measurement model and the structural equation model.

The **measurement model** specifies how latent variables or hypothetical constructs depend upon or are indicated by the observed variables. It describes the measurement properties (reliabilities and validities) of the observed variables.

The **structural equation model** specifies the causal relationships among the latent variables, describes the causal effects, and assigns the explained and unexplained variance.

The LISREL method estimates the unknown coefficients of a set of linear structural equations. It is particularly designed to accommodate models that include latent variables, measurement errors in both dependent and independent variables, reciprocal causation, simultaneity, and interdependence.

As implemented in the LISREL 7 program, the method includes as special cases such procedures as confirmatory factor analysis, multiple regression analysis, path analysis, economic models for time-dependent data, recursive and non-recursive models for cross-sectional and longitudinal data, and covariance structure models.

1.1   The general LISREL model

The full LISREL model for single samples is defined, for deviations about the mean, by the following three equations:

The structural equation model:

$$\eta = \mathbf{B}\eta + \mathbf{\Gamma}\xi + \zeta \tag{1.1}$$

The measurement model for **y**:

$$\mathbf{y} = \mathbf{\Lambda}_y\eta + \epsilon \tag{1.2}$$

The measurement model for **x**:

$$\mathbf{x} = \mathbf{\Lambda}_x\xi + \delta \tag{1.3}$$

The terms in these models are defined as follows:

    y   is a $p \times 1$ vector of observed response or outcome variables.

    x   is a $q \times 1$ vector of predictors, covariates, or input variables.

    η is an $m \times 1$ random vector of latent dependent, or endogenous, variables.

    ξ is an $n \times 1$ random vector of latent independent, or exogenous, variables.

    ϵ is a $p \times 1$ vector of measurement errors in **y**.

    δ is a $q \times 1$ vector of measurement errors in **x**.

    $\mathbf{\Lambda}_y$ is a $p \times m$ matrix of coefficients of the regression of **y** on η.

    $\mathbf{\Lambda}_x$ is a $q \times n$ matrix of coefficients of the regression of **x** on ξ.

    $\mathbf{\Gamma}$ is an $m \times n$ matrix of coefficients of the ξ-variables in the structural relationship.

    B   is an $m \times m$ matrix of coefficients of the η-variables in the structural relationship. **B** has zeros in the diagonal, and $\mathbf{I} - \mathbf{B}$ is required to be non-singular.

    ζ is an $m \times 1$ vector of equation errors (random disturbances) in the structural relationship between η and ξ.

Assumptions

The random components in the LISREL model are assumed to satisfy the following minimal assumptions:

    ϵ is uncorrelated with η

    δ is uncorrelated with ξ

    ζ is uncorrelated with ξ

ζ, ϵ, and δ are mutually uncorrelated

Covariance matrices:

$$\text{Cov}(\boldsymbol{\xi}) = \boldsymbol{\Phi}\ (n \times n) \qquad \text{Cov}(\boldsymbol{\zeta}) = \boldsymbol{\Psi}\ (m \times m)$$
$$\text{Cov}(\boldsymbol{\epsilon}) = \boldsymbol{\Theta}_\epsilon\ (p \times p) \qquad \text{Cov}(\boldsymbol{\delta}) = \boldsymbol{\Theta}_\delta\ (q \times q)$$

The covariance matrix of the observations as implied by the LISREL model

The assumptions in the previous section imply the following form for the covariance matrix of the observed variables:

$$\boldsymbol{\Sigma} = \begin{pmatrix} \boldsymbol{\Lambda}_y \mathbf{A}(\boldsymbol{\Gamma}\boldsymbol{\Phi}\boldsymbol{\Gamma}' + \boldsymbol{\Psi})\mathbf{A}'\boldsymbol{\Lambda}'_y + \boldsymbol{\Theta}_\epsilon & \boldsymbol{\Lambda}_y \mathbf{A}\boldsymbol{\Gamma}\boldsymbol{\Phi}\boldsymbol{\Lambda}'_x \\ \boldsymbol{\Lambda}_x \boldsymbol{\Phi}\boldsymbol{\Gamma}'\mathbf{A}'\boldsymbol{\Lambda}'_y & \boldsymbol{\Lambda}_x\boldsymbol{\Phi}\boldsymbol{\Lambda}'_x + \boldsymbol{\Theta}_\delta \end{pmatrix} \qquad (1.4)$$

where $\mathbf{A} = (\mathbf{I} - \mathbf{B})^{-1}$.

Fixed, free, and constrained parameters

The general LISREL model is specialized by fixing and constraining the parameters that comprise the elements in $\boldsymbol{\Lambda}_y$, $\boldsymbol{\Lambda}_x$, $\mathbf{B}$, $\boldsymbol{\Gamma}$, $\boldsymbol{\Phi}$, $\boldsymbol{\Psi}$, $\boldsymbol{\Theta}_\epsilon$ and $\boldsymbol{\Theta}_\delta$. The elements are of three kinds:

Fixed parameters — assigned specified values
Constrained parameters — unknown but equal to one or more other unknown parameters
Free parameters — unknown and not constrained to be equal to other parameters

LISREL notation for numbers of variables

Variables	Number	Notation
y	p	NY
x	q	NX
η	m	NE
ξ	n	NK

1.2 Path diagrams and the LISREL equations

A path diagram represents the relationship among variables in the LISREL model. If drawn and labeled correctly and in sufficient detail, the diagram can specify exactly the fixed, constrained or free status of all parameters in the model.

The following are rules for drawing path diagrams:

- The observed x- and y-variables are enclosed in boxes.
- The latent variables ξ and η are enclosed in circles or ellipses.
- The error variables ϵ, δ, and ζ appear in the diagram but are not enclosed.
- A one-way arrow between two variables indicate a postulated direct influence of one variable on another. A two-way arrow between two variables indicates that these variables may be correlated without any assumed direct relationship. One-way arrows are drawn straight, while two-way arrows are generally curved.
- There is a fundamental distinction between independent variables (ξ-variables) and dependent variables (η-variables). Variation and covariation in the dependent variables is to be accounted for or explained by the independent variables. In the path diagram this corresponds to the statements,
  1 no one-way arrow can point to a ξ-variable;
  2 all one-way arrows pointing to an η-variable come from ξ- and η-variables.
- Coefficients are associated with each arrow as follows:
  One-way arrows ($\rightarrow$):

  An arrow from ξ_i to x_b is denoted $\lambda_{bi}^{(x)}$.

  An arrow from η_g to y_a is denoted $\lambda_{ag}^{(y)}$.

  An arrow from η_h to η_g is denoted β_{gh}.

  An arrow from ξ_i to η_g is denoted γ_{gi}.

  Two-way arrows ($\leftrightarrow$):

  A two-way arrow from ξ_j to ξ_i is denoted ϕ_{ij}.

  A two-way arrow from ζ_h to ζ_g is denoted ψ_{gh}.

  A two-way arrow from δ_b to δ_a is denoted $\theta_{ab}^{(\delta)}$.

A two-way arrow from ϵ_d to ϵ_c is denoted $\theta_{cd}^{(\epsilon)}$.

- Each coefficient has two subscripts: the first is the subscript of the variable to which the arrow is pointing; the second is the subscript of the variable from which the arrow is coming. In Figure 1.1, for example, γ_{23} corresponds to the arrow from ξ_3 to η_2. For two-way arrows, the two subscripts may be interchanged ($\phi_{21} = \phi_{12}$ in Figure 1.1). Arrows that have no explicit coefficient in the path diagram are assumed to have a unit coefficient (unless space limits prevents their appearance).
- All direct influences of one variable on another must be included in the path diagram. The non-existence of an arrow between two variables means that the two variables are assumed not directly related. (They may still be indirectly related, however, see Section 1.10.)

If the above conventions for path diagrams are followed exactly, it is possible to write the corresponding model equations by means of the following general rules:

1   For each variable which has a one-way arrow pointing to it there will be one equation in which this variable is a left-hand variable.

2   The right-hand side of each equation is the sum of a number of terms equal to the number of one-way arrows pointing to that variable and each term is the product of the coefficient associated with the arrow and the variable from which the arrow is coming.

Equations for the path diagram

With these rules, the equations for the path diagram in Figure 1.1 can be written as follows.

The diagram shows there are seven x-variables as indicators of three latent ξ-variables. Note that x_3 is a variable measuring both ξ_1 and ξ_2. There are two latent η-variables each with two y-indicators. The five latent variables are connected in a two-equation interdependent system. The model involves errors in equations (the ζ's) and errors in variables (the ϵ's and δ's).

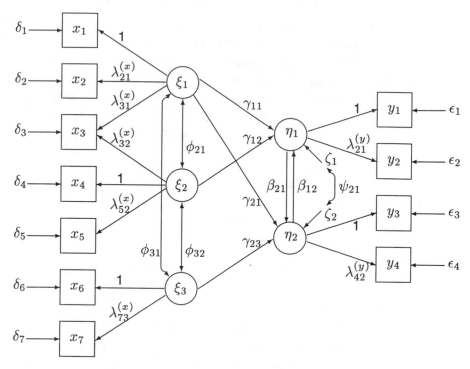

Figure 1.1   Path Diagram for Hypothetical Model

The *structural equations* are

$$\eta_1 = \beta_{12}\eta_2 + \gamma_{11}\xi_1 + \gamma_{12}\xi_2 + \zeta_1$$
$$\eta_2 = \beta_{21}\eta_1 + \gamma_{21}\xi_1 + \gamma_{23}\xi_3 + \zeta_2$$

or in matrix form

$$\begin{pmatrix} \eta_1 \\ \eta_2 \end{pmatrix} = \begin{pmatrix} 0 & \beta_{12} \\ \beta_{21} & 0 \end{pmatrix} \begin{pmatrix} \eta_1 \\ \eta_2 \end{pmatrix} + \begin{pmatrix} \gamma_{11} & \gamma_{12} & 0 \\ \gamma_{21} & 0 & \gamma_{23} \end{pmatrix} \begin{pmatrix} \xi_1 \\ \xi_2 \\ \xi_3 \end{pmatrix} + \begin{pmatrix} \zeta_1 \\ \zeta_2 \end{pmatrix} .$$

Either of these forms corresponds to the structural equation model represented in Figure 1.1.

The *measurement model* equations for y-variables are

$$y_1 = \eta_1 + \epsilon_1$$

$$y_2 = \lambda_{21}^{(y)}\eta_1 + \epsilon_2$$
$$y_3 = \eta_2 + \epsilon_3$$
$$y_4 = \lambda_{42}^{(y)}\eta_2 + \epsilon_4$$

or in matrix form

$$
\begin{pmatrix} y_1 \\ y_2 \\ y_3 \\ y_4 \end{pmatrix} =
\begin{pmatrix} 1 & 0 \\ \lambda_{21}^{(y)} & 0 \\ 0 & 1 \\ 0 & \lambda_{42}^{(y)} \end{pmatrix}
\begin{pmatrix} \eta_1 \\ \eta_2 \end{pmatrix} +
\begin{pmatrix} \epsilon_1 \\ \epsilon_2 \\ \epsilon_3 \\ \epsilon_4 \end{pmatrix}.
$$

The *measurement model* equations for x-variables are

$$x_1 = \xi_1 + \delta_1$$
$$x_2 = \lambda_{21}^{(x)}\xi_1 + \delta_2$$
$$x_3 = \lambda_{31}^{(x)}\xi_1 + \lambda_{32}^{(x)}\xi_2 + \delta_3$$
$$x_4 = \xi_2 + \delta_4$$
$$x_5 = \lambda_{52}^{(x)}\xi_2 + \delta_5$$
$$x_6 = \xi_3 + \delta_6$$
$$x_7 = \lambda_{73}^{(x)}\xi_3 + \delta_7$$

or in matrix form

$$
\begin{pmatrix} x_1 \\ x_2 \\ x_3 \\ x_4 \\ x_5 \\ x_6 \\ x_7 \end{pmatrix} =
\begin{pmatrix}
1 & 0 & 0 \\
\lambda_{21}^{(x)} & 0 & 0 \\
\lambda_{31}^{(x)} & \lambda_{32}^{(x)} & 0 \\
0 & 1 & 0 \\
0 & \lambda_{52}^{(x)} & 0 \\
0 & 0 & 1 \\
0 & 0 & \lambda_{73}^{(x)}
\end{pmatrix}
\begin{pmatrix} \xi_1 \\ \xi_2 \\ \xi_3 \end{pmatrix} +
\begin{pmatrix} \delta_1 \\ \delta_2 \\ \delta_3 \\ \delta_4 \\ \delta_5 \\ \delta_6 \\ \delta_7 \end{pmatrix}.
$$

These equations correspond to the measurement models represented in Figure 1.1.

One λ in each column of Λ_y and Λ_x has been set equal to 1 to fix the scales of measurement in the latent variables.

In these equations, note that the second subscript on each coefficient is always equal to the subscript of the variable that follows the coefficient. This correspondence serves to check that the terms are correct.

In the matrices $\mathbf{B}$, $\boldsymbol{\Gamma}$, $\boldsymbol{\Lambda}_y$, and $\boldsymbol{\Lambda}_x$, the subscripts on each coefficient, as originally defined in the path diagram, correspond to the row and column of the matrix in which they appear. Note that possible paths that are *not* included in the diagram correspond to *zeros* in these matrices.

Each of the parameter matrices contain fixed elements (the zeros and ones) and free parameters (the coefficients with two subscripts).

The four remaining parameter matrices are symmetric matrices:

the covariance matrix of $\boldsymbol{\xi}$,

$$\boldsymbol{\Phi} = \begin{pmatrix} \phi_{11} & & \\ \phi_{21} & \phi_{22} & \\ \phi_{31} & \phi_{32} & \phi_{33} \end{pmatrix},$$

the covariance matrix of $\boldsymbol{\zeta}$,

$$\boldsymbol{\Psi} = \begin{pmatrix} \psi_{11} & \\ \psi_{21} & \psi_{22} \end{pmatrix},$$

the covariance matrix of $\boldsymbol{\epsilon}$, a diagonal matrix,

$$\boldsymbol{\Theta}_\epsilon = \mathrm{diag}(\theta_{11}^{(\epsilon)}, \theta_{22}^{(\epsilon)}, \ldots, \theta_{44}^{(\epsilon)}),$$

and the covariance matrix of $\boldsymbol{\delta}$, also a diagonal matrix,

$$\boldsymbol{\Theta}_\delta = \mathrm{diag}(\theta_{11}^{(\delta)}, \theta_{22}^{(\delta)}, \ldots, \theta_{77}^{(\delta)}).$$

1.3 LISREL submodels

Various submodels of LISREL are obtained by setting the numbers of certain variables to zero. (Numbers not specified are zero by default.)

The measurement (factor analysis) model for x (NX $\neq$ 0; NK $\neq$ 0)

$$\mathbf{x} = \mathbf{\Lambda}_x \boldsymbol{\xi} + \boldsymbol{\delta} \qquad (1.5)$$

Parameter matrices:

$\mathbf{\Lambda}_x$ is the matrix of factor loadings $(q \times n)$.

$\boldsymbol{\xi}$ is the vector of latent factors $(n \times 1)$.

$\boldsymbol{\delta}$ is the vector of unique components $(q \times 1)$.

$\boldsymbol{\Phi}$ is the factor covariance or correlation matrix (covariance matrix of $\boldsymbol{\xi}$) $(n \times n)$.

$\boldsymbol{\Theta}_\delta$ is the covariance matrix of unique components $(q \times q)$.

Chapter 3 discusses this LISREL model, Submodel 1.

Structural equation model where y and x are observed without error (NY $\neq$ 0; NX $\neq$ 0)

$$\underline{\mathbf{y}} = \mathbf{B}\underline{\mathbf{y}} + \mathbf{\Gamma}\underline{\mathbf{x}} + \boldsymbol{\zeta} \qquad (1.6)$$

Special case: $\mathbf{B} = \mathbf{0}$. The multivariate multiple regression model (canonical correlation):

$$\mathbf{y} = \mathbf{\Gamma}\mathbf{x} + \boldsymbol{\zeta} \,. \qquad (1.7)$$

$\mathbf{B}$ is the structural coefficient matrix $(p \times p)$ of $\mathbf{y}$; $\|\mathbf{I} - \mathbf{B}\| \neq \mathbf{0}$.

$\mathbf{\Gamma}$ is the structural coefficient matrix $(p \times q)$ of $\mathbf{x}$.

$\boldsymbol{\zeta}$ is the vector $(p \times 1)$ of structural disturbance terms or residuals.

$\boldsymbol{\Psi}$ is the residual covariance matrix (conditional covariance matrix of $\mathbf{y}$, given $\mathbf{x}$).

Chapter 4 discusses this LISREL model, Submodel 2.

Errors in y-variables only (NY $\neq$ 0; NE $\neq$ 0; NK $\neq$ 0)

$$\boldsymbol{\eta} = \mathbf{B}\boldsymbol{\eta} + \mathbf{\Gamma}\boldsymbol{\xi} + \boldsymbol{\zeta} \quad {\scriptstyle (I - B)\eta\, =\, \Gamma\xi + \zeta}$$
$$\text{and } \mathbf{y} = \mathbf{\Lambda}_y \boldsymbol{\eta} + \boldsymbol{\epsilon}$$
$$\text{or } \mathbf{y} = \mathbf{\Lambda}_y (\mathbf{I} - \mathbf{B})^{-1}(\mathbf{\Gamma}\boldsymbol{\xi} + \boldsymbol{\zeta}) + \boldsymbol{\epsilon} \qquad (1.8)$$

Special case: $\mathbf{B} = \mathbf{0}$. The second-order factor analysis model for $\mathbf{y}$:

$$\mathbf{y} = \mathbf{\Lambda}_y(\mathbf{\Gamma}\boldsymbol{\xi} + \boldsymbol{\zeta}) + \boldsymbol{\epsilon} \, . \tag{1.9}$$

$\mathbf{\Lambda}_y$ is the matrix of first-order factor loadings ($p \times m$).
$\mathbf{\Gamma}$ is the matrix of second-order factor loadings ($m \times n$).
$\boldsymbol{\xi}$ is the vector of second-order factors ($n \times 1$).
$\boldsymbol{\zeta}$ is the vector of second-order unique components ($n \times 1$).
$\boldsymbol{\epsilon}$ is the vector of first-order unique components ($p \times 1$).

$\mathbf{\Phi}$ is the covariance matrix of second-order factors (covariance matrix of $\boldsymbol{\xi}$) ($n \times n$).
$\mathbf{\Psi}$ is the covariance matrix of second-order uniquenesses ($m \times m$).
$\mathbf{\Theta}_\epsilon$ is the diagonal covariance matrix of first-order uniquenesses ($p \times p$).

Chapter 6 discusses this LISREL model, Submodel 3A.

No x-variables (NY $\neq$ 0; NE $\neq$ 0)

$$
\begin{aligned}
\mathbf{y} &= \mathbf{\Lambda}_y\boldsymbol{\eta} + \boldsymbol{\epsilon} \\
\text{and } \boldsymbol{\eta} &= \mathbf{B}\boldsymbol{\eta} + \boldsymbol{\zeta} \\
\text{or } \mathbf{y} &= \mathbf{\Lambda}_y(\mathbf{I} - \mathbf{B})^{-1}\boldsymbol{\zeta} + \boldsymbol{\epsilon}
\end{aligned}
\tag{1.10}
$$

Special case: $\mathbf{B} = \mathbf{0}$. The factor analysis model for $\mathbf{y}$:

$$\mathbf{y} = \mathbf{\Lambda}_y\boldsymbol{\zeta} + \boldsymbol{\epsilon} \, . \tag{1.11}$$

$\mathbf{\Lambda}_y$ is the matrix of factor loadings ($p \times m$).
$\boldsymbol{\zeta}$ is the vector of factors ($m \times 1$).
$\boldsymbol{\epsilon}$ is the vector of unique components ($p \times 1$).
$\mathbf{\Psi}$ is the factor covariance or correlation matrix ($m \times m$).

Note: Because of a special provision for specifying factor covariances, it is more convenient to specify the factor analysis for the x-variables (see section *The measurement model for* x on page 9).

Chapter 6 discusses this LISREL model, Submodel 3B.

Summary of LISREL submodels

Table 1.1 gives an overview of the LISREL submodels. The four submodels 1, 2, 3A, and 3B are described in the four previous sections and discussed more fully in Chapters 3–6.

Table 1.1 Submodels in LISREL

Type	Specified	Default	Model	Parameters
1	NX,NK	NY,NE	$\mathbf{x} = \mathbf{\Lambda}_x \boldsymbol{\xi} + \boldsymbol{\delta}$	$\mathbf{\Lambda}_x, \mathbf{\Phi}, \mathbf{\Theta}_\delta$
2	NY,NX	NE,NK	$\mathbf{y} = \mathbf{B}\mathbf{y} + \mathbf{\Gamma}\mathbf{x} + \boldsymbol{\zeta}$	$\mathbf{B}, \mathbf{\Gamma}, \mathbf{\Psi}$
3A	NY,NE,NK	NX	$\mathbf{y} = \mathbf{\Lambda}_y(\mathbf{I} - \mathbf{B})^{-1}(\mathbf{\Gamma}\boldsymbol{\xi} + \boldsymbol{\zeta}) + \boldsymbol{\epsilon}$	$\mathbf{\Lambda}_y, \mathbf{B}, \mathbf{\Gamma}, \mathbf{\Phi}, \mathbf{\Psi}, \mathbf{\Theta}_\epsilon$
3B	NY,NE	NX,NK	$\mathbf{y} = \mathbf{\Lambda}_y(\mathbf{I} - \mathbf{B})^{-1}\boldsymbol{\zeta} + \boldsymbol{\epsilon}$	$\mathbf{\Lambda}_y, \mathbf{B}, \mathbf{\Psi}, \mathbf{\Theta}_\epsilon$

Default values for parameter matrices

For the eight parameter matrices in LISREL, Table 1.2 gives their LISREL names, their possible and default forms, and their default modes.

Table 1.2
Parameter Matrices in LISREL: Their Possible Forms and Default Values

Name	Math Symbol	LISREL Name	Order	Possible Forms	Default Form	Default Mode
LAMBDA-Y	$\mathbf{\Lambda}_y$	LY	NY × NE	ID,IZ,ZI,DI,FU	FU	FI
LAMBDA-X	$\mathbf{\Lambda}_x$	LX	NX × NK	ID,IZ,ZI,DI,FU	FU	FI
BETA	$\mathbf{B}$	BE	NE × NE	ZE,SD,FU	ZE	FI
GAMMA	$\mathbf{\Gamma}$	GA	NE × NK	ID,IZ,ZI,DI,FU	FU	FR
PHI	$\mathbf{\Phi}$	PH	NK × NK	ID,DI,SY,ST	SY	FR
PSI	$\mathbf{\Psi}$	PS	NE × NE	ZE,DI,SY	SY	FR
THETA-EPSILON	$\mathbf{\Theta}_\epsilon$	TE	NY × NY	ZE,DI,SY	DI	FR
THETA-DELTA	$\mathbf{\Theta}_\delta$	TD	NX × NX	ZE,DI,SY	DI	FR

The meaning of the possible form values is as follows:

ZE   **0** (zero matrix)

ID   **I** (identity matrix)

IZ $\left(\begin{array}{cc} \mathbf{I} & \mathbf{0} \end{array} \right)$ or $\left(\begin{array}{c} \mathbf{I} \\ \mathbf{0} \end{array} \right)$ (partitioned identity and zero)

ZI $\left(\begin{array}{cc} \mathbf{0} & \mathbf{I} \end{array} \right)$ or $\left(\begin{array}{c} \mathbf{0} \\ \mathbf{I} \end{array} \right)$ (partitioned zero and identity)

DI   a diagonal matrix

SD   a full square matrix with fixed zeros in and above the diagonal and all elements under the diagonal free (refers to **B** only)

SY   a symmetric matrix that is not diagonal

ST   a symmetric matrix with fixed ones in the diagonal (a correlation matrix; refers to $\mathbf{\Phi}$ only)

FU   a rectangular or square non-symmetric matrix

1.4   LISREL notation for specifying free, fixed, and constrained parameters

Parameter matrices may be specialized with the following specifications:

1. Elements are entered rowwise within parameter matrices.
2. Elements are specified by the LISREL name of their matrix followed by their row and column positions in parentheses.
   Example: LY(2,3) refers to the element in row 2 and column 3 of the $\mathbf{\Lambda}_y$ matrix.
3. Elements may be specified by their serial position (linear index) in the matrix.
   Example: if $\mathbf{\Lambda}_y$ is 3×2, the position numbers of its elements are

$$\mathbf{\Lambda}_y(3 \times 2) : \begin{bmatrix} 1 & 2 \\ 3 & 4 \\ 5 & 6 \end{bmatrix} ;$$

   thus, LY(2,1) $\equiv$ LY(3).
4. Elements in consecutive order across rows may be specified by their first and last element separated by a hyphen.

Example:

    LY(2,1) – LY(3,1)

    LY(3) – LY(5)

    LY(3) LY(4) LY(5)

5 If a matrix is specified as diagonal (DI), only the diagonal elements are stored and may be referred to.

    Example: TE(1,1) TE(2,2) $\cdots$ TE(p,p) $\equiv$ TE(1) TE(2) $\cdots$ TE(p)

6 If a matrix is specified as symmetric (SY), only the elements in or below the diagonal are stored. The serial positions run as follows:

$$\Phi(3 \times 3) : \begin{bmatrix} 1 & & \\ 2 & 3 & \\ 4 & 5 & 6 \end{bmatrix}.$$

Symmetrically situated elements are equal:

    PH(1,2) = PH(2,1) $\equiv$ PH(2).

7 The zero (0) and identity (**I**) matrices are not physically stored in memory and cannot be referenced.

Specification of fixed and free elements

See also section *Default values for parameter matrices* on page 11.

1 All elements in a matrix may be specified fixed or free by the notation: LISREL NAME = MATRIX FORM, MATRIX MODE

    Example: PH=DI,FI fixes the elements in a diagonal form of PHI.

2 Individual elements may be fixed with the word FIX or freed with the the word FREE, followed by a list of the elements separated by spaces.

    Example: FIX BE(3,1) BE(4,1) BE(4,2).

3 Later specifications override earlier specifications.

    Example:

      BE=SD

      FIX BE(3,1) BE(4,1) BE(4,2)

The first statement sets all subdiagonal elements of BETA free; the second leaves only the elements in the first subdiagonal free.

4 For the symmetric Φ matrix, the specification PH=ST means that the diagonal elements of Φ are fixed at one and the off-diagonal elements are free. The specifications PH=ST,FI and PH=ST,FR are contradictory and not permitted.

5 For the error covariance matrices, Θ_ϵ(TE) and Θ_δ(TD), note:
   o The default is diagonal (DI) and free (FR).
   o TE=SY or TD=SY means that these matrices are symmetric with free diagonal and fixed off-diagonal elements.
   o TE=SY,FR or TD=SY,FR means that all elements of the symmetric matrix are free.

Specification of equality constraints

Equality is specified by the word EQUAL followed by the list of elements that are constrained to be equal. The first element in the list must previously have been specified free (FR).

Example: $\beta_{35} = \gamma_{41} = \phi_{21}$ is specified as

   EQUAL GA(4,1) BE(3,5) PH(2,1), assuming γ_{41} has been declared free.

It is possible to use a fixed first element, thereby fixing the following elements to the same value. But such a purpose is better served with the VALUE command, described in the following section.

Specification of non-zero fixed parameters

The value of each parameter, whether free or fixed, is zero by default. Fixed parameters may be set at a specific value by the word VALUE followed by the value (with decimal point) and the list of elements to be set to that value. If the value is an integer, the decimal point may be omitted.

   Example: VALUE 0.065 LY(4,2) BE(6,1) PS(5,4) TE(7,3).

Any statement of this type overrides any previous VALUE statement with the same referents.

1.5 Kinds of input data and type of moment matrix to be analyzed

LISREL 7 accepts data in the following forms; the LISREL notation is on the left (see also Chapter 2).

RA	Case-by-case raw data.
CM	A covariance matrix represented by variances in the diagonal and covariances below the diagonal only.
KM	A matrix of product moment correlations based on raw scores or normal scores.
OM, PM	A correlation matrix consisting of tetrachoric, polychoric, biserial, polyserial, canonical or product-moment correlations, as produced by the PRELIS program (see Section 1.6).
MM	A moment matrix (*i.e.*, second-order moments about zero; squares and cross-products *not* corrected to the mean).
ME	A vector of means.
SD	A vector of standard deviations.

The matrices CM, KM, MM, OM, or PM may be analyzed directly, of course, or computed from the raw data (RA). The covariance matrix (CM) may also be computed from a product moment correlation matrix (KM) and a vector of standard deviations (SD), or from a moment matrix (MM) and a vector of means (ME). The product moment correlation matrix (KM) may be analyzed after computation from a covariance matrix (CM) and a vector of standard deviations (SD). The moment matrix (MM) may be computed from a covariance matrix (CM) and a vector of means (ME). And finally, an augmented moment matrix (AM) may be obtained from a moment matrix (MM) and a vector of means (ME).

Since the program uses zero for means and one for standard deviations as default values, the matrix to be analyzed (CM, KM, MM, or AM) can always be computed, regardless of what has been input (RA, CM, KM, or MM). Before the actual analysis, variables may be deleted from the matrix or reordered. The resulting matrix is printed in the output file and may also be saved for further use.

1.6 PRELIS

LISREL 7 is designed to accept a covariance or correlation matrix computed by the PRELIS program. PRELIS is required if the data include ordinal or censored variables; it computes the moment matrices used by LISREL 7 for the analysis of non-continuous data or data of mixed scale types.

If all variables are measured continuously, PRELIS is not required, as LIS-REL 7 provides for input of such data. But even in this case, the user may find PRELIS useful for pre-screening the data to detect inadmissible values.

PRELIS has the following features:

- PRELIS reads raw data of any numeric form, case after case. The data is not stored in memory, and the number of cases (the sample size) is unlimited. PRELIS can also read grouped data and weighted data in which each case carries a weight.

- The scale type of each variable may be declared as ordinal, censored, or continuous. Groups of variables (including all variables) of the same scale type may be declared collectively. Ordinal variables may have up to 15 categories.

- A distinct numeric value may be defined for each variable to represent a missing value. Such a numeric value can also be defined collectively for a group of variables or globally for all variables.

- Moment matrices may be computed either under listwise deletion or pairwise deletion when there are missing values.

- Continuous variables may be transformed using any one of a large family of transformations. Ordinal variables may be recoded or transformed to normal scores, or they may first be recoded and then transformed to normal scores. Maximum and/or minimum values of censored variables may also be transformed to normal scores.

- In addition to moment and covariance matrices based on raw scores or normal scores, the program can compute a number of different types of correlation coefficients — namely, product-moment (Pearson), canonical, polychoric (including tetrachoric), polyserial (including biserial), and product-moment correlations based on normal or optimal scores. The program can also estimate correlations between censored variables and ordinal or continuous variables.

- The program saves the computed moment matrix in a file that can be read directly by LISREL.

- PRELIS can produce an estimate of the *asymptotic* (large sample) *covariance matrix* of the estimated sample variances and covariances under arbitrary non-normal distributions (see Browne, 1982, 1984). This can be used to compute a weight matrix for WLS (Weighted

Least Squares, equivalent to Browne's ADF) analysis in LISREL 7 (see below). PRELIS can also compute estimates of the asymptotic variances and covariances of estimated product-moment correlations, polychoric correlations and polyserial correlations; these can also be used with WLS estimation in LISREL 7. Optionally, PRELIS may be used to compute a diagonal matrix consisting of estimates of the *asymptotic variances* of estimated variances, covariances, or correlations. These diagonal matrices can be used with DWLS estimation (Diagonally Weighted Least Squares) in LISREL 7 (see below).

1.7 Methods of estimation

For problems that do not include a structure on the means (see Chapter 10 for that case), LISREL 7 can perform any of seven methods of estimation:

- o   Instrumental Variables (IV)
- o   Two-Stage Least Squares (TSLS)
- o   Unweighted Least Squares (ULS)
- o   Generalized Least Squares (GLS)
- o   Maximum Likelihood (ML)
- o   Generally Weighted Least Squares (WLS)
- o   Diagonally Weighted Least Squares (DWLS)

The purpose of these methods is to estimate the free and constrained parameters of the model from the sample covariance matrix S.

Properties of the alternative methods are described in this section. The ridge option (see section *The ridge option in LISREL 7* on page 24) may also be used with some of these estimation methods.

Instrumental variables (IV) and two-stage least squares (TSLS)

The ULS, GLS, ML, WLS, and DWLS methods of estimation are iterative and require approximations to the parameters in order to begin the computations. These starting values of the parameters are computed in LISREL by the IV and TSLS methods. Although the resulting estimates are not *efficient* in the sense of having minimum large-sample variance, they are *consistent* and have the advantage of being very easy to compute. IV and TSLS do not provide standard errors of the estimated parameters.

When the model fits the data well, the starting values produced by the program are often so close to the iterated solution that only a few iterations are required to compute these solutions. For some models, the estimated starting values are identical to ML and other estimates. To emphasize the fact that the starting values are estimates in their own right, we call them *initial estimates* instead of starting values. One can choose to obtain only these initial estimates and not to compute ML or other estimates. In particular, this may be used with large models to save computer time, especially when the model is only tentative. In such a situation the initial estimates themselves or other information in the output may suggest ways to improve the model.

In most cases, one need only specify the non-zero fixed values in each column of Λ_y and Λ_x necessary to fix the scales for η and ξ, and leave it to the program to compute estimates of all the free parameters. However, one *can* specify starting values for any number of free parameters. These are sometimes necessary in non-standard models to give the program some help in starting the iterations.

A key concept in the computation of initial estimates (IV and TSLS) is that of a *reference variable*. A reference variable for a latent variable is an observed variable that represents the latent variable in the sense of being a valid and reliable measure of it. There can be only one reference variable for each latent variable. Although the selection of reference variables is done automatically by the program, there is a connection between the selection of reference variables and the assignment of scales to the latent variables. If one assigns scales to the latent variables by fixing a non-zero value in each column of Λ_y and Λ_x, then the variables for which these non-zero values have been fixed will be reference variables. In this way, users can specify the reference variables explicitly.

The initial estimates are computed in four steps as follows:

1. *Reference variables* are determined as follows. If the scales for η and ξ have been fixed by assigning a non-zero fixed value in each column of Λ_y and Λ_x, LISREL will determine non-singular submatrices of Λ_y and Λ_x of m and n rows, respectively, if this is possible. The rows

of these submatrices determine the reference variables. In this way $m + n$ reference variables can be determined, provided $\mathbf{\Lambda}_y$ and $\mathbf{\Lambda}_x$ contain m and n linearly independent rows, respectively. Note that this requires that $m \leq p$ and $n \leq q$.

Remember that all parameters are zero by default. This means that, when this process is applied, all elements of $\mathbf{\Lambda}_y$ and $\mathbf{\Lambda}_x$ are zero except those that have been assigned non-zero values by the user. If no non-zero values have been assigned, both $\mathbf{\Lambda}_y$ and $\mathbf{\Lambda}_x$ are zero so that this procedure fails.

If the scales of $\boldsymbol{\xi}$ have been fixed by standardizing $\mathbf{\Phi}$, the program will automatically assign fixed values in the columns of $\mathbf{\Lambda}_x$, relax the fixed diagonal elements of $\mathbf{\Phi}$ and use the same procedure as above to determine the reference variables. When the initial estimates for $\mathbf{\Lambda}_x$ have been determined in Step 2, the program will rescale the ξ-variables so that $\mathrm{diag}(\mathbf{\Phi}) = \mathbf{I}$.

2. For each row of $\mathbf{\Lambda}$ ($\mathbf{\Lambda}_y$ or $\mathbf{\Lambda}_x$), the free parameters, if any, are estimated from the linear relation between each observed variable and the reference variables using all other observed variables as instrumental variables.

3. For given $\mathbf{\Lambda}_y$ and $\mathbf{\Lambda}_x$, the joint covariance matrix of $\boldsymbol{\eta}$, $\boldsymbol{\xi}$, $\boldsymbol{\epsilon}$, and $\boldsymbol{\delta}$ is estimated by unweighted least squares (ULS) applied to $\mathbf{S} - \mathbf{\Sigma}$. For given $\mathbf{\Lambda}_y$ and $\mathbf{\Lambda}_x$ this leads to a quadratic function which can be minimized easily. Parameters in $\mathbf{\Phi}$, $\mathbf{\Theta}_\epsilon$ and $\mathbf{\Theta}_\delta$ that have non-zero values are held fixed during this minimization.

4. When the joint covariance matrix of $\boldsymbol{\eta}$ and $\boldsymbol{\xi}$ has been estimated as in Step 3, the structural equation system can be estimated by instrumental variables methods. We estimate each equation separately using all the ξ-variables as instrumental variables. Again, non-zero parameters in $\mathbf{B}$ and $\mathbf{\Gamma}$ are held fixed. The estimates computed in this step are identical to the well-known instrumental variables or two-stage least-squares estimators; see, for example, Goldberger (1964).

Unweighted least squares (ULS)

The ULS estimator minimizes the function

$$F = \frac{1}{2}\mathrm{tr}[(\mathbf{S} - \mathbf{\Sigma})^2] \,, \tag{1.12}$$

where $\mathrm{tr}[(\mathbf{S} - \mathbf{\Sigma})^2]$ represents the sum of squares of the elements in the (symmetric) residual matrix, $\mathbf{S} - \mathbf{\Sigma}$, of order $p + q$.

The ULS estimator is consistent and relatively quick to compute, but is not efficient — that is, it does not attain minimum large-sample variances. Standard errors for ULS are estimated under normal theory.

Generalized least squares (GLS)

GLS minimizes

$$F = \frac{1}{2}\mathrm{tr}[(\mathbf{I} - \mathbf{S}^{-1}\mathbf{\Sigma})^2] \,, \tag{1.13}$$

equivalent to minimizing the sum of squares of the residuals weighted by the inverse of the sample covariance matrix. The estimator is consistently efficient, and has large-sample standard errors computed by LISREL under normal theory.

Maximum likelihood (ML)

ML maximizes the likelihood of the parameters, given the data. In the present context, it is equivalent to minimizing

$$F = \log||\mathbf{\Sigma}|| + \mathrm{tr}(\mathbf{S}\mathbf{\Sigma}^{-1}) - \log||\mathbf{S}|| - (p + q) \,. \tag{1.14}$$

ML has the same properties as GLS and is about equally time consuming to compute.

Generally weighted least-squares (WLS)

The ULS, GLS, and ML fit functions are, in effect, special cases of the more general function for fitting covariance structures,

$$F(\boldsymbol{\theta}) = (\mathbf{s} - \boldsymbol{\sigma})'\mathbf{W}^{-1}(\mathbf{s} - \boldsymbol{\sigma}) \tag{1.15}$$

$$= \sum_{g=1}^{k}\sum_{h=1}^{g}\sum_{i=1}^{k}\sum_{j=1}^{i} w^{gh,ij}(s_{gh} - \sigma_{gh})(s_{ij} - \sigma_{ij}),$$

where

$$\mathbf{s}' = (s_{11}, s_{21}, s_{22}, s_{31}, \ldots, s_{kk}),$$

is a vector of the elements in the lower half, including the diagonal, of the covariance matrix $\mathbf{S}$ of order $k \times k$ used to fit the model to the data;

$$\boldsymbol{\sigma}' = (\sigma_{11}, \sigma_{21}, \sigma_{22}, \sigma_{31}, \ldots, \sigma_{kk}),$$

is the vector of corresponding elements of $\boldsymbol{\Sigma}(\boldsymbol{\theta})$ reproduced from the model parameters $\boldsymbol{\theta}$;

$$w^{gh,ij}$$

is a typical element of a positive definite matrix $\mathbf{W}^{-1}$ of order $u \times u$, where $u = k(k+1)/2$. In most cases, the elements of $\mathbf{W}^{-1}$ are obtained by inverting a matrix $\mathbf{W}$ whose typical element is denoted $w_{gh,ij}$. The usual way of choosing $\mathbf{W}$ in weighted least squares is to let $w_{gh,ij}$ be a consistent estimate of the asymptotic covariance between s_{gh} and s_{ij}. If this is the case, we say that $\mathbf{W}^{-1}$ is the *correct weight matrix*. To estimate the model parameters $\boldsymbol{\theta}$, the fit function is minimized with respect to $\boldsymbol{\theta}$.

To obtain consistent estimates, any positive definite matrix $\mathbf{W}$ may be used. Under very general assumptions, if the model holds in the population and if the sample variances and covariances in $\mathbf{S}$ converge in probability to the corresponding elements in the population covariance matrix $\boldsymbol{\Sigma}$ as the sample size increases, any fit function with a positive definite $\mathbf{W}$ will give a consistent estimator of $\boldsymbol{\theta}$. In practice, numerical results obtained by one fit function are often close enough to the results that would be obtained by another fit function to give the same substantive interpretations of the results.

Further assumptions must be made, however, if one needs an asymptotically correct chi-square measure of goodness-of-fit and asymptotically correct standard errors of parameter estimates.

"Classical" theory for covariance structures (see, for example, Browne, 1974 or Jöreskog, 1981a) assumes that the asymptotic variances and covariances of the elements of S are of the form

$$\text{ACov}(s_{gh}, s_{ij}) = (1/N)(\sigma_{gi}\sigma_{hj} + \sigma_{gj}\sigma_{hi}) , \qquad (1.16)$$

where N is the total sample size. This holds, in particular, if the observed variables have a multivariate normal distribution, or if S has a Wishart distribution. The GLS and ML methods and their chi-square values and standard errors are based on (1.16). The GLS method corresponds to using in (1.15) a matrix $\mathbf{W}^{-1}$, which has as a general element

$$w^{gh,ij} = N(2 - \delta_{gh})(2 - \delta_{ij})(s^{gi}s^{hj} + s^{gj}s^{hi}) , \qquad (1.17)$$

where δ_{gh} and δ_{ij} are Kronecker deltas. The fit function (1.14) for ML is not of the form (1.15) but may be shown to be equivalent to using a $\mathbf{W}^{-1}$ of the form (1.17), with s replaced by an estimate of σ, which is then updated in each iteration.

In recent fundamental work by Browne (1982, 1984), this classical theory for covariance structures has been generalized to any multivariate distribution for continuous variables satisfying very mild assumptions. This approach uses a $\mathbf{W}$ matrix with typical element

$$w_{gh,ij} = m_{ghij} - s_{gh}s_{ij} , \qquad (1.18)$$

where

$$m_{ghij} = (1/N) \sum_{a=1}^{N} (z_{ag} - \bar{z}_g)(z_{ah} - \bar{z}_h)(z_{ai} - \bar{z}_i)(z_{aj} - \bar{z}_j) \qquad (1.19)$$

are the fourth-order central moments. Using such a $\mathbf{W}$ in (1.15) gives what Browne calls "asymptotically distribution-free best GLS estimators," for which asymptotically correct chi-squares and standard errors may be obtained. As shown by Browne, this $\mathbf{W}$ matrix may also be used to compute asymptotically correct chi-squares and standard errors for estimates which have been obtained by the classical ML and GLS methods.

When $\mathbf{W}$ is defined by (1.18), we call the fit function WLS (Weighted Least Squares) to distinguish it from GLS, where $\mathbf{W}$ is defined by (1.17). WLS and GLS are different forms of weighted least squares: WLS is asymptotically distribution free, while GLS is based on normal theory.

While WLS is attractive in theory it presents several difficulties in practical applications. First, the matrix $\mathbf{W}$ is of order $u \times u$ and has $u(u+1)/2$ distinct elements. This increases rapidly with k, demanding large amounts of computer memory when k is at all large. For example, when $k = 20$, $\mathbf{W}$ has 22,155 distinct elements. Second, to estimate moments of fourth order with reasonable precision requires very large samples. Third, when there are missing observations in the data, different moments involved in (1.18) may be based on different numbers of cases unless listwise deletion is used. When pairwise deletion is used, it is not clear how to deal with this problem.

Browne's (1984) development is a theory for sample covariance matrices for continuous variables. In practice, correlation matrices are often analyzed; *i.e.*, covariance matrices scaled by stochastic standard deviations. The elements of such a correlation matrix do not have asymptotic variances and covariances of the form (1.16), even if $\mathbf{S}$ has a Wishart distribution. In PRELIS, we have extended Browne's (1984) work so that an estimate of the asymptotic covariance matrix of estimated correlations can also be obtained under the same general assumptions of non-normality. This approach can also be used when some or all of the variables are ordinal or censored, if the raw scores are replaced by normal scores. PRELIS can also compute estimates of the asymptotic variances and covariances of estimated polychoric and polyserial correlations.

Diagonally weighted least-squares (DWLS)

Computation of asymptotic covariance matrices of estimated coefficients is very time consuming and demands large amounts of memory when the number of variables is large. An alternative approach, which may be used even when the number of variables is large, is to compute only the asymptotic variances of the estimated coefficients.

Let w_{gh} be an estimate of the asymptotic variance of s_{gh}. These estimates may be used with a fit function of the form

$$F(\theta) = \sum_{g=1}^{k} \sum_{h=1}^{k} (1/w_{gh})(s_{gh} - \sigma_{gh})^2 \ . \qquad (1.20)$$

This corresponds to using a diagonal weight matrix $\mathbf{W}^{-1}$ in (1.15). In LISREL 7 we call this DWLS (Diagonally Weighted Least Squares). This does not lead to asymptotically efficient estimates of model parameters, but is offered as a compromise between unweighted least squares (ULS) and fully weighted least squares (WLS). DWLS can be used also when correlation matrices are analyzed.

The ridge option in LISREL 7

The GLS, ML, and WLS methods of estimation require that the sample covariance matrix, $\mathbf{S}$, be positive-definite. To provide for situations in which $\mathbf{S}$ is not quite positive-definite, as sometimes happens in econometric models containing identities and in regression problems with near-multicollinearity among predictors, LISREL 7 includes a provision for so-called *ridge* estimation.

In ridge estimation, a constant times the diagonal of $\mathbf{S}$ is added to $\mathbf{S}$; the constant is determined by the program, but may also be set by the user (see the OU(1) command in Chapter 2).

The ridge option may be used with ULS, GLS, ML, WLS, and DWLS; it has no effect on IV and TSLS.

The information matrix

Associated with each of the iterative estimation procedures, that minimize a fit function, is an information matrix for the parameters. The order of this matrix is equal to the number of free parameters in the model. The elements of the matrix are the expected values of the second derivatives of the fit function at the solution point (*i.e.*, the expected Hessian matrix).

The inverse of the information matrix contains the sampling variances, or large-sample variances, of the parameters as its diagonal elements. The off-diagonal elements are the covariances between all of the possible pairs of parameter estimates.

The standard errors of LISREL parameter estimates are the square roots of the diagonal elements of the inverse information matrix; the correlations between the estimates are the off-diagonal elements of the inverse information matrix divided by the corresponding pairs of standard errors. The information matrix must be positive-definite for the model to be identified.

Admissibility of the estimates

LISREL 7 does not constrain the parameter estimates to be admissible (for example, diagonal elements of Φ, Ψ, Θ_ϵ, or Θ_δ can become negative if the data are unfavorable relative to the assumed model). The program has a built-in check on admissibility of the solution, however, and will stop if the solution becomes non-admissible, unless the check is turned off (AD=OFF). The *admissibility* check is that

1: Λ_y and Λ_x have full column ranks and no rows of only zeros,
2: Φ, Ψ, Θ_ϵ, and Θ_δ are positive definite.

It is often possible, though not always, to use various tricks to force the program to stay within the admissible parameter space (see Rindskopf, 1983a–b, 1984, or for an example, see Jöreskog, 1981b). See also Chapter 8.

1.8   Evaluation of the LISREL solution

LISREL 7 provides five types of information for evaluating the adequacy of the assumed model:

1: Standard errors and correlations of the parameter estimates
2: Measures of variation accounted for
3: Overall goodness-of-fit measures
4: Analysis of residuals

The definitions and properties of these quantities are outlined in this section.

Standard errors and correlations of estimates

The program provides a standard error for each estimated parameter in the units of measurement of the corresponding observed or latent variable. It also computes the ratio of the estimate to its standard error (t-statistic or critical ratio statistic), which are unitless quantities.

Standard errors are not given for IV or TSLS and are only approximate for ULS and DWLS. Those for ML and GLS are correct under multivariate normality of the observed variables and for WLS if the correct weight matrix is used. Standard errors for ML and GLS are robust against moderate departures from normality.

LISREL 7 also computes correlations of the estimates from the information matrix. Very high correlations are an indication that the information matrix is close to nonpositive-definite and the model nearly non-identified.

Variation accounted for

The program provides squared multiple correlations for each observed variable separately and coefficients of determination for all the observed variables jointly. It also gives squared multiple correlations for each structural equation and coefficients of determination for all structural equations jointly. The squared multiple correlation is a measure of the strength of a linear relationship and the coefficient of determination is a measure of the strength of several relationships jointly.

These coefficients are defined as follows. The *squared multiple correlation* for the i-th observed variable is

$$1 - \frac{\hat{\theta}_{ii}}{\hat{\sigma}_{ii}} \, ,$$

where $\hat{\theta}_{ii}$ is the estimated error variance and $\hat{\sigma}_{ii}$ is the estimated total variance of the i-th variable.

The *coefficient of determination* is

$$1 - \frac{||\hat{\Theta}||}{||\hat{\Sigma}||} \, ,$$

where $||\hat{\Theta}||$ is the determinant of $\hat{\Theta}$ and $||\hat{\Sigma}||$ is the determinant of the fitted covariance matrix $\hat{\Sigma}$ of the observed variables. These measures show how well the observed variables serve, separately or jointly, as measurement instruments for the latent variables. The measure should be between zero and one, large values being associated with good models.

The squared multiple correlation for the i-th structural equation is defined as

$$1 - \frac{\widehat{\mathrm{Var}(\zeta_i)}}{\widehat{\mathrm{Var}(\eta_i)}} \, ,$$

where $\widehat{\mathrm{Var}(\zeta_i)}$ and $\widehat{\mathrm{Var}(\eta_i)}$ are the estimated variances of ζ_i and η_i, respectively.

The total coefficient of determination for all structural equations jointly is defined as

$$1 - \frac{||\hat{\Psi}||}{||\widehat{\mathrm{Cov}(\eta)}||} \, ,$$

where $||\hat{\Psi}||$ is the determinant of $\hat{\Psi}$ and $||\widehat{\mathrm{Cov}(\eta)}||$ is the determinant of the estimated covariance matrix of η.

Goodness-of-fit measures

The third part of the model evaluation concerns the assessment of the overall fit of the model to the data. The goodness of fit of the whole model may be judged by means of four measures of overall fit:

- ☐ Chi-square (χ^2)
- ☐ Goodness-of-fit index (GFI)
- ☐ Adjusted goodness-of-fit index (AGFI)
- ☐ Root mean square residual (RMR)

Chi-square

For ML, GLS, and WLS, the χ^2-measure is $(N-1)$ times the minimum value of the fit function for the specified model. The χ^2-measure is distributed asymptotically as a chi-square distribution under certain conditions. For ULS and DWLS, certain adjustments are made so as to make the χ^2-measure also asymptotically correct for these methods, see Browne (1984). The χ^2-measure is correct for ULS, ML, GLS, and DWLS under multinormality of the observed variables if a covariance matrix is analyzed. With WLS, the χ^2-measure is correct if a correct weight matrix is used. If a correlation matrix is analyzed with ML, χ^2 is correct only if the model is scale-invariant and $\text{diag}(\hat{\Sigma}) = \text{diag}(S)$. For other cases, see Section 1.12.

If the model is correct and the sample size is sufficiently large, the χ^2-measure may be used as a test statistic for testing the model against the alternative that Σ is unconstrained. The degrees of freedom for χ^2 are

$$df = \frac{1}{2}(p+q)(p+q+1) - t \,, \qquad (1.21)$$

where $p+q$ is the number of observed variables analyzed and t is the total number of independent parameters estimated. The p-value reported by the program is the probability level of χ^2, that is, the probability of obtaining a χ^2-value larger than the value actually obtained, given that the model is correct.

Although the χ^2-measure may be viewed theoretically as a test statistic for testing the hypothesis that Σ is of the form implied by the model against the alternative that Σ is unconstrained (see Jöreskog, 1977), it must be emphasized that such a use of χ^2 is not valid in most applications. In most empirical work, the model is only tentative and is only regarded as an approximation to reality. From this point of view the statistical problem is not one of testing a given hypothesis (which *a priori* may be considered false), but rather one of fitting the model to the data and to decide whether the fit is adequate or not.

Instead of regarding χ^2 as a test statistic, one should regard it as a goodness-of-fit (or badness-of-fit) measure in the sense that large χ^2-values correspond to bad fit and small χ^2-values to good fit. The degrees of freedom serves as a standard by which to judge whether χ^2 is large or small. The χ^2-measure is sensitive to sample size and very sensitive to departures from multivariate normality of the observed variables. In large samples, departures from normality tend to increase χ^2 over and above what can be expected due to specification error in the model. One reasonable way to use χ^2-measures in comparative model fitting is to use χ^2-differences in the following way. If a value of χ^2 is obtained that is large compared to the number of degrees of freedom, the fit may be examined and assessed by an inspection of the fitted residuals, the standardized residuals, and the modification indices (see below). Often these quantities will suggest ways to relax the model by introducing more parameters. The new model usually yields a smaller χ^2. A large drop in χ^2, compared to the difference in degrees of freedom, indicates that the changes made in the model represent a real improvement. On the other hand, a drop in χ^2 close to the difference in number of degrees of freedom indicates that the improvement in fit is obtained by "capitalizing on chance," and the added parameters may not have real significance and meaning.

Goodness-of-fit indices

Following Tanaka & Huba (1984), the goodness-of-fit index is defined as

$$\text{GFI} = 1 - \frac{(\mathbf{s} - \hat{\sigma})' \mathbf{W}^{-1} (\mathbf{s} - \hat{\sigma})}{\mathbf{s}' \mathbf{W}^{-1} \mathbf{s}} . \qquad (1.22)$$

The numerator in (1.22) is the minimum of the fit function after the model has been fitted; the denominator is the fit function before any model has been fitted.

The goodness-of-fit index adjusted for degrees of freedom, or the adjusted GFI, AGFI, is defined as

$$\text{AGFI} = 1 - \frac{(p + q)(p + q + 1)}{2d} (1 - \text{GFI}) , \qquad (1.23)$$

where d is the degrees of freedom of the model. This corresponds to using mean squares instead of total sums of squares in the numerator and denominator of $1 - \text{GFI}$. Both of these measures should be between zero and one, although it is theoretically possible for them to become negative.

(This should not happen, of course, for it means that the model fits worse than any model at all.) Although GFI is not explicitly a function of sample size, its distribution depends on sample size.

Root mean squared residual

The root mean squared residual RMR, is defined as

$$\text{RMR} = \left[2 \sum_{i=1}^{p+q} \sum_{j=1}^{i} (s_{ij} - \hat{\sigma}_{ij})^2 / (p+q)(p+q+1) \right]^{\frac{1}{2}}. \qquad (1.24)$$

RMR is a measure of the average of the fitted residuals and can only be interpreted in relation to the sizes of the observed variances and covariances in $\mathbf{S}$. This measure works best if all observed variables are standardized.

The root mean squared residual can be used to compare the fit of two different models for the same data. The goodness of fit index can be used for this purpose too but can also be used to compare the fit of models for different data.

It should be emphasized that the measures χ^2, GFI, and RMR are measures of the overall fit of the model to the data and do not express the quality of the model judged by any other internal or external criteria. For example, it can happen that the overall fit of the model is very good but with one or more relationships in the model very poorly determined, as judged by the squared multiple correlations, or vice versa. Furthermore, if any of the overall measures indicate that the model does not fit the data well, it does not tell what is wrong with the model or which part of the model is wrong.

Residuals

Using estimates of the parameters, the program computes from the formula (1.4) (see section *The covariance matrix of the observations as implied by the LISREL model* on page 3) the matrix $\hat{\mathbf{\Sigma}}$, called the "fitted covariance matrix." The matrix is printed in the output, if requested, and may be saved in a file (see the OU command in Chapter 2). This matrix may be useful for checking the identification of the model and for power calculations (see Chapter 8).

The elements of $S - \hat{\Sigma}$, the difference between the sample moment matrix and the fitted matrix, are called "fitted residuals."

Although the program will print the fitted residuals on request, the so-called "standardized" residuals computed by the program are usually easier to interpret. A standardized residual is a fitted residual divided by the large-sample standard error of the residual.

LISREL 7 computes standardized residuals by a more exact formula than that used in previous versions of the program. This formula is valid for GLS and ML under normal theory and for WLS if the correct weight matrix is used. The residuals are correlated, but the program does not compute these correlations.

The program provides information about the sample distribution of the standardized residuals in the form of a stem-and-leaf plot and a quantile plot or "Q-plot." The annotated example in section *An annotated example of LISREL input and output* on page 97 shows the stem-and-leaf and Q-plot for some simulated data.

In the Q-plot, the standardized residuals are ordered by size and their percentage points in the sample distribution are calculated. Then the residuals are plotted against the normal deviates corresponding to these percentage points, called normal quantiles, as shown in the annotated example.

Model-modification indices

The modification indices are measures associated with the fixed and constrained parameters of the model. For each fixed and constrained parameter, the modification index is a measure of predicted decrease in χ^2 if a single fixed parameter or equality constraint is relaxed and the model is reestimated. For GLS, ML, and WLS, these indices, therefore, may be judged by means of a χ^2-distribution with 1 degree of freedom. The fixed parameter corresponding to the largest such index is the one that, when relaxed, will improve fit maximally. The improvement in fit is measured by a reduction in χ^2, which is expected to equal the modification index. This procedure seems to work well in practice, but is recommended only when relaxing a parameter makes sense from a substantive point of view and when the estimated value of the parameter can be clearly interpreted.

A new feature in LISREL 7 is that not only are measures of expected improvement of fit provided but also a prediction of the *estimated change* of each fixed and constrained parameter. These predictions give useful information about the sensitivity of the measure of fit to changes in parameters. The practical use of modification indices is discussed in Chapters 3 and 8.

Modification indices are useful not only for fixed parameters but also for equality constraints. We use the notation MI(θ) and CH(θ) for the modification index of θ and the estimated change in θ. If $\theta_1 = \theta_2$, then MI(θ_1) = MI(θ_2). If $\theta_1 = \theta_2 = \theta_3$, there will be three modification indices, MI(θ_1), MI(θ_2), and MI(θ_3), which will generally not be equal. MI(θ_3), say, measures the predicted decrease in χ^2 if θ_3 is freed while the equality constrained $\theta_1 = \theta_2$ is retained and CH(θ_3) measures the predicted change of θ_3 under this condition.

1.9 Standardized solutions

In LISREL 7 there are two kinds of standardized solutions: SS (Standardized Solution) and SC (Completely Standardized Solution). In the SS solution, the latent variables are scaled to have standard derivations equal to unity; the *observed* variables are left in their original metric. In the SC solution, the observed as well as the latent variables are standardized.

These standardized solutions can only be obtained after the model has been fitted with the variables in their original metric. After that, the standard deviations of the observed and latent variables are estimated and applied as scale factors in the rows and columns of the estimated parameter matrices. For formulas, see *LISREL 7: A Guide to the Program and Applications* (Jöreskog & Sörbom, 1989).

1.10   Direct, indirect, and total effects

The path diagram in Figure 1.1 includes both direct and indirect effects of ξ_1 on η_2. For example, in addition to the direct effect γ_{21} of ξ_1 on η_2 there is an indirect effect $\beta_{21}\gamma_{11}$ mediated by η_1. Similarly, although there is no direct effect of ξ_3 on η_1, there is an indirect effect $\beta_{12}\gamma_{23}$ mediated by η_2.

There are never direct effects of an η on itself, *i.e.*, all diagonal elements of $\mathbf{B}$ are zero. Nevertheless, there may be a total effect of each η on *itself*. But this can only occur in non-recursive models and can best be understood by defining a cycle. A cycle is a causal chain going from one η, passing over some other η's, and returning to the original η. The two η's in Figure 1.1 are shown in isolation in Figure 1.2.

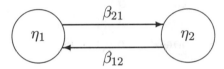

Figure 1.2   Reciprocal Causation Between η_1 and η_2

One cycle for η_1 consists of one path to η_2 and a return to η_1. The effect of one cycle on η_1 is $\beta_{21}\beta_{12}$. After two cycles the effect will be $\beta_{21}^2\beta_2^2$, after three cycles $\beta_{21}^3\beta_{12}^3$, etc. The total effect on η_1 will be the sum of the infinite geometric series $\beta_{21}\beta_{12} + \beta_{21}^2\beta_{12}^2 + \beta_{21}^3\beta_{12}^3 + \cdots$, which is $\beta_{21}\beta_{12}/(1 - \beta_{21}\beta_{12})$ for $\beta_{21}\beta_{12} < 1$.

In general, the total effect of $\boldsymbol{\eta}$ on itself is

$$\mathbf{B} + \mathbf{B}^2 + \mathbf{B}^3 + \cdots = (\mathbf{I} - \mathbf{B})^{-1} - \mathbf{I} , \qquad (1.25)$$

provided the infinite series converges. Similarly, one finds that the total effect of $\boldsymbol{\xi}$ on $\boldsymbol{\eta}$ is

$$(\mathbf{I} + \mathbf{B} + \mathbf{B}^2 + \mathbf{B}^3 + \cdots)\boldsymbol{\Gamma} = (\mathbf{I} - \mathbf{B})^{-1}\boldsymbol{\Gamma}. \qquad (1.26)$$

A necessary and sufficient condition for convergence of the series in (1.25) and (1.26), *i.e.*, for stability of the system, is that all the eigenvalues of $\mathbf{B}$

are within the unit circle. In general the eigenvalues of $\mathbf{B}$ are complex numbers somewhat difficult to compute. However, a *sufficient* condition for convergence is that the largest eigenvalue of $\mathbf{BB}'$ is less than one, and this is very easy to verify. The program prints the largest eigenvalue of $\mathbf{BB}'$ under the name STABILITY INDEX.

General formulas for indirect and total effects are given in Table 1.3.

Table 1.3   Decomposition of Effects

	$\xi \longrightarrow \eta$	$\eta \longrightarrow \eta$
Direct	$\mathbf{\Gamma}$	$\mathbf{B}$
Indirect	$(\mathbf{I}-\mathbf{B})^{-1}\mathbf{\Gamma}-\mathbf{\Gamma}$	$(\mathbf{I}-\mathbf{B})^{-1}-\mathbf{I}-\mathbf{B}$
Total	$(\mathbf{I}-\mathbf{B})^{-1}\mathbf{\Gamma}$	$(\mathbf{I}-\mathbf{B})^{-1}-\mathbf{I}$
	$\xi \longrightarrow \mathbf{y}$	$\eta \longrightarrow \mathbf{y}$
Direct	$\mathbf{0}$	$\mathbf{\Lambda}_y$
Indirect	$\mathbf{\Lambda}_y(\mathbf{I}-\mathbf{B})^{-1}\mathbf{\Gamma}$	$\mathbf{\Lambda}_y(\mathbf{I}-\mathbf{B})^{-1}-\mathbf{\Lambda}_y$
Total	$\mathbf{\Lambda}_y(\mathbf{I}-\mathbf{B})^{-1}\mathbf{\Gamma}$	$\mathbf{\Lambda}_y(\mathbf{I}-\mathbf{B})^{-1}$

1.11   Covariances among all LISREL variables

The general form of the LISREL model involves the vectors of the four basic variables, $\mathbf{y}$, η, $\mathbf{x}$, and ξ. The equations and assumptions of the sections on pages 1–3 imply that the covariance matrix of these variables is

$$
\text{Cov}\begin{bmatrix} \mathbf{y} \\ \eta \\ \mathbf{x} \\ \xi \end{bmatrix} = \begin{bmatrix} \mathbf{\Lambda}_y(\mathbf{\Pi\Phi\Pi}'+\mathbf{\Psi}^*)\mathbf{\Lambda}_y'+\mathbf{\Theta}_\epsilon & & & \\ (\mathbf{\Pi\Phi\Pi}'+\mathbf{\Psi}^*)\mathbf{\Lambda}_y' & \mathbf{\Pi\Phi\Pi}'+\mathbf{\Psi}^* & & \\ \mathbf{\Lambda}_x\mathbf{\Phi\Pi}'\mathbf{\Lambda}_y' & \mathbf{\Lambda}_x\mathbf{\Phi\Pi}' & \mathbf{\Lambda}_x\mathbf{\Phi\Lambda}_x'+\mathbf{\Theta}_\delta & \\ \mathbf{\Phi\Pi}'\mathbf{\Lambda}_y' & \mathbf{\Phi\Pi}' & \mathbf{\Phi\Lambda}_x' & \mathbf{\Phi} \end{bmatrix},
$$

where $\mathbf{\Pi} = (\mathbf{I}-\mathbf{B})^{-1}\mathbf{\Gamma}$ and $\mathbf{\Psi}^* = (\mathbf{I}-\mathbf{B})^{-1}\mathbf{\Psi}(\mathbf{I}-\mathbf{B}')^{-1}$.

It is possible to obtain estimates of all the submatrices of this large matrix, but the various parts will appear in different sections of the output.

The (y, y), (x, y), and (x, x) parts are contained in the fitted covariance matrix $\hat{\Sigma}$ that will appear if requested with the RS option on the OU command, or that may be saved into a file if requested with SI=*filename* on the OU command. The (η, η), (η, ξ), and (ξ, ξ) parts are contained in the joint covariance matrix of η and ξ that is always given in the section LIS-REL ESTIMATES. The covariance parts (y, η), (y, ξ), (x, η), and (x, ξ) are printed if requested with the option MR on the OU command.

1.12   Analysis of correlation matrices

The general rule is that the covariance matrix should be analyzed. However, in many behavioral sciences applications units of measurement in the observed variables have no definite meaning and are often arbitrary or irrelevant. For these reasons, for convenience, and for interpretational purposes, the correlation matrix is often analyzed as if it is a covariance matrix. This is a common practice.

The analysis of correlation matrices is problematic in several ways. Such an analysis may

(a)   modify the model being analyzed,
(b)   produce incorrect χ^2 and other goodness-of-fit measures, and
(c)   give incorrect standard errors.

Problem (a) can occur when the model includes constrained parameters. For example, if $\lambda_{11}^{(x)}$ and $\lambda_{21}^{(x)}$ are constrained to be equal but the variances $\sigma_{11}^{(xx)}$ and $\sigma_{22}^{(xx)}$ are not equal, then analysis of the correlation matrix will give estimates of

$$\lambda_{11}^{(x)}/\sqrt{\sigma_{11}^{(xx)}} \quad \text{and} \quad \lambda_{21}^{(x)}/\sqrt{\sigma_{22}^{(xx)}}$$

which are not equal. Correlation matrices should not be analyzed if the model contains equality constraints of this kind.

The main question is whether the standard errors and χ^2 goodness-of-fit measures produced when correlation matrices are analyzed are asymptotically correct. The exact conditions under which this is the case are extremely complicated and give little practical guidance. However, crucial conditions are that the model is scale-invariant and that

$$\text{diag}(\hat{\boldsymbol{\Sigma}}) = \text{diag}(\mathbf{S}) \ .$$

These conditions hold for some, *but not all*, models and for some, *but not all*, methods. For example, they hold for Examples 3.2, 3.4, and 4.5, but not for Examples 5.5 and 6.6.

2 The LISREL problem run

This chapter contains the complete LISREL command specifications.[1]

2.1 Preparing the LISREL command file

Execution of LISREL problems is controlled by a command file describing three phases of processing:

1) data input; 2) model construction; 3) output of results.

Commands

A typical LISREL command consists of a two-letter command name, one or more option names, and one or more keywords set equal to values.[2] The order of options and keywords is immaterial. In the command descriptions to follow, a command is represented in the form:

Name   Keyword$_1 = a$ Keyword$_2 = b$ $\cdots$ | Option 1A | | Option 2A | $\cdots$
                                                     | Option 1B | | Option 2B |
                                                     $\vdots$ $\vdots$

Only one of the options enclosed in boxes may be selected. The equals sign is required in keywords. Options and keywords may be separated by

---

[1] In this edition of the guide, this chapter has been updated to LISREL 8.

[2] Messages (errors or warnings) in the program output still use the term "parameter" instead of "keyword" or "option." To avoid confusion with model parameters, this guide uses the new terminology.

commas or blanks. Blanks on either side of an equals sign are permitted. The command ends with a return character. More than one command may appear on a physical line provided they are separated by semicolons and the line does not exceed 127 columns. A command may be continued on the next physical line by writing a C in place of an option or keyword, then starting the next line with that option or keyword.

Significant characters. Only the first two characters are significant in command names, options, keywords, and character keyword values. Any additional characters up to the first blank, comma, semicolon, or equals sign will be ignored. Thus,

DA, DATA, DAta, and data

are all equivalent.

Detail lines

A command may be followed by detail lines giving additional information. The RA command, for example, may be followed by the data for the problem if desired. Large data sets are usually placed in a separate file, however. In general it is recommended that all data be read from external files, not from the command file. In that way the program can better detect errors in the data.

FORTRAN format statements in the command file

When data (labels, raw data, summary statistics) are used in fixed format, a FORTRAN format statement is needed to instruct the program how to read the data. The general form of such a statement is

(rCw) or *(rCw.d),*

where:
- *r* Repeat count; if omitted, 1 is assumed.
- *C* Format code:
  - A   Code for character values (used in LA, LK, and LE commands)

	Code for integer values (used in PA command)
I	
F	Code for real numbers (used in RA, CM, ME, SD, etc., commands)
w	Field width, or number of columns.
d	Number of decimal places (for F-format).

The format statement should be enclosed in parentheses. Blanks within the statement are ignored: (r C w . d) is acceptable. Anything after the right parenthesis and on the same line is also ignored by the program, thus comments may be placed after the format statement.

Examples:

The labels HEIGHT, WEIGHT, AGE, and IQ could be read in fixed format as:

```
(A6,A6,A3,A2)
HEIGHTWEIGHTAGEIQ
```

Or, with the same result, as:

```
(4A6)
HEIGHTWEIGHT  AGE   IQ
```

Note that the first method lets the repeat count default to 1, and that it describes several different fields, separated by commas, with one statement.

The following example shows three ways to read five integers, with the same result:

```
(5I1)
12345
(5I2)
 1 2 3 4 5
(I1,I2,3I3)
1 2  3  4  5
```

The F-format requires the number of decimal places in the field description, so if there are none (and eight columns) specify (F8.0), (F8) is not allowed. However, if a data value contains a decimal point, then this overrides the location of the decimal point as specified by the general field description. If the general field description is given by (F8.5), then 12345678 would result in the real number $+123.45678$, but the decimal point in -1234.56 would not change. Just a decimal point, or only blanks will result in the value zero. The plus sign is optional.

It is possible to use the format statement to skip over variables in the data file, when they are not needed in the analysis. For example, the format statement (F7.4,8X,2F3.2) informs the program that the data file has 21 columns per line. The first value can be found in the first seven columns (and there are four decimal places), then eight columns should be skipped, and a second and third value are in columns 16–21, both occupying three columns (with two decimal places).

Another possibility is the use of the tabulator format descriptor T, followed by a column number n. For instance, (1F8.5, T60, 2F5.1) describes three data fields; in columns 1–8, with five decimal digits, next in columns 61–65 and 66–70, both with one decimal digit. If the number n is smaller than the current column position, left-tabbing results. Left tabs should be used cautiously. No problems are known when data records are shorter than 256 columns. But under certain operating systems, some PRELIS/LISREL versions support left tabs reliably only if the line length of the data file is 512 columns or less.

A forward slash (/) in an F-format means "skip the rest of this line and continue on the next line." Thus, (F10.3/5F10.3) instructs the program to read the first variable on the first line, then to skip the remaining variables on that line and to read five variables on the next line.

For other uses of a format statement, a FORTRAN textbook should be consulted, because there are more possibilities then can be explained here. Note, however, that LISREL allows selection (and reordering) of variables with the SE command.

Rules for line length

The command file can normally have lines of up to 127 characters, except under some operating systems that restricts input lines to 80 characters.

The maximum record length for external data files depends on the mode of the input. If data are read in free format, the maximum record length is 127 characters. When fixed format is used, all systems support record lengths of up to 1024 characters.

Note that some systems support left-tabbing only when the record length is 512 or less (see Section 2.4.3 above). Format statements are always processed like command lines. Even if the format statement is given in the first line of a data file, only its first 127 columns will be processed. However, the format statement may be continued over up to five records.

Stacked problems

The program stops reading input after the first OU command, or in the case of a multigroup problem after the OU command for the last group, as indicated with the keyword NG=n on the DA command. Then, after the data for this problem has been analyzed, it proceeds reading the next problem in the command file, if there is one; else the program stops.

Thus, any number of problems may be stacked together and analyzed in one run. See, for instance, Example 3.3 in Chapter 3.

Because the PRELIS and LISREL programs close files when they terminate and not when a problem is completed, there may be many open data files at the end of a set of "stacked" input problems. When the program reaches a problem specification in the middle of the stacked file, all files used by previous problems are still open.

When an output file is assigned in several problems, output lines from a later problem will simply be appended at the end of the file. For input files, two cases should be distinguished:

a. The data file is also "stacked." After LISREL has read from it the lines needed for previous problems, the next problem will read data from the next line of the data file.

   Example:
   The data file STACKED1.DAT contains two covariance matrices, each preceded by a format statement.

```
(4F8.3)                                          Sample 1
   63.382
   70.984 110.237
   41.710   52.747   60.584
   30.218   37.489   36.392   32.295
(3F8.5)                                          Sample 2
107.3305
  55.3437 63.2032
  38.8969 39.2611 35.4037
```

The two LISREL problems specified in the following command file read the two covariance matrices from STACKED1.DAT in turn:

```
Problem 1 using sample 1
DA NI=4 NO=898
CM FILE=STACKED1.DAT                        reads first five lines
MO . . .
OU . . .
Problem 2 using sample 2
DA NI=3 NO=500
CM FILE=STACKED1.DAT                        reads last four lines
MO . . .
OU . . .
```

b. The same data are to be read repeatedly. At the conclusion of each problem, the data file must be rewound. In each problem specification, the last command that reads the data must contain the RE option to specify rewinding the file.

Example:

The dataset DATAB contains a covariance matrix and variable labels:

```
63.382                                       covariance matrix
70.984   110.237
41.710    52.747   60.584
V-ONE     V-TWO   V-THREE                    variable labels
```

The commands below would read DATAB once for the first problem, rewind the file, and read it again for the second problem specification:

```
Problem 1
DA NI=3 NO=898
CM FILE=DATAB                                reads lines 1–3
```

```
LA FILE=DATAB REwind                    reads line 4, rewinds  DATAB
MO . . .
OU . . .
Problem 2
DA NI=3 NO=898
CM FILE=DATAB                            reads lines 1–3
LA FILE=DATAB                              reads line 4
MO . . .
OU . . .
```

Order of commands

The order of the LISREL commands is arbitrary except for the following conditions:

- ☐ After optional title lines, a DA (data) command must always come first.
- ☐ The OU (output) command must always be last.
- ☐ LK, LE, FR, FI, EQ, CO, IR, PA, VA, ST, MA, PL, and NF commands must always come after the MO (model) command.
- ☐ The MO command is optional only if no LISREL model is analyzed. If the MO command is missing, only the matrix to be analyzed will be printed out. Otherwise, the MO command must appear in the command file.
- ☐ Although the order of other commands is relatively free, a later command will overrule an earlier command, in so far as the same elements are referenced.

PURPOSE

Title lines are not commands and are optional. The LISREL commands for each problem may be preceded by one or more title lines naming and describing the problem. The program will read, and print at the head of the problem output, all lines preceding the DA (data description) command, thereafter it prints only the first title line as a heading for each section of output.

The title lines must *not* use as the first two non-blank characters DA, LA, or OB. Those characters signal the start of the LISREL data description (DA) command or the SIMPLIS commands: Labels or Observed Variables. To avoid this problem, it is good practice to begin all title lines with an exclamation mark (!) or the slash-asterisk combination (/*).

See Example 5.6 for an illustration.

FORMAT

... *text* ...
... *text* ...

PURPOSE

To specify the structure of the data and the type of moment matrix to be analyzed.

FORMAT

DA   NG $= n$ NI $= k$ NO $= N$ MA $=$ *type of matrix*

        XM $=$ *global missing value*   RP $=$ *number of repetitions*

KEYWORDS

NG   Number of groups
Default: NG=1
(For multigroup problems only; see Chapter 9.)

NI   Number of input variables
Default: None; required keyword.
The value of k must be specified or the program will stop. The number of variables is limited only by machine capacity.

NO   Number of cases
Default: NO=0
If raw data is to be read from an external file, leave NO default and the program will compute N. Otherwise, if NO is not specified, the program will stop.

MA   Type of matrix to be analyzed
Default: MA=CM
Possible values for MA:

     MM   for a matrix of moments about zero

     AM   for an augmented moment matrix

     CM   for a covariance matrix

     KM   for a matrix of product moment correlations based on raw scores or normal scores

     OM   for a correlation matrix of optimal scores produced by PRELIS

     PM   for a matrix which includes polychoric or polyserial correlations

     RM   for a matrix of Spearman rank correlations

     TM   for a matrix of Kendall's tau-c correlations

XM   Value for missing data. If this keyword is specified, c is a global numeric value that represents all missing values in the whole data matrix. LISREL uses *listwise deletion*. Use PRELIS for *pairwise deletion* and for different missing value representations, as well as other raw data problems (see Section 1.6).

RP   Number of repetitions.
Default: RP=1
This keyword is new with LISREL 8. It is intended for Monte Carlo and bootstrap studies (see Appendix C in the *PRELIS 2 User's Reference Guide*).

For example, RP=100 means *repeat 100 times* and has the same effect as stacking 100 command files after each other, *i.e.*, the command file will be read and executed 100 times.

NOTES

The MA value specifies the kind of matrix to be *analyzed*, not the kind of matrix to be *input*. The program will convert the *input* matrix to the form specified before analysis, and starts the output with this matrix. The variables may be selected or reordered (see SE command below) before the matrix is analyzed.

LISREL stops reading raw data when a record with *all* zero values (an empty record) is encountered.

PURPOSE
To assign names to each observed variable.

FORMAT
LA   FI = *filename* FO RE

> *(Variable format statement)*
> *

Data (labels)

KEYWORDS
FI   User specified name of file containing the labels.
      With LISREL 8, the shorter command format LA=*filename* may be used.
      Default: Labels are in the command file.

OPTIONS (only relevant for external file)
FO   If this option appears, the variable format statement describing the label records will appear as the next line.
      Default: Format statement (if any) is at the head of the label file.

RE   If this option appears, the label file will be rewound after the labels are read. Only an external file may be rewound.
      Default: No rewind.

DETAIL LINES
(Variable format statement)
      If the FI keyword and the FO option do appear (or nothing at all), and the labels are in *fixed* format, a FORTRAN A-format statement, enclosed in parentheses, is inserted here to describe the column assignments of the label records.

*   Otherwise, an asterisk (*) may appear in column 1 to indicate that the labels are in free format (separated by spaces, commas, or return characters).
      Default: *

Data (y- and x-labels)
      If an extenal file is not specified, the labels must appear at this point in the command file.

NOTES

If no LA command appears, the default labels for observed variables (VAR 1, VAR 2, . . .) are used.

The order of the labels follows the order of the input variables. The necessary order, when both x- and y-variables are present, is y-variables first; if this is not the case, the SE command below should be used to reorder the variables and their labels.

There are eight columns available for labels. In free format longer labels will be cut off at the right. In fixed format longer labels, like (A9), will be cut off at the left. Labels shorter than eight columns will be padded with spaces to the left, in both formats.

EXAMPLES

The four following examples demonstrate the various possibilities for the LA command. Assume that the number of input variables equals eight, *i.e.*, NI=8.

```
1. LA
   *
   'LABEL 1',, 'LABEL 3' 'LABEL 4'
   'LABEL 5', 'LABEL 6'/
```

The LA command, without anything, indicates that format and labels will be next. The line with the asterisk, indicating free format, is optional. The labels are separated by a comma, a space or a return character, hence the labels themselves are in right quotes (or apostrophes) to protect the space within each label. The double comma (,,) tells the program that no label will be given here and the default should be used. A triple comma (,,,) would skip two labels, etc. The forward slash (/) ends the list of labels before their number equals NI on the DA command, otherwise it is not needed. Again, default labels will be used. So, the result of example 1 would be:

```
LABEL 1   VAR 2 LABEL 3 LABEL 4 LABEL 5 LABEL 6 VAR 7 VAR 8
```

```
2. LA
   (4A7)
   LABEL 1LABEL 2LABEL 3LABEL 4
   LABEL 5LABEL 6LABEL 7LABEL 8
```

This time, a fixed format is used, informing the program that four labels of seven characters will follow. Since NI=8, two such lines are expected. In fixed format no defaults are available, of course.

```
3. LA FI=LABEL
```

No detail lines are expected after the DA command. The labels are in the external file called LABEL. If the labels are in fixed format, LABEL will start with a variable format statement, otherwise, in free format, the labels start immediately or they are optionally preceded with a line containing an asterisk. The RE option could be added if the same labels are to be used again in the next problem of a command file with several (stacked) problems.

```
4. LA=LABEL FO ! Note the shorter LISREL 8 notation.
   (8A7)
```

The difference with the example above is that the FO option indicates that a format statement will follow in the command file. This format shows that the labels are in fixed format, with eight labels per record.

PURPOSE

To input case records containing values of the variables for analysis.

FORMAT

RA   FI = *filename* FO RE

> *(Variable format statement)*
> *

Data (observations)

KEYWORDS

FI   User specified name of file containing the labels.

With LISREL 8, the shorter command format RA=*filename* may be used.

Default: Observations are in the command file.

OPTIONS (only relevant for external file)

FO   If this option appears, the variable format statement describing the observation records will appear as the next line.

Default: Format statement (if any) is at the head of the observation file.

RE   If this option appears, the observation file will be rewound after the observations are read. Only an external file may be rewound.

Default: No rewind.

DETAIL LINES

(Variable format statement)

If the FI keyword and the FO option do appear (or nothing at all), and the observations are in *fixed* format, a FORTRAN F-format statement, enclosed in parentheses, is inserted here to describe the column assignments of the observation records.

*   Otherwise, an asterisk (*) may appear in column 1 to indicate that the observations are in free format (separated by spaces, commas, or return characters).

Default: *

Data (observations)

If an external file is not specified, the observations must appear at this point in the command file.

NOTES

The raw data are read one case after another. There must be NI data values (see DA command) for each case. Preferably, data are read from an external file. Then, the program will determine the sample size if NO on the DA command is default or set to 0. Or, if NO is erroneously set too large, the program will terminate input when an end-of-file is encountered and will use the correct case count in the computations. If NO is set too small, only NO cases will be read, regardless of how many cases exist. When the data are included in the command file, NO should indicate the number of cases correctly, otherwise the program will stop with an error message. When reading a raw data case in free format, blanks, commas and return characters are used as delimiters and the following options are available:

- Ending a case record with a forward slash may be used to indicate that all remaining data values for this case are the same as the corresponding data values for the previous case.
- Two consecutive commas may be used to specify that the corresponding data value for the previous case should be inserted between the commas. Three consecutive commas imply that two data values from the previous case will be inserted, etc.
- Repetitions of the same data value can be specified by an $*$ preceded by a repeat factor. For example, 4*1 means 1 1 1 1.
- LISREL interprets all data values as floating point decimal numbers. However, for data values that are integers, the decimal point may be omitted.

EXAMPLES

1. Raw data are read from an external file, called DATA. The data are in fixed format and the format statement follows the RA command in the command file, as indicated by the option FO. The number of observations will be computed by the program from the data, because the NO keyword on the DA command was not given.

```
DA NI=5
RA FI=DATA FO
(5F3.1)
```

2. Raw data follow the RA command in free format.

```
DA NI=5 NO=20
RA
3.5 4.2 6.8, 9.3, 10.1
3.7 5.1 /
3.2 ,, 7.2 3.4 9
2*3.8 4.1
6.2 4.1
.
.
.
```

Note that the optional asterisk (*) to indicate free format is not used. The first four cases of the raw data are equivalent to:

```
(5F3.1)
 35 42 68 93101
 37 51 68 93101
 32 51 72 34 90
 38 38 41 62 41
```

PURPOSE

To read summary statistics for the LISREL analysis: covariances, correlations, or moments about zero.

FORMAT

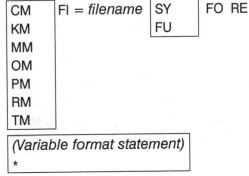

Data *(summary statistics)*

KEYWORDS

FI   User specified name of file containing the summary statistics. With LISREL 8, the shorter command format, for example, CM=*filename* may be used.
Default: Summary statistics are in the command file.

OPTIONS

SY   Only elements in and below the main diagonal are present; they are read across successive rows up to and including the diagonal element.

FU   *All* elements in the symmetric data matrix are present and are read rowwise.
Default: SY (But see NOTES below)

FO   If this option appears, the variable format statement describing the summary statistics records will appear as the next line.
Default: Format statement (if any) is at the head of the summary statistics file.

RE   If this option appears, the summary statistics file will be rewound after the summary statistics are read. Only an external file may be rewound.
Default: No rewind.

DETAIL LINES
(Variable format statement)

If the FI keyword and the FO option do appear (or nothing at all), and the summary statistics are in *fixed* format, a FORTRAN format statement, enclosed in parentheses, is inserted here to describe the column assignments of the summary statistics records.

*   Otherwise, an asterisk (*) may appear in column 1 to indicate that the summary statistics are in free format (separated by spaces, commas, or return characters).
Default: *

Data (summary statistics)

If an external file is not specified, the summary statistics must appear at this point in the command file.

NOTES

The summary statistics are in the form of a covariance, correlation, or moment matrix as specified by CM, KM, or MM, respectively. Besides a product moment correlation matrix (KM), a correlation matrix based on optimal scores (OM) or a matrix that includes polychoric and/or polyserial correlations (PM) can be input. (PRELIS can produce both OM and PM.)

PRELIS 2 also computes Spearman rank correlations or Kendall's tau-c correlations. These matrices may be input with the RM and TM commands, respectively.

If the MA keyword in the DA command indicates that a covariance matrix is to be analyzed but a correlation matrix has been input by the KM command, standard deviations for the observations must be read in (see SD command).

If the MA keyword in the DA command indicates that the moments about zero are to be analyzed but a covariance matrix has been input by the CM command, means for the observations must be read in (see ME command).

If MA=MM appears and a correlation matrix has been input, both the means and the standard deviations must be read in.

When neither the FU nor the SY option has been specified, and the data are in fixed format, the lower half of the matrix should be entered rowwise *as one long line*. In free format, when return characters are treated as delimiters, the matrix can be entered with one row per line. See EXAMPLES below.

EXAMPLES

Given the following covariance matrix,

$$\mathbf{S} = \left(\begin{array}{ccc} 1.13 & -0.87 & 1.08 \\ -0.87 & 2.17 & 1.83 \\ 1.08 & 1.83 & 3.25 \end{array} \right),$$

using the format F5.2, the input in the three alternatives will be (note the blanks):

```
CM FU
(3F5.2)
  113  -87  108
  -87  217  183
  108  183  325


CM SY
(3F5.2)
  113
  -87  217
  108  183  325


CM
(6F5.2)
  113  -87  217  108  183  325
```

Another possibility is to read the matrix in free format. If blanks and return characters are used as delimiters, there is no distinction between starting a new line for each row of the matrix and reading all elements as one long line. For example, the full matrix can be read by giving

```
CM FU
1.13 -.87 1.08
-.87 2.17 1.83
1.08 1.83 3.25
```

When reading only the lower half of the matrix, the option SY is redundant (for free format).

```
CM
1.13 -.87 2.17 1.08 1.83 3.25
```

or, equivalently,

```
CM
1.13
-.87    2.17
1.08    1.83    3.25
```

PURPOSE

To read the means and/or the standard deviations of the observations.

FORMAT

| ME | FI = *filename* FO RE |
| SD | |

| *(Variable format statement)* |
| * |

Data (vector of NI means or standard deviations)

KEYWORDS

FI   User specified name of file containing the means and/or standard deviations.

With LISREL 8, the shorter command format, for example, ME=*filename* may be used.

Default: Means or standard deviations are in the command file.

OPTIONS (only relevant for external file)

FO   If this option appears, the variable format statement describing the means or standard deviation records will appear as the next line.

Default: Format statement (if any) is at the head of the file with the means or standard deviations.

RE   If this option appears, the means or standard deviations file will be rewound after the means or standard deviations are read. Only an external file may be rewound.

Default: No rewind.

DETAIL LINES

(Variable format statement)

If the FI keyword and the FO option do appear (or nothing at all), and the means or standard deviations are in *fixed* format, a FORTRAN format statement, enclosed in parentheses, is inserted here to describe the column assignments of the means or standard deviation records.

           *   An asterisk (*) may appear in column 1 to indicate that the means
                   or standard deviations are in free format (separated by spaces,
                   commas, or return characters).
                   Default: *

Data (vector of NI *means or standard deviations)*
                   If an external file is not specified, the means or standard devia-
                   tions must appear at this point in the command file.

EXAMPLES The following part of a command file instructs the program to read first a covariance matrix, from a file called COVMEANS, next it reads the means of the input variables from the same external file, in a format specified after the ME command in the command file.

```
DA NI=3 MA=MM
CM FI=COVMEANS
ME FI=COVMEANS FO
(3F5.3)
```

The file COVMEANS looks like:

```
(3F5.2)
  113
  -87   217
  108   183   325
 1015  2185  3753
```

The first line is the format for the covariance matrix, which occupies itself the next three lines, followed by the three means.

ME,SD

PURPOSE

To read the asymptotic covariance matrix of the elements of the co-variance or the correlation matrix to be analyzed by the WLS method.

For the WLS estimation method, use either the AC or the WM command.

FORMAT

AC   FI = *filename*

KEYWORDS

FI   User specified name of file containing the asymptotic covariance matrix.

With LISREL 8, the shorter command format AC=*filename* may be used.

Default: None.

NOTES

The AC command can only be used with MA=CM, KM, or PM on the DA command. It (or a weight matrix, see the WM command) is necessary for use of the WLS estimation method, the default method (i.s.o. ML) if the AC command appears. If DWLS is requested on the OU command only the diagonal elements of the asymptotic covariance matrix will be used. For ULS, GLS, or ML the matrix is ignored.

The number of distinct elements in the asymptotic covariance matrix is

$\frac{1}{2}k(k+1)[\frac{1}{2}k(k+1)+1]$ if MA=CM

$\frac{1}{2}k(k-1)[\frac{1}{2}k(k-1)+1]$ if MA=KM or PM,

where k is specified by the NI keyword on the DA command.

The asymptotic covariance matrix can only be read from an external file. If this matrix is produced by PRELIS, no format is necessary. Otherwise, specify the format in the first line of the external file if the elements of the asymptotic covariance matrix are in fixed format. This matrix should be read in SY form only (see CM, KM, MM, OM, PM, RM, TM commands). Note that the FO and RE options are not allowed on the AC command.

PURPOSE

To read a symmetric Moore-Penrose generalized inverse $\mathbf{W}^-$ instead of $\mathbf{W}^{-1}$ as a weight matrix in the fit function for WLS.

For the WLS estimation method, use either the AC or the WM command.

FORMAT

WM   FI = *filename*

KEYWORDS

FI   User specified name of file containing the weight matrix.
With LISREL 8, the shorter command format WM=*filename* may be used.
Default: None.

NOTES

This weight matrix can only be read from an external file.

There are situations where the asymptotic covariance matrix $\mathbf{W}$ produced by PRELIS 2 may be singular or ill-conditioned (very nearly singular). In such a situation it is better to use a symmetric Moore-Penrose generalized inverse $\mathbf{W}^-$ instead of $\mathbf{W}^{-1}$ as a weight matrix in the fit function for WLS.

To do so, put the asymptotic covariance matrix $\mathbf{W}$ produced by PRELIS 2 in the file *infile*.AC, run the utility program GINV with the DOS command line

GINV *infile*.AC *outfile*.WM

where *outfile*.WM is the filename where the weight matrix $\mathbf{W}^-$ is to be stored. Then, in the LISREL 8 input file, use the command line

WM= *outfile*.WM

to read this weight matrix.

If a WM command is used, no selection of variables is possible in LISREL 8 since the selection of variables must be done in $\mathbf{W}$ before the generalized inverse is computed. If selection of variables is necessary, they can be done, by using SD commands, for example, in PRELIS 2.

The weight matrix $\mathbf{W}^-$ produced by GINV is stored in binary form in *outfile*.WM. It is obtained by computing all eigenvalues of $\mathbf{W}$ greater than ϵ, k say, and the corresponding eigenvectors and then using the formula

$$\mathbf{W}^- = \mathbf{U}_k \mathbf{D}_k^{-1} \mathbf{U}_k' \,,$$

where $\mathbf{D}_k$ is a diagonal matrix of the k largest eigenvalues of $\mathbf{W}$ and $\mathbf{U}_k$ is a matrix with the corresponding orthonormal eigenvectors as columns.

In addition to the binary file *outfile*.WM, GINV gives an ordinary output file called OUTPUT which gives all the eigenvalues of $\mathbf{W}$. This can be used to inspect the eigenvalues and to decide on a suitable value of ϵ.

The default value of ϵ is 10^{-12}. Larger values can be used but ϵ should not be chosen too large. To change ϵ, use the following DOS command line to execute GINV:

```
GINV  infile.AC  outfile.WM -EPS= e
```

where e is the required value of ϵ.

The WM command can only be used with MA=CM, KM, or PM on the DA command. Either this weight matrix or the asymptotic covariance matrix (see AC command) is necessary for use of the WLS estimation method, the default method (i.s.o. ML) if the AC or the WM command appear.

If DWLS is requested on the OU command only the diagonal elements of the weight matrix will be used. For ULS, GLS, or ML the matrix is ignored.

PURPOSE

To read the asymptotic variances of the elements of the covariance or correlation matrix to be analyzed by the DWLS method.

For the DWLS estimation method, use either the AV or the DM command.

FORMAT

AV   FI = *filename*

KEYWORDS

FI   User specified name of file containing the asymptotic variances. With LISREL 8, the shorter command format AV=*filename* may be used.
Default: None.

NOTES

The AV command can only be used with MA=CM, KM, or PM on the DA command. It is necessary for use of the DWLS estimation method, the default method (i.s.o. ML) if the AV command appears. If ULS, GLS, or ML is requested on the OU command, the asymptotic variances are ignored, while the choice of WLS leads to an error message.

The number of elements in the asymptotic variances file is

$\frac{1}{2}k(k+1)$ if MA=CM
$\frac{1}{2}k(k-1)$ if MA=KM or PM,

where k is specified by the NI keyword on the DA command.

The asymptotic variances can only be read from an external file. If these variances are produced by PRELIS, no format is necessary. Otherwise, specify the format in the first line of the external file if the variances are in fixed format. Note that the FO and RE options are not allowed on the AV command.

PURPOSE

To read user supplied weights for DWLS analysis.

For the DWLS estimation method, use either the AV or the DM command.

FORMAT

DM   FI = *filename*

KEYWORDS

FI   User specified name of file containing the diagonal weights.
With LISREL 8, the shorter command format DM=*filename* may be used.
Default: None.

NOTES

The DM command can only be used with MA=CM, KM, PM, or MM on the DA command. It is necessary for the DWLS estimation method, the default method (i.s.o. ML) if the DM command appears. No standard errors, *t*-values, chi-squares, etc., can be obtained. The diagonal weights are ignored if ULS, GLS, or ML is requested on the OU command.

The number of elements in the diagonal weights matrix is

$\frac{1}{2}k(k+1)$ if MA=CM or MM
$\frac{1}{2}k(k-1)$ if MA=KM or PM,

where k is specified by the NI keyword on the DA command.

The weights can only be read from an external file. Specify the format in the first line of the external file if the weights are in fixed format. Note that the FO and RE options are not allowed on the DM command.

See the sections *Generally weighted least-squares* on page 21 and *Diagonally weighted least-squares* on page 23 for a definition of the weights.

PURPOSE

To select in any order any number of variables from the NI input variables.

FORMAT

SE   FI = *filename*

List of variable names or numbers

KEYWORDS

FI   User specified name of file containing the list of variable names or numbers.

With LISREL 8, the shorter command format SE=*filename* may be used.

Default: The list of names follows the SE command.

DETAIL LINES

List of variable names or numbers

If an external file is not specified, the list of variables must appear at this point in the command file.

NOTES

The selected variables should be listed either by number or by label (see: LA command) in the order that they are wanted in the model and *the y-variables should be listed first.*

The variable names are listed in free-format separated by blanks, commas, or return characters (a variable format statement is not required).

If the number of names in the list is less than NI, the list must terminate with a forward slash (/).

See Examples 4.3 and 4.5 for illustrations.

The selection and reordering of variables specified by the SE command will affect not only the covariance or correlation matrix to be analyzed but also the asymptotic covariance matrix or the asymptotic variances if these have been entered. See Example 7.2 for an illustration.

PURPOSE

To specify the model for the LISREL analysis.

FORMAT

MO   NY $= p$ NX $= q$ NE $= m$ NK $= n$ AP $= k$ FI

LY $= mf,mm$ LX $= mf,mm$

BE $= mf,mm$ GA $= mf,mm$

PH $= mf,mm$ PS $= mf,mm$

TE $= mf,mm$ TD $= mf,mm$ TH $= mf,mm$

TY $= mf,mm$ TX $= mf,mm$ AL $= mf,mm$ KA $= mf,mm$

KEYWORDS

NY   The number of y-variables in the model
      Default: NY = 0

NX   The number of x-variables in the model
      Default: NX = 0

NE   The number of η-variables in the model
      Default: NE = 0

NK   The number of ξ-variables in the model
      Default: NK = 0

AP   The number of additional parameters
      See the section *General covariance structures* on page 347 in Appendix A for an explanation of this new feature for LISREL 8.
      Default: AP = 0

TH   With LISREL 8, the full LISREL model has been extended with a parameter matrix $\Theta_{\delta\epsilon}$ of order $q \times p$ representing the covariance matrix between δ and ϵ. The LISREL name for this matrix is TH. This matrix is a fixed zero matrix by default. It *cannot* be declared free on the MO command. However, any of its elements can be declared free on a FR command.
      Default: TH = ZE,FI

TY, TX, AL, KA

> Chapter 10 introduces these four parameter matrices (actually vectors). They are used for models with mean structures, the extended LISREL model.
>
> Default: TY = ZE,FI   TX = ZE,FI   AL = ZE,FI   KA = ZE,FI

The remaining keywords are discussed in the NOTES below.

OPTION

FI   One option may be given on the MO command, namely the logical option FIxed-x. This signifies that the x-variables are fixed or unconstrained random variables. See the section *Unconstrained x* on page 341 in Appendix A.

If FI is given on the MO command, the program *automatically* sets NK=NX, $\Lambda_x = \mathbf{I}$, $\Theta_\delta = 0$, $\Phi = \mathbf{S}_{xx}$ (fixed), *i.e.*, $\xi \equiv \mathbf{x}$.

LISREL 8 automatically recognizes this kind of model if NK is omitted or NK=0 on the MO command. It is no longer necessary to use the FI option to specify such models. In LISREL 8, FI means that Φ is to be considered fixed and equal to $\mathbf{S}_{xx}$. Thus,

- o Without FI, Φ will be estimated as a free parameter matrix along with the standard errors of $\hat{\Phi}$.
- o With FI, $\Phi = \mathbf{S}_{xx}$ is fixed and no standard errors of $\hat{\Phi}$ are computed.

See Examples 5.3B and 5.5.

NOTES

The remaining keywords specify the form *mf* and/or mode *mm* of the parameter matrices. The order of *mf* and *mm* is immaterial; if both are used, a comma should separate them (a space is not allowed). The possible forms and modes of the matrices are summarized in Table 2.1. Note that ST can only be the form of the PH matrix, while SD is only possible for BE.

The specification PH=ST on the MO command has a special meaning. It means that the diagonal elements of Φ are fixed at one and the off-diagonal elements are free. This specification cannot be overridden by fixing and/or

**Table 2.1   Keyword Summary for Specifying
the Form and Mode of the LISREL Parameter Matrices**

Mathematical Notation: *LISREL Name:*		Λ_y LY	Λ_x LX	**B** BE	Γ GA	Φ PH	Ψ PS	Θ_ϵ TE	Θ_δ TD	$\Theta_{\delta\epsilon}$ TH
Matrix Form:	*mf*									
Zero (**0**)	ZE			*			+	+	+	*
Identity (**I**)	ID	+	+		+	+				
Identity, Zero (**I 0**)	IZ	+	+		+					
Zero, Identity (**0 I**)	ZI	+	+		+					
Diagonal	DI	+	+		+	+	*	*	*	+
Symmetric	SY					*	+	+	+	+
Subdiagonal	SD			+						
Standardized Symmetric	ST					+				
Full (nonsymmetric)	FU	*	*	+	*					
Matrix mode:	*mm*									
Fixed	FI	*	*	*	+	+	+	+	+	*
Free	FR	+	+	+	*	*	*	*	*	
Legend:		* Default						+ Permissible		

freeing elements of Φ on FI, FR, or PA commands (see FI, FR commands below). The specifications PH=ST,FI and PH=ST,FR are not permitted.

To obtain something different from PH=ST, specify PH=FI or let PH default on the MO command and then specify the fixed-free status of each element of Φ on the FI or FR commands. For example, suppose Φ is required to be

$$
\Phi = \begin{pmatrix}
1 & & & \\
* & 1 & & \\
0 & 0 & * & \\
0 & 0 & 0 & *
\end{pmatrix},
$$

where $*$'s are free parameters and 0's and 1's are fixed parameters. This form can be specified by:

```
MO ... PH=FI ...
FR PH(2,1) PH(3,3) PH(4,4)
VA 1 PH(1,1) PH(2,2)
```

In this case it is absolutely essential that a scale has been defined for ξ_3 and ξ_4 by fixing a non-zero value in columns 3 and 4 of Λ_x.

The default mode for **B**, namely FI, does not apply to the matrix form SD in the same way as for the other parameter matrices. The form SD for **B**, without any mode specification, sets the elements below the main diagonal free, keeping those in and above the main diagonal fixed at zero. The specification BE=SD,FI would fix the elements below the diagonal as well, and would give the same result as BE=FU (with the default mode FI). Similarly, the specification BE=SD,FR would free all the elements of **B** (but such a model is normally not identified).

The general form above is given as though it occupies only *one* physical record. In practice, when the MO command is continued on a next physical record, a C should be written in place of a keyword or option and the new record should then start with that keyword or option.

PURPOSE

To assign names to the η-variables and/or the ξ-variables.

FORMAT

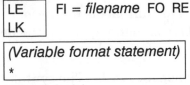

Data (labels)

KEYWORDS

FI   User specified name of file containing the labels.
      With LISREL 8, the shorter command format, for example,
      LE=*filename* may be used.
      Default: Labels are in the command file.

OPTIONS (only relevant for external file)

FO   If this option appears, the variable format statement describing
      the label records will appear as the next line.
      Default: Format statement (if any) is at the head of the label file.

RE   If this option appears, the label file will be rewound after the labels
      are read. Only an external file may be rewound.
      Default: No rewind.

DETAIL LINES

(Variable format statement)
      If the FI keyword and the FO options do appear (or nothing at all),
      and the labels are in *fixed* format, a FORTRAN A-format statement,
      enclosed in parentheses, may be inserted here to describe the col-
      umn assignments of the label records.

*   Otherwise, an asterisk (*) may appear in column 1 to indicate that
      the labels are in free format (separated by spaces, commas, or re-
      turn characters).
      Default: *

Data (ξ- or η-labels)

> If an external file is not specified, the labels must appear at this point in the command file.

NOTES

If no LE command appears, the default labels for latent η-variables ((ETA 1, ETA 2, ...) are used. If no LK command appears, the default labels for latent ξ-variables (KSI 1, KSI 2, ...) are used.

There are eight columns available for labels. The syntax rules are equivalent to those for the LA command.

PURPOSE

To set specified elements fixed or free in the LISREL parameter matrices.

FORMAT

FI
FR
List of parameter matrix elements

OPTION

List of parameter matrix elements

Each element should be written as a parameter matrix name (LY, LX, BE, GA, PH, PS, TE, TD, or TH), followed by row and column index of the specific element. Row and column indices may be separated by a comma and enclosed in parentheses, like LY(3,2), LX(4,1), or separated from the matrix name and each other by spaces, like LY 3 2 LX 4 1. See NOTES below.

NOTES

With the MO command, one can specify that an entire parameter matrix is to be fixed or free, *i.e.*, that *all* the elements of the matrix are fixed or free.

With the PA command, the fixed-free status of all the elements in a particular parameter matrix can be specified quickly.

The FR and FI commands can be used to define the fixed-free status of *single matrix elements*.

There are three important rules for FR and FI commands:

o   If a matrix has been specified as ZE or ID on the MO command, it is not stored in computer memory and none of its elements may be referred to.

o   If a matrix has been specified as DI on the MO command, only the diagonal elements are stored in memory and may be referred to.

o   If one specifies PH=ST on the MO command, one cannot refer to any elements of Φ on FI or FR commands (see MO command above).

Any number of these commands may appear, and later commands over-rule earlier commands with the same referents.

Continuation of a list of elements on a following record is established by writing a C in place of an element (*not* an index) and starting the new record with that element.

EXAMPLES

```
FIX LX(1,2),LX(2,2),LX(3,1),GA(2,2)-GA(2,5)
FI  LX 1 2  LX 2 2  LX 3 1  GA 2 2 -GA 2 5
```

Because both commas and parentheses may be replaced with blanks, the two commands are equivalent. The hyphen (or minus sign), with or without blanks, may be used for a range of parameters in consecutive order. Above, the parameters γ_{22}, γ_{23}, γ_{24} and γ_{25} are declared fixed.

It is also possible to refer to elements using linear indices, that is, counting the elements of a parameter matrix rowwise, starting at position (1,1). Assuming the LX matrix has only three columns, and GA five (and both are FU,FR), the following commands are also equivalent to the ones above:

```
FI  LX(2) LX(5) LX(7) GA(7) - GA(10)
FI  LX 2  LX 5  LX 7  GA 7  - GA 10
```

Consequently, when TD has been specified as diagonal and only the diagonal elements may be referred to, the following commands are equivalent:

```
FR   TD(1,1), TD(2,2), TD(3,3)
FREE TD 1 - TD 3
```

Since later commands overrule earlier ones, the command

```
FR PS(1) PS(2) PS(4) - PS(7)
```

could also be specified with the two commands

```
FR  PS(1,1) - PS(7,7)
FI  PS(3,3)
```

provided the matrix Ψ has been specified as fixed and diagonal.

PURPOSE

To constrain other parameters to be equal to a specified parameter (the first in the list).

FORMAT

EQ   *List of parameter matrix elements*

OPTION

List of parameter matrix elements

Each element should be written as a parameter matrix name (LY, LX, BE, GA, PH, PS, TE, TD, or TH), followed by row and column index of the specific element. Row and column indices may be separated by a comma and enclosed in parentheses, like LY(3,2), LX(4,1), or separated from the matrix name and each other by spaces, like LY 3 2 LX 4 1. See NOTES below.

NOTES

The first parameter listed is normally a free parameter. However, it is possible to use the EQ command to fix parameters and set them equal to the value of the first, fixed parameter in the list. The rules for writing the list of elements are equal to those given for the FI,FR commands above.

With the PA command, one can specify simple equality constraints within and across parameter matrices. This use of the PA command is explained in the section *Simplified pattern matrices for equality constraints* on page 343 in Appendix A.

Use the CO command for other than simple equality constraints and the IR command to impose interval restrictions on specific parameters.

PURPOSE

To constrain a parameter to be equal to a function of other parameters.

FORMAT

CO   *parameter matrix element = expression with other parameters*

KEYWORD

parameter matrix element

> The equation defining the constraint is written in a straightforward way. Multiplication is specified by * and exponentiation by ** or ˆ. Exponents need not be integers. Parentheses are not permitted except in matrix elements. Division is not permitted although exponents may be negative. Constants are written as usual. If they are written without a decimal point, they are taken to be integers.
>
> Default: none

NOTES

See the section *Linear and non-linear constraints* on page 345 in Appendix A.

Constraints must be used with the utmost care. The constraints must make sense both from a substantive and a mathematical point of view. Make sure the constraints are written correctly and correspond to the constraints intended. To be safe, follow these rules:

- ○ Find out exactly which parameters are free. This may involve choosing a particular set so that the constraints can be expressed in a form that LISREL can handle.

- ○ All the non-fixed elements in all the parameter matrices and in all the groups must be expressed as functions of the free parameters. Only free parameters should appear on the right-hand side on CO commands. Thus,

  - • Implicit equations, in which the parameter on the left also appears on the right side are not permitted.

  - • Parameters that are constrained on previous CO commands, *i.e.*, that are on the left side, should not appear on the right side on any CO command. Constraints cannot be used recursively.

- Parameters which are equal to one of the free parameters, can be specified either by CO commands or by EQ commands, but in the latter case, the free parameter must be listed first.

EXAMPLES

There should be one constraint defined on each CO command. If the constraint is so complex that it does not fit on a line of 127 characters, just enter a C for Continue and continue on the next line.

```
CO TD(1,1)=1-LX(1,1)**2-LX(1,2)**2
CO LX(1,4)=LX(1,5)-LX(1,6)**4
CO BE(1,2)=-BE(2,1)
CO BE(3,2)=1.5634*GA(1,2)*GA(1,3)*GA(4,2)**1.37
CO LY(3,3)=TE(3,3)**-1
CO LY(1,1)=3.27*BE(1,2)*GA(1,1)*PH(2,2)*1.7*PS(1,1)+TD(1,1)*TE(1,1)**-1
```

PURPOSE

To constrain one or more parameters to a specific interval.

FORMAT

IR   *list of parameter matrix elements* $> a < b$

SPECIFICATIONS

list of parameter matrix elements

Each element should be written as a parameter matrix name (LY, LX, BE, GA, PH, PS, TE, TD, or TH), followed by row and column index of the specific element. Row and column indices may be separated by a comma and enclosed in parentheses, like LY(3,2), LX(4,1), or separated from the matrix name and each other by spaces, like LY 3 2 LX 4 1.

Default: none

$> a < b$

Interval restrictions of the forms $\theta \geq a$, $\theta \leq b$ and $a \leq \theta \leq b$ may be placed on any LISREL parameter θ, where a and b are specified constants.

NOTES

See also the section *Interval restrictions* on page 348 in Appendix A.

It is recommended to run the problem without the interval restrictions first and then apply only those interval restrictions which are needed. Chi-square and standard errors will be affected if parameter estimates are on the boundary of the interval and standard errors may not be valid.

EXAMPLE

The following three commands

```
IR TD(2,2) >0
IR GA(2,4) <1
IR PH(2,1) >-1 <1
```

correspond to $\theta_{22}^{(\delta)} \geq 0$, $\gamma_{24} \leq 1$, and $-1 \leq \phi_{21} \leq 1$.

PURPOSE

To set elements of the LISREL parameter matrices fixed or free using a pattern of 1's and 0's (1 ≡ free; 0 ≡ fixed).

To specify equality constraints. This use of the PA command is explained in the section *Simplified pattern matrices for equality constraints* on page 343 in Appendix A.

FORMAT

PA   FI = *filename* FO RE *matrix name*

```
(Integer format statement)
*
```

Data (pattern of integers)

KEYWORDS

FI   User specified name of file containing the pattern matrix.
With LISREL 8, the shorter command format PA=*filename* may be used.
Default: Pattern matrix is in the command file.

OPTIONS

Matrix name
        Replace with the name of the parameter matrix whose elements are to be set fixed or free (LY LX BE GA PH PS TE TD TH).

FO   If this option appears, the integer format statement describing the pattern matrix will appear as the next line.
        Default: Format statement (if any) is at the head of the pattern matrix file.

RE   If this option appears, the pattern matrix file will be rewound after the labels are read. Only an external file may be rewound.
        Default: No rewind.

DETAIL LINES

Integer format statement

> If the FI keyword and the FO option do appear (or nothing at all), and the pattern matrix is in *fixed* format, a FORTRAN I-format statement, enclosed in parentheses, may be inserted here to describe the column assignments of the pattern matrix records.

*   An asterisk (*) may appear in column 1 to indicate that the pattern matrix is in free format (separated by spaces, commas, or return characters).

> Default: *

Data (pattern matrix)

> If an external file is not specified, the pattern matrix must appear at this point in the command file.

NOTES

One of these command lines may appear for each matrix.

If the pattern matrix is in free format (with its elements separated by spaces, commas, or return characters) and the number of elements is less than the total number of elements in the matrix, the pattern must end with a forward slash (/). The elements after the slash default to 0's, indicating free elements.

EXAMPLES

1. The following are four alternative ways of reading the pattern matrix for

$$\Gamma = \begin{pmatrix} free & fixed & fixed \\ fixed & free & free \end{pmatrix}$$

```
PA GA
(6I1)
100011

PA GA
(3I1)
100
011
```

```
PA GA
*
1 0 0 0 1 1
```

```
PA GA
*
1 0 0
0 1 1
```

As before, the line containing the * may be omitted.

2. If a matrix is symmetric, only the elements in the lower half, including the diagonal should be read. If a matrix is specified to be diagonal, only the diagonal elements should be read. For example, if $\boldsymbol{\Phi}(4 \times 4)$ is symmetric with fixed diagonal elements and free off-diagonal elements, and if $\boldsymbol{\Psi}(4 \times 4)$ is diagonal, with elements ψ_{11} and ψ_{33} fixed and ψ_{22} and ψ_{44} free, the pattern matrices are read as:

```
PA PH
*
0 1 0 1 1 0 1 1 1 0
PA PS
*
0 1 0 1
```

3. Suppose the symmetric matrix $\boldsymbol{\Phi}$ is of order 10×10 and partitioned as

$$\boldsymbol{\Phi} = \begin{pmatrix} \mathbf{I} & \\ \mathbf{0} & \mathbf{0} \end{pmatrix} ,$$

where $\mathbf{I}$ is an identity matrix of order 5×5, say. One can read this matrix as:

```
PA PH
1
0 1
0 0 1
0 0 0 1
0 0 0 0 1/
```

The forward slash (/) implies that the remaining elements will all be zero. Data containing repetitions of the same number or group of numbers can be read very conveniently. For example, the matrix Φ can also be read as:

```
PA PH
1 0 1 2*0 1 3*0 1 4*0 1/
```

Here 3*0 is equivalent to 0 0 0.

4. Suppose one wants to read the following pattern matrix for Λ_x.

$$\begin{pmatrix} 1 & 0 & 0 \\ 1 & 0 & 0 \\ 1 & 0 & 0 \\ 0 & 1 & 0 \\ 0 & 1 & 0 \\ 0 & 1 & 0 \\ 0 & 0 & 1 \\ 0 & 0 & 1 \\ 0 & 0 & 1 \end{pmatrix}$$

This can be read as:

```
PA LX
3*(1 0 0) 3*(0 1 0) 3*(0 0 1)
```

or even more simply (by omitting the asterisks) as:

```
PA LX
3(1 0 0) 3(0 1 0) 3(0 0 1)
```

PURPOSE

To assign numerical values to fixed parameters (VA); to assign starting values for iterative estimation of free parameters (ST).

FORMAT

VA ST	value	List of parameter matrix elements ALL

OPTIONS

value Numerical value to be assigned (with decimal point).
         Default: none; required option.

List of parameter matrix elements
         Each element should be written as a parameter matrix name (LY, LX, BE, GA, PH, PS, TE, TD, or TH), followed by row and column index of the specific element. Row and column indices may be separated by a comma and enclosed in parentheses, like LY(3,2), LX(4,1), or separated from the matrix name and each other by spaces, like LY 3 2 LX 4 1. See NOTES below.

ALL Set all free elements in all parameter matrices to starting value (with ST; see NOTES below). "ALL" may *not* be given as "AL."
     Default: VA values are zero. ST values will be computed by the program, if possible.

NOTES

Setting elements fixed by the FI, PA, or EQ commands does not set their values. All elements, whether fixed, free, or constrained, are zero by default.

Setting ST values to good approximations from similar analyses may save some computing time. Otherwise, the default values estimated by IV or TSLS will be supplied by the program.

The rules for writing the list of elements are equal to those given for the FI,FR commands above.

These commands may appear any number of times. Values in later commands override those in earlier commands with the same referents.

The VA and ST commands are equivalent and may be used synonymously. Whether the assigned value will be a starting value or a fixed value is dependent on the mode of each element, as specified in the relevant command lines. There is one exception, however. When a range of elements is specified, as LY(1,1)-LY(2,2), then fixed elements in this range are changed by VA, but not by ST. Hence, the option "ALL" behaves differently for VA and ST, and, although allowed for the VA command, it is only useful for the ST command.

EXAMPLES

1.

```
VA 1.5 LX(2,1) LY(6,2) GA(1,2)
```

assigns the value 1.5 to $\lambda_{21}^{(x)}$, $\lambda_{62}^{(y)}$, and γ_{12}.

2. As a second example, suppose that $\mathbf{B}$ is subdiagonal, $\mathbf{\Psi}$ is symmetric and $\mathbf{\Theta}_\epsilon$ is diagonal, with the following starting values for the free parameters.

$$\mathbf{B} = \begin{pmatrix} 0 & 0 & 0 \\ 0.5 & 0 & 0 \\ 0.5 & 0.5 & 0 \end{pmatrix} \qquad \mathbf{\Psi} = \begin{pmatrix} 1.5 & & \\ 0.5 & 1.9 & \\ 0.7 & 0.5 & 1.5 \end{pmatrix}$$

$$\mathbf{\Theta}_\epsilon = \mathrm{diag}(1.5, 1.5, 1.5)$$

The starting values for the free parameters may then be set by the following ST commands.

```
ST  0.5 BE(2,1) BE(3,1)-BE(3,2) PS(2,1) PS(3,2)
ST  1.5 PS(1,1) PS(3,3) TE(1)-TE(3)
ST  1.9 PS(2,2)
ST  0.7 PS(3,1)
```

Whenever a range of elements is specified, only those elements in this range which have been specified as non-fixed (free or constrained) elements will be set. Thus, the first of the ST commands above can also be written, with the same effect, as:

```
ST 0.5 BE(1,1)-BE(3,3) PS(2,1) PS(3,2)
```

3. All non-fixed elements in all parameter matrices are set at the same starting value. Next, PS(1,1) is assigned a different starting value.

```
ST 0.5 ALL
ST 5 PS 1 1
```

Note that the option "ALL" must be entered with all *three* significant characters.

PURPOSE

To set all elements of a parameter matrix to values specified by an input matrix; these values will be starting values for the free parameters and fixed values otherwise.

FORMAT

MA   FI = *filename* FO RE *matrix name*

> (Variable format statement)
> *

Data (matrix values)

KEYWORDS

FI   User specified name of file containing the matrix values.
With LISREL 8, the shorter command format MA=*filename* may be used.
Default: Matrix values are in the command file.

OPTIONS

Matrix name

Replace with the name of the parameter matrix whose elements are to be set to the fixed and/or starting values specified (LY, LX, BE, GA, PH, PS, TE, TD, or TH).

FO   If this option appears, the variable format statement describing the matrix value records will appear as the next line.
Default: Format statement (if any) is at the head of the matrix values file.

RE   If this option appears, the matrix values file will be rewound after the matrix values are read. Only an external file may be rewound.
Default: No rewind.

DETAIL LINES

(Variable format statement)

If the FI keyword and the FO option do appear (or nothing at all), and the matrix values are in *fixed* format, a FORTRAN format statement, enclosed in parentheses, may be inserted here to describe the column assignments of the matrix values.

* An asterisk (*) may appear in column 1 to indicate that the matrix values are in free format (separated by spaces, commas, or return characters).

   Default: *

Data (matrix values)

   If an external file is not specified, the matrix values must appear at this point in the command file.

EXAMPLES

The matrices from example 2 of the VA,ST command above could be read as:

```
MA BE
(3F1.1)
000
500
550
MA PS
*
1.5 0.5 1.9 0.7 0.5 1.5
MA TE
1.5 1.5 1.5
```

Or, of course, from an external file (using FI=*filename* and possibly FO and RE on the MA command). With free format (*) it is possible to read only a leading subset of elements in a matrix by terminating the list with a forward slash (/). The remaining elements will then default to zero.

See also the OU(4) command below for a possible use of the MA command.

PURPOSE

To plot the fit functions for ULS, GLS, ML, WLS, or DWLS against any parameter, fixed or free.

FORMAT

PL   *list of parameter matrix elements* FROM a TO b

OPTIONS

List of parameter matrix elements

Each element should be written as a parameter matrix name (LY, LX, BE, GA, PH, PS, TE, TD, or TH), followed by row and column index of the specific element. Row and column indices may be separated by a comma and enclosed in parentheses, like LY(3,2), LX(4,1), or separated from the matrix name and each other by spaces, like LY 3 2 LX 4 1. See NOTES below.

a, b The *range* of parameter values to be plotted.

Default: An approximate 95 percent confidence interval for free parameters. For fixed parameters, the predicted estimated change in the parameter when set free.

NOTES

The parameter plots in LISREL 6 and LISREL 7 differ. The plot in LISREL 7 is a plot of the *concentrated* fit function, *i.e.*, for each value of θ, the *minimum* of the fit function with respect to all other free parameters is plotted. For an illustration, see Example 3.4.

Several PL commands may be included in each problem, but the total number of plots cannot exceed 10.

The rules for writing the list of elements are equal to those given for the FI,FR commands above.

EXAMPLES

To plot the parameters LX(2,1), LY(4,3), TD(1,1), write:

```
PL LX(2,1) LY(4,3) TD(1,1)
```

And to plot TD(1,1) and TD(2,2) from 0.4 to 0.5, write:

```
PL TD(1,1) TD(2,2) FROM 0.4 TO 0.5
```

PURPOSE

To specify elements for which modification indices should not be computed.

FORMAT

NF   *List of parameter matrix elements*

OPTION

List of parameter matrix elements

Each element should be written as a parameter matrix name (LY, LX, BE, GA, PH, PS, TE, TD, or TH), followed by row and column index of the specific element. Row and column indices may be separated by a comma and enclosed in parentheses, like LY(3,2), LX(4,1), or separated from the matrix name and each other by spaces, like LY 3 2 LX 4 1. A hyphen (or minus sign) may be used for a range of parameters in consecutive order. See NOTES below.

NOTES

If the option MI (modification indices) is chosen on the OU command and no NF commands appear in the command file, the program will compute a modification index for each fixed or constrained element. Many of these may not be of interest because it is meaningless to have these elements as parameters of the model. Excluding those elements also results in faster program execution. The NF command provides the possibility to specify such elements.

For example, if LX is specified as ID or IZ, modification indices for elements of Λ_x are usually of no interest. One can specify this by

    NF LX(1) - LX(k)

where k is the serial index of the last element of Λ_x. The rules for writing the list of elements are equal to those given for the FI,FR commands above.

Only fixed parameters will be affected by the NF command. See also the NOTES section for FI,FR commands above.

Only elements in the original model will be relaxed. For example, if Θ_δ is diagonal, no off-diagonal element will be relaxed and none should appear in a NF command. See also notes for FI,FR commands above.

Modification indices and estimated changes for elements specified on NF commands will appear as 0.000 in the output file. In the parameter specifications such elements appear as -1.

PURPOSE

To request display of a path diagram with the current model solution.

FORMAT

```
PD
PATH DIAGRAM
```

NOTES

The path diagram will be displayed on screen after successful execution of
the problem. The book *LISREL 8: Structural Equation Modeling with the
SIMPLIS Command Language* discusses the use of path diagrams with
LISREL in detail (Jöreskog & Sörbom, 1993b).

PURPOSE

To establish the estimation procedures of LISREL.

FORMAT

OU　　　ME= $\begin{array}{|c|} \hline \text{IV} \\ \text{TS} \\ \text{UL} \\ \text{GL} \\ \text{ML} \\ \text{WL} \\ \text{DW} \\ \hline \end{array}$　RC=c　SL=100α　NS　RO　AM　SO

KEYWORDS

ME　Method of estimation.

Default: ML

Possible values:

IV　　Instrumental variables

TS　　Two-stage least squares

UL　　Unweighted least squares

GL　　Generalized least squares

ML　　Maximum likelihood

WL　　Generally weighted least squares

DW　　Diagonally weighted least squares

RC　The ridge constant. This constant will be multiplied repeatedly by 10 until the matrix becomes positive-definite. See RO option below.

Default: RC=0.001

SL　The significance level of the model modification procedure expressed as an integral percent. See AM option below.

For example, SL=5 sets the significance level for the modification indices to 0.05.

Default: SL=1

OPTIONS

NS　If this option appears, the program will not compute starting values. The user must supply starting values with ST or MA commands.

RO   Ridge option (see Section 1.7.7 and Example 4.6).
If this option appears, the program will analyze the matrix

$$S + c(\text{diag}[S])$$

in place of S. This option will be invoked automatically if S is not positive-definite.

AM   Automatic model modification.
If this option is present, the program will modify the model sequentially by freeing at each step the fixed or constrained parameter that has the largest modification index (see Example 4.2). It will continue the modification for as long as any index is statistically significant at the α level of the SL keyword. (Use the NF command to prevent specific parameters from being modified).

SO   Scaling check off.
If this option is present, the program will *not* check whether a scale has been defined for each latent variable (see Section 1.7.1). The SO option is needed for very special models where scales for latent variables are defined in a different way. See Example 6.1 for an illustration.

NOTES

Although the OU command is presented here in four separate parts, all chosen keywords and options should be placed on one and the same OU command. Write a C instead of a keyword or option (before column 128), then continue on the next physical record, if needed.

An AC command in the command file changes the default method of estimation from ML to WLS, while the presence of an AV command or a DM command makes DWLS the default method of estimation (see AC command, AV command, and DM command above).

Starting values or initial estimates are not printed at all unless requested with PT on the OU command, *i.e.*, starting values are only printed with the technical output.

All options and keywords on the OU command may be omitted, but a line with the two characters OU must be included as the last line of the command file.

PURPOSE
To select the printed output of LISREL.

FORMAT

OU   SE TV PC PT RS EF MR MI XM XI FS SS SC ALL $\boxed{\begin{array}{l}\text{TO}\\\text{WP}\end{array}}$

     ND=d

OPTIONS

SE   Standard errors

TV t-values (estimate/standard error)

PC   Correlation matrix of parameter estimators

PT   Print technical output

RS   Residuals, standardized residuals, Q-plot and fitted covariance (or correlation, or moment) matrix $\hat{\Sigma}$

EF   Total effects and indirect effects

MR   Miscellaneous results; see Section 1.11

MI   Model modification indices

XM   Suppress computation of the modification indices; see NOTES below.

XI   Limit the fit statistics; see NOTES below.

FS   Factor-scores regression

SS   Standardized solution

SC   Solution completely standardized

ALL   **Print everything** (may be given as "AL")

TO   Print 80 characters per line (PC default) (TO for terminal output)

WP   Print 132 characters per line (Mainframe default)

ND   Number of decimals (0–8) in the printed output
      Default: ND=2

NOTES

Standard errors and t-values now appear together with parameter estimates within each parameter matrix and are always printed, whenever possible (in LISREL 7 standard errors and t-values had to be requested). Therefore, the SE and TV options on the OU command are no longer needed.

Also, the MI option is no longer needed because modification indices are always printed unless one puts the option XM on the OU command (note that *computation* of the modification indices cannot be suppressed when a path diagram is requested).

Starting values or initial estimates are not printed at all unless requested with PT on the OU command, *i.e.*, starting values are only printed with the technical output.

LISREL 8 will standardize all latent variables, *even the η-variables*, unless otherwise specified. This is a new unique feature in LISREL 8, see Section *Scaling the latent variables* in Appendix A.

If both EF and SS appear on the OU command, LISREL 8 will give the standardized effects for the SS solution, *i.e.*, the solution in which the latent variables are standardized but not the observed. If both EF and SC appear on the OU command, LISREL 8 will give the standardized effects for the SC solution, *i.e.*, the solution in which both the latent and the observed variables are standardized. With multiple groups, the standardized effects are based on the within group standardized solutions. See also the section *Standardized effects* on page 344 in Appendix A.

If the XI option is specified, the list output has only one line with fit statistics (chi-square, degrees of freedom, and P-value). The GF file, if requested, gives only five quantities: RP, error indicator, *df*, chi-square, and P-value. This option is useful for Monte Carlo studies, where it may be convenient to have only the essential fit statistics instead of all fit statistics. See Appendix C in the *PRELIS 2: User's Reference Guide* for a description of the GF file.

PURPOSE
To save various matrices in specified files at termination.

FORMAT
OU $matrix_1 = filename_1$ $matrix_2 = filename_2$ $\cdots$

KEYWORDS
$matrix_i$

Replace with the matrix name to be saved.

Possible names:

LY, LX, BE, GA, PH, PS, TE, TD, TH, AL, KA, TX, TY, or

MA   The matrix analyzed after selection and/or reordering of variables

SI   The fitted (moment, covariance, or correlation) matrix, $\hat{\Sigma}$ (SI for Sigma)

RM   The regression matrix of latent variables on observed variables. Printout of the matrix must also have been requested with the FS option described under output requests (2) above

EC   The estimated asymptotic covariance matrix of the LISREL parameter estimates.

GF   All the goodness-of-fit measures.

PV   The vector of estimated free parameters.

SV   The vector of corresponding standard errors.

TV   The vector of corresponding t-values.

NOTES
The matrices are written in format (6D13.6), preceded by a line with the format and the name of the saved matrix. This format means that each value occupies 13 columns, the last six being the decimal places, and that there are six values per record.

PURPOSE

To control the performance of the LISREL iterative estimation procedures. (See Chapter 11 for advanced technical control.)

FORMAT

OU   TM=t IT=n AD=$\boxed{\begin{array}{c} m \\ \text{OFF} \end{array}}$ EP=ε

KEYWORDS

TM   The maximum number of CPU seconds for the current problem.
Default: PC version, TM=172800 (2 days); Mainframe, TM=60

IT   Maximum number of iterations for the current problem.
Default: IT=*three times the number of free parameters*

AD   Check the admissibility of the solution after m iterations and stop the program if the admissibility check fails. In that case, an intermediate solution will be printed. Note that the program will always check the admissibility of the final solution, regardless of the value of the AD keyword.
Default: AD=20
Turn the check off with AD=OFF (see Section 1.7.9).

EP   Convergence criterion, epsilon. The default value normally results in a solution that is accurate to three significant digits. However, this cannot be guaranteed for all problems.
Default: EPS=0.000001

NOTES

If t seconds are exceeded, the iterations are stopped and the current "solution" is written onto a file called DUMP unless another filename is specified on the OU command, see below. The "solution" LY, LX, BE, GA, PH, PS, TE, and TD is written in format (6D13.6), and is preceded by a line with this format and the name of the matrix. A matrix saved in this way can be read by LISREL with an MA command, see above. For example:

```
MA LY FI=DUMP
```

This termination of the program will also occur if the program iterates for more than n iterations or if numerical instabilities are encountered.

2.2 An annotated example of LISREL input and output

In this section we illustrate the processes of (a) writing input for LISREL and (b) interpreting the output from the program. To maintain continuity, the example presented is the hypothetical model discussed in Section 1.2; the path diagram for this model is contained in Figure 1.1. This model is typical of the structural equation models often tested by researchers. It does not demonstrate all the features of LISREL: it is limited to one group; it does not model the means of the variables; it has no equality restrictions on the parameters; and it assumes that the variables are continuous and have a multivariate normal distribution.

For most models, the commands perform the following tasks:

1. Specify characteristics of the data set, such as the number of variables, the names of the variables, the form of the data (raw data, or summary statistics such as variances and covariances).

2. Read the data.

3. Specify the general characteristics of the model: how many latent and observed exogenous and endogenous variables are there; what will be the form of each matrix in the model (for example, if square, is it symmetric or diagonal?); will each matrix consist primarily of free or of fixed parameters?

4. Specify modifications to individual elements of matrices to make them fixed in a predominantly free matrix, or vice versa; or specify sets of parameters to be equal.

5. Assign values to nonzero fixed parameters, and any other values necessary to start the iteration procedure.

6. Specify what output is desired, and nondefault settings to determine characteristics of the estimation process or output.

Input

The command file for testing this model is listed below, followed by a detailed explanation of each line.

```
HYPOTHETICAL MODEL ESTIMATED BY ML
DA NI=11  NO=100
CM FI=EX1.COV SY
LA
Y-1 Y-2 Y-3 Y-4 X-1 X-2 X-3 X-4 X-5 X-6 X-7
MO NY=4 NX=7 NE=2 NK=3 BE=FU PS=SY,FR
FR LY 2 1 LY 4 2 LX 2 1 LX 3 1 LX 3 2 LX 5 2 LX 7 3 BE 2 1 BE 1 2
FI GA 1 3 GA 2 2
VA 1 LY 1 1 LY 3 2 LX 1 1 LX 4 2 LX 6 3
LE
ETA-1 ETA-2
LK
KSI-1 KSI-2 KSI-3
OU RS EF MR SS SC
```

The first line is a title. The title can extend for as many lines as needed; the program assumes that the title ends when it finds the characters "DA" as the first two characters of a line, which signals the DA command. On this command, the keyword NI indicates the number of variables, which for this problem is 11. The keyword NO indicates the number of observations.

The CM command indicates that the data are in the form of a covariance matrix. To show that the matrix is symmetric, and that only the lower triangular part (including the diagonal) is included, the option SY is specified. The data are not included in the command file; the keyword FI tells that the data are in the file EX1.COV. The contents of the file EX1.COV are:

```
(16F5.3)
 3204
 2722 2629
 3198 2875 4855
 3545 3202 5373 6315
  329  371 -357 -471 1363
  559  592 -316 -335 1271 1960
 1006 1019 -489 -591 1742 2276 3803
  468  456 -438 -539  788 1043 1953 1376
  502  539 -363 -425  838 1070 2090 1189 1741
 1050  960 1416 1714  474  694  655   71  104 1422
 1260 1154 1923 2309  686  907  917  136  162 1688 2684
```

The LA command is used to specify that labels will be provided for the observed variables. The following line gives the labels for these variables. These labels may continue over as many lines as needed.

The MO command is used to specify the general form of the matrices in the model. There are four y-variables (NY=4), seven x-variables (NX=7), two η-variables (NE=2), and three ξ-variables (NK=3). The default form is used for most of the matrices; for example, Λ_x and Λ_y are FU (*i.e.*, rectangular, not square) matrices with FI (fixed) elements. The nondefault matrices are specified as BE=FU and PS=SY,FR. This makes BE (Beta) a full rectangular matrix instead of the default, a ZE (zero) matrix, and PS (Psi) a full symmetric matrix instead of the default, a DI (diagonal) matrix.

The specifications for individual elements that will depart from the general form specified in the MO command are given next. The FR command allows parameters in matrices that were fixed to be free. The elements to be freed are specified by two-character names and indices to specify the row and column. For example, the first element freed is LY 2 1, which is the element in row 2, column 1, of Λ_y. The FI command serves a similar purpose: it fixes elements in matrices that were specified to be free.

The VA command gives specified values to parameters. If these parameters are fixed, then the values do not change during the estimation process. If no value is specified for a fixed parameter, its value defaults to zero. Here, the value 1 is given to various elements of Λ_y and Λ_x.

Just as labels can be given to observed variables, they can also be given to latent variables. The LE command gives labels to the η-variables, and the LK command gives labels to the ξ-variables. In the example, we have given generic names to these variables.

The OU command serves several purposes. Most commonly, it is used to specify the method of estimation (here maximum likelihood by default, since no other method is specified), and to specify what output is desired. Here we have requested the printing of the fitted covariance matrix, residuals, standardized residuals, and a Q-plot of residuals (RS), total and indirect effects (EF), miscellaneous results (MR) and a standardized solution (SS). As this job was run on a PC version of LISREL, the program automatically produces 80-column output; on a mainframe, this would be requested by listing the additional option TO.

The printing of standard errors (SE), t-values (TV), and modification indices (MI) is included by default.

Output

The (edited) output file follows. Some segments are omitted to save space. Comments are interspersed, and are set off in italics to differentiate them from the actual output.

The program first reproduces the command file, followed by the general form of the problem.

```
The following lines were read from file C:\LISREL8W\EXAMPLES\LS8EX\EX1.LS8:

HYPOTHETICAL MODEL ESTIMATED BY ML
DA NI=11  NO=100
 . . .
 . . .
OU RS EF MR SS SC

HYPOTHETICAL MODEL ESTIMATED BY ML

                        NUMBER OF INPUT VARIABLES 11
                        NUMBER OF Y - VARIABLES    4
                        NUMBER OF X - VARIABLES    7
                        NUMBER OF ETA - VARIABLES  2
                        NUMBER OF KSI - VARIABLES  3
                        NUMBER OF OBSERVATIONS   100
```

The covariance matrix is listed. In some cases, this is calculated by the program from raw data, or from correlations and standard deviations.

LISREL 8 uses two decimals in the output by default rather than three decimals as used in LISREL 7. With the ND keyword on the OU command, you may specify a different number.

```
COVARIANCE MATRIX TO BE ANALYZED

                Y-1       Y-2       Y-3       Y-4       X-1       X-2
              -------   -------   -------   -------   -------   -------
      Y-1      3.20
      Y-2      2.72      2.63
      Y-3      3.20      2.88      4.86
      Y-4      3.54      3.20      5.37      6.32
      X-1      0.33      0.37     -0.36     -0.47      1.36
      X-2      0.56      0.59     -0.32     -0.34      1.27      1.96
      X-3      1.01      1.02     -0.49     -0.59      1.74      2.28
      X-4      0.47      0.46     -0.44     -0.54      0.79      1.04
      X-5      0.50      0.54     -0.36     -0.42      0.84      1.07
      X-6      1.05      0.96      1.42      1.71      0.47      0.69
      X-7      1.26      1.15      1.92      2.31      0.69      0.91
```

COVARIANCE MATRIX TO BE ANALYZED

	X-3	X-4	X-5	X-6	X-7
X-3	3.80				
X-4	1.95	1.38			
X-5	2.09	1.19	1.74		
X-6	0.66	0.07	0.10	1.42	
X-7	0.92	0.14	0.16	1.69	2.68

For each matrix, the free and fixed elements are listed. Each parameter is assigned a number. The number zero indicates that an element is fixed; a positive integer that an element is free. When there are equality constraints, elements restricted to have the same value are assigned the same number. The specifications are a result of the general forms for the matrices that were specified in the MO *command, and the specifications for individual parameters in* FI *and* FR *commands.*

Lambda-Y has only two free parameters, which were specified on the FR *command in the input. Remember that the value "0" for the other six parameters merely indicates that they are fixed, NOT that they are fixed at the value 0. In fact, two of them are fixed at the value 1, as can be seen in the section with the parameter estimates.*

PARAMETER SPECIFICATIONS

LAMBDA Y

	ETA-1	ETA-2
Y-1	0	0
Y-2	1	0
Y-3	0	0
Y-4	0	2

LAMBDA X

	KSI-1	KSI-2	KSI-3
X-1	0	0	0
X-2	3	0	0
X-3	4	5	0
X-4	0	0	0
X-5	0	6	0
X-6	0	0	0
X-7	0	0	7

BETA

	ETA-1	ETA-2
ETA-1	0	8
ETA-2	9	0

GAMMA

	KSI-1	KSI-2	KSI-3
ETA-1	10	11	0
ETA-2	12	0	13

For symmetric matrices such as PHI *and* PSI *below, only the lower triangular part is specified.*

PHI

	KSI-1	KSI-2	KSI-3
KSI-1	14		
KSI-2	15	16	
KSI-3	17	18	19

PSI

	ETA-1	ETA-2
ETA-1	20	
ETA-2	21	22

For diagonal matrices such as THETA EPS *and* THETA DELTA, *only the diagonal elements are listed. Each of these matrices is actually a square matrix.*

THETA EPS

Y-1	Y-2	Y-3	Y-4
23	24	25	26

THETA DELTA

X-1	X-2	X-3	X-4	X-5	X-6	X-7
27	28	29	30	31	32	33

Since the free parameters are numbered consecutively, it is easy to calculate the degrees of freedom: there are (11 × 12)/2 = 66 variances and covariances, and 33 free parameters, resulting in 66 − 33 = 33 degrees of freedom.

Next the maximum-likelihood estimates are reported. Starting values or initial estimates are not printed at all unless requested with PT *on the* OU *command, i.e., starting values are only printed with the technical output.*

Standard errors and t-values now appear together with parameter estimates within each parameter matrix and are always printed, whenever possible (in LISREL 7 *standard errors and t-values had to be requested).*

The standard errors show how accurately the values of the free parameters have been estimated. If these are small, as they mostly are here, then the parameters have been estimated accurately.

For each free parameter, the parameter estimate divided by its standard error produces a t-value. If a t-value is between −1.96 and 1.96, it is not significantly different from zero, so fixing it to zero will not make the fit of the model significantly worse.

```
LISREL ESTIMATES (MAXIMUM LIKELIHOOD)

  LAMBDA-Y

               ETA-1       ETA-2
             _____    _____

    Y-1        1.00         - -

    Y-2        0.92         - -
              (0.04)
              25.99

    Y-3        - -          1.00

    Y-4        - -          1.14
                           (0.03)
                           38.74


  LAMBDA-X

               KSI-1       KSI-2       KSI-3
             _____    _____    _____

    X-1        1.00         - -         - -
```

X-2	1.29	- -	- -
	(0.10)		
	12.33		
X-3	0.92	1.09	- -
	(0.12)	(0.12)	
	7.46	9.32	
X-4	- -	1.00	- -
X-5	- -	1.08	- -
		(0.08)	
		12.80	
X-6	- -	- -	1.00
X-7	- -	- -	1.44
			(0.09)
			15.48

BETA

	ETA-1	ETA-2
ETA-1	- -	0.54
		(0.06)
		9.53
ETA-2	0.94	- -
	(0.18)	
	5.25	

GAMMA

	KSI-1	KSI-2	KSI-3
ETA-1	0.21	0.50	- -
	(0.15)	(0.15)	
	1.39	3.35	
ETA-2	-1.22	- -	1.00
	(0.12)		(0.15)
	-10.05		6.57

The variances and covariances among the ksi's, in the lower right hand part, are the elements of the parameter matrix phi. The remaining elements are not part of the parameter estimates, but are derived from them.

COVARIANCE MATRIX OF ETA AND KSI

	ETA-1	ETA-2	KSI-1	KSI-2	KSI-3
ETA-1	2.96				
ETA-2	3.12	4.72			
KSI-1	0.48	-0.22	0.97		
KSI-2	0.55	-0.31	0.79	1.12	
KSI-3	0.93	1.40	0.52	0.13	1.18

PHI

	KSI-1	KSI-2	KSI-3
KSI-1	0.97		
	(0.19)		
	5.17		
KSI-2	0.79	1.12	
	(0.15)	(0.20)	
	5.21	5.72	
KSI-3	0.52	0.13	1.18
	(0.13)	(0.13)	(0.20)
	3.93	1.06	5.78

PSI

	ETA-1	ETA-2
ETA-1	0.49	
	(0.13)	
	3.83	
ETA-2	-0.07	0.13
	(0.17)	(0.08)
	-0.41	1.70

Now some other estimates that are derived from the parameter estimates are printed in between the remaining estimates. These will help determine how well the observed variables measure the constructs, both individually and as a group. Here, the multiple correlations for the observed variables are all high, so none is a poor measure of its latent variable. The squared multiple correlations for the structural equations indicate the proportion of variance in the endogenous variables accounted for by the variables in the structural equations. Here they are very high.

SQUARED MULTIPLE CORRELATIONS FOR STRUCTURAL EQUATIONS

ETA-1	ETA-2
0.84	0.97

THETA-EPS

Y-1	Y-2	Y-3	Y-4
0.25	0.12	0.14	0.20
(0.05)	(0.04)	(0.04)	(0.05)
4.66	3.24	3.32	3.60

SQUARED MULTIPLE CORRELATIONS FOR Y - VARIABLES

Y-1	Y-2	Y-3	Y-4
0.92	0.95	0.97	0.97

THETA-DELTA

X-1	X-2	X-3	X-4	X-5	X-6	X-7
0.39	0.34	0.06	0.26	0.44	0.25	0.26
(0.06)	(0.07)	(0.05)	(0.05)	(0.07)	(0.05)	(0.09)
6.09	5.00	1.23	5.14	5.88	4.60	2.83

SQUARED MULTIPLE CORRELATIONS FOR X - VARIABLES

X-1	X-2	X-3	X-4	X-5	X-6	X-7
0.71	0.83	0.98	0.81	0.75	0.83	0.90

The measures of fit for the model follow.

GOODNESS OF FIT STATISTICS

CHI-SQUARE WITH 33 DEGREES OF FREEDOM = 29.10 (P = 0.66)
ESTIMATED NON-CENTRALITY PARAMETER (NCP) = 0.0
90 PERCENT CONFIDENCE INTERVAL FOR NCP = (0.0 ; 12.26)

MINIMUM FIT FUNCTION VALUE = 0.29
POPULATION DISCREPANCY FUNCTION VALUE (F0) = 0.0
90 PERCENT CONFIDENCE INTERVAL FOR F0 = (0.0 ; 0.12)
ROOT MEAN SQUARE ERROR OF APPROXIMATION (RMSEA) = 0.0
90 PERCENT CONFIDENCE INTERVAL FOR RMSEA = (0.0 ; 0.061)
P-VALUE FOR TEST OF CLOSE FIT (RMSEA < 0.05) = 0.90

EXPECTED CROSS-VALIDATION INDEX (ECVI) = 0.96
90 PERCENT CONFIDENCE INTERVAL FOR ECVI = (1.00 ; 1.12)
ECVI FOR SATURATED MODEL = 1.33
ECVI FOR INDEPENDENCE MODEL = 14.79

```
        CHI-SQUARE FOR INDEPENDENCE MODEL WITH 55 DEGREES OF FREEDOM = 1441.95
                      INDEPENDENCE AIC = 1463.95
                            MODEL AIC = 95.10
                        SATURATED AIC = 132.00
                     INDEPENDENCE CAIC = 1503.61
                           MODEL CAIC = 214.07
                       SATURATED CAIC = 369.94

            ROOT MEAN SQUARE RESIDUAL (RMR) = 0.065
                      STANDARDIZED RMR = 0.027
                 GOODNESS OF FIT INDEX (GFI) = 0.95
        ADJUSTED GOODNESS OF FIT INDEX (AGFI) = 0.91
       PARSIMONY GOODNESS OF FIT INDEX (PGFI) = 0.48

                  NORMED FIT INDEX (NFI) = 0.98
              NON-NORMED FIT INDEX (NNFI) = 1.00
         PARSIMONY NORMED FIT INDEX (PNFI) = 0.59
             COMPARATIVE FIT INDEX (CFI) = 1.00
             INCREMENTAL FIT INDEX (IFI) = 1.00
               RELATIVE FIT INDEX (RFI) = 0.97

                     CRITICAL N (CN) = 187.35
```

The residuals compare the observed variances and covariances with those resulting from the model's parameter estimates. In a model that fits well, these will be small. The square root of the average squared residual (RMR) was reported above as .065; the table following the fitted covariance matrix shows where the large residuals were, and how many there were.

When examining these, keep in mind that their size will vary with the scale of the variables; changing the unit of measurement of a variable will change the variances and covariances, and thus the size of the residuals. Thus caution is needed in the interpretation of these residuals.

FITTED COVARIANCE MATRIX

	Y-1	Y-2	Y-3	Y-4	X-1	X-2
Y-1	3.20					
Y-2	2.72	2.63				
Y-3	3.12	2.87	4.85			
Y-4	3.55	3.27	5.37	6.31		
X-1	0.48	0.44	-0.22	-0.25	1.36	
X-2	0.62	0.57	-0.28	-0.32	1.26	1.96
X-3	1.05	0.96	-0.54	-0.61	1.76	2.27
X-4	0.55	0.51	-0.31	-0.35	0.79	1.02
X-5	0.60	0.55	-0.34	-0.38	0.85	1.10
X-6	0.93	0.86	1.40	1.60	0.52	0.68
X-7	1.34	1.23	2.01	2.29	0.75	0.97

	X-3	X-4	X-5	X-6	X-7
X-3	3.80				
X-4	1.95	1.38			
X-5	2.10	1.21	1.74		
X-6	0.63	0.13	0.14	1.42	
X-7	0.90	0.19	0.21	1.69	2.68

FITTED RESIDUALS

	Y-1	Y-2	Y-3	Y-4	X-1	X-2
Y-1	0.00					
Y-2	0.00	0.00				
Y-3	0.08	0.01	0.00			
Y-4	0.00	-0.06	0.00	0.00		
X-1	-0.15	-0.07	-0.14	-0.22	0.00	
X-2	-0.06	0.02	-0.04	-0.02	0.01	0.00
X-3	-0.04	0.05	0.05	0.02	-0.01	0.01
X-4	-0.09	-0.05	-0.13	-0.18	0.00	0.03
X-5	-0.10	-0.01	-0.03	-0.04	-0.01	-0.03
X-6	0.12	0.10	0.01	0.12	-0.05	0.02
X-7	-0.08	-0.08	-0.09	0.02	-0.07	-0.07

	X-3	X-4	X-5	X-6	X-7
X-3	0.00				
X-4	0.01	0.00			
X-5	-0.01	-0.02	0.00		
X-6	0.03	-0.06	-0.04	0.00	
X-7	0.01	-0.06	-0.04	0.00	0.00

SUMMARY STATISTICS FOR FITTED RESIDUALS
SMALLEST FITTED RESIDUAL =   -0.22
  MEDIAN FITTED RESIDUAL =   0.00
 LARGEST FITTED RESIDUAL =   0.12

The stem-leaf plot is useful for detecting outlying residuals, and for examining the general shape of the distribution of residuals. Standardized residuals are residuals divided by their standard errors.

```
STEMLEAF PLOT
- 2-2
- 1-85
- 1-430
- 0-9988777666655
- 0-4444433221111000000000000000000
  0-111111222233
  0-558
  1-022
```

STANDARDIZED RESIDUALS

	Y-1	Y-2	Y-3	Y-4	X-1	X-2
Y-1	0.00					
Y-2	0.00	0.00				
Y-3	1.66	0.21	0.00			
Y-4	-0.04	-1.66	0.00	0.00		
X-1	-1.50	-0.83	-1.14	-1.59	0.00	
X-2	-0.71	0.27	-0.36	-0.14	0.58	0.00
X-3	-0.56	1.27	0.93	0.35	-0.45	0.35
X-4	-1.02	-0.77	-1.29	-1.63	0.00	0.60
X-5	-0.86	-0.12	-0.20	-0.27	-0.20	-0.48
X-6	1.64	1.74	0.20	1.45	-0.76	0.26
X-7	-1.11	-1.58	-1.55	0.23	-0.84	-1.01

	X-3	X-4	X-5	X-6	X-7
X-3	0.00				
X-4	0.53	0.00			
X-5	-0.37	-1.08	0.00		
X-6	0.35	-0.98	-0.49	0.00	
X-7	0.25	-0.79	-0.46	0.00	0.00

The summary statistics, stem-and-leaf display, and list of outlying standardized residuals below make it much easier than examining the above display to see how bad the fit is. But the display of all the standardized residuals may help locate the reasons why a model does not fit well.

SUMMARY STATISTICS FOR STANDARDIZED RESIDUALS

```
SMALLEST STANDARDIZED RESIDUAL =    -1.66
  MEDIAN STANDARDIZED RESIDUAL =    -0.02
 LARGEST STANDARDIZED RESIDUAL =     1.74
```

```
STEMLEAF PLOT
-  1-766655
-  1-3111000
-  0-988888765555
-  0-44322110000000000000000
   0-222233334
   0-5669
   1-34
   1-677
```

QPLOT OF STANDARDIZED RESIDUALS

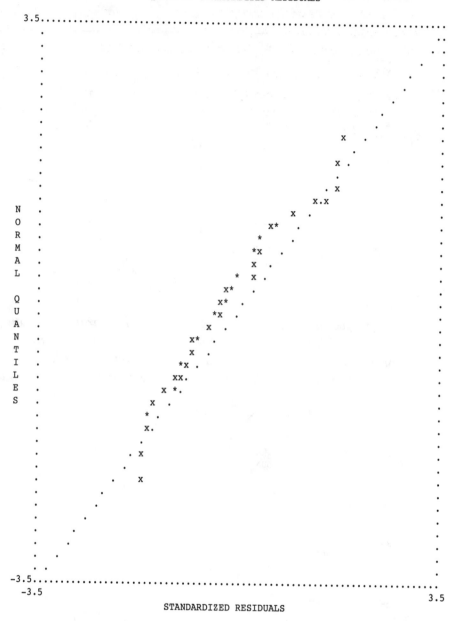

The plot above is another way of examining standardized residuals. If the model fits poorly, as is the case here, the plot will be shallower than the

2 THE LISREL PROBLEM RUN

diagonal line. If the standardized residuals are very small, then the plot will be steeper than the diagonal line. An x represents a single point, an * multiple points. Non-linearities in the plotted points are indicative of specification errors in the model or of departures from linearity or normality.

When a model does not fit well, the modification indices will often be the most useful way of deciding how to change the model to improve the fit. They give an estimate of how much the chi-square will decrease if a fixed parameter is freed. Of course, a parameter should only be freed if it makes sense to do so. The estimated change shows approximately how much the parameter will change when it is freed.

MODIFICATION INDICES AND ESTIMATED CHANGE

MODIFICATION INDICES FOR LAMBDA Y

	ETA-1	ETA-2
Y-1	- -	0.99
Y-2	- -	0.99
Y-3	2.11	- -
Y-4	2.11	- -

EXPECTED CHANGE FOR LAMBDA-Y

	ETA-1	ETA-2
Y-1	- -	0.06
Y-2	- -	-0.05
Y-3	0.09	- -
Y-4	-0.10	- -

STANDARDIZED EXPECTED CHANGE FOR LAMBDA-Y

	ETA-1	ETA-2
Y-1	- -	0.13
Y-2	- -	-0.12
Y-3	0.15	- -
Y-4	-0.17	- -

COMPLETELY STANDARDIZED EXPECTED CHANGE FOR LAMBDA-Y

	ETA-1	ETA-2
Y-1	- -	0.07
Y-2	- -	-0.07
Y-3	0.07	- -
Y-4	-0.07	- -

MODIFICATION INDICES FOR LAMBDA-X

	KSI-1	KSI-2	KSI-3
X-1	- -	0.11	1.05
X-2	- -	0.11	0.34
X-3	- -	- -	3.38
X-4	0.30	- -	1.37
X-5	0.30	- -	0.24
X-6	0.21	0.00	- -
X-7	0.21	0.00	- -

EXPECTED CHANGE FOR LAMBDA-X

	KSI-1	KSI-2	KSI-3
X-1	- -	-0.04	-0.08
X-2	- -	0.06	-0.05
X-3	- -	- -	0.15
X-4	0.08	- -	-0.08
X-5	-0.09	- -	-0.04
X-6	0.03	0.00	- -
X-7	-0.05	0.00	- -

STANDARDIZED EXPECTED CHANGE FOR LAMBDA-X

	KSI-1	KSI-2	KSI-3
X-1	- -	-0.05	-0.09
X-2	- -	0.06	-0.06
X-3	- -	- -	0.16
X-4	0.08	- -	-0.08
X-5	-0.09	- -	-0.04
X-6	0.03	0.00	- -
X-7	-0.05	0.00	- -

COMPLETELY STANDARDIZED EXPECTED CHANGE FOR LAMBDA-X

	KSI-1	KSI-2	KSI-3
X-1	- -	-0.04	-0.08
X-2	- -	0.04	-0.04
X-3	- -	- -	0.08
X-4	0.07	- -	-0.07
X-5	-0.07	- -	-0.03
X-6	0.03	0.00	- -
X-7	-0.03	0.00	- -

NO NON-ZERO MODIFICATION INDICES FOR BETA
NO NON-ZERO MODIFICATION INDICES FOR GAMMA
NO NON-ZERO MODIFICATION INDICES FOR PHI
NO NON-ZERO MODIFICATION INDICES FOR PSI

2 THE LISREL PROBLEM RUN

MODIFICATION INDICES FOR THETA-EPS

	Y-1	Y-2	Y-3	Y-4
Y-1	- -			
Y-2	- -	- -		
Y-3	0.53	0.00	- -	
Y-4	0.55	0.00	- -	- -

EXPECTED CHANGE FOR THETA-EPS

	Y-1	Y-2	Y-3	Y-4
Y-1	- -			
Y-2	- -	- -		
Y-3	0.02	0.00	- -	
Y-4	-0.03	0.00	- -	- -

COMPLETELY STANDARDIZED EXPECTED CHANGE FOR THETA-EPS

	Y-1	Y-2	Y-3	Y-4
Y-1	- -			
Y-2	- -	- -		
Y-3	0.01	0.00	- -	
Y-4	-0.01	0.00	- -	- -

MODIFICATION INDICES FOR THETA-DELTA-EPS

	Y-1	Y-2	Y-3	Y-4
X-1	0.13	0.50	2.04	4.21
X-2	0.24	0.10	0.35	0.62
X-3	0.00	0.06	0.01	0.05
X-4	0.91	0.03	0.04	0.37
X-5	1.03	0.10	0.11	0.71
X-6	0.95	1.12	2.40	0.17
X-7	0.29	1.70	0.02	0.91

EXPECTED CHANGE FOR THETA-DELTA-EPS

	Y-1	Y-2	Y-3	Y-4
X-1	-0.01	0.02	0.05	-0.08
X-2	-0.02	0.01	-0.02	0.03
X-3	0.00	-0.01	0.00	0.01
X-4	0.03	0.00	-0.01	-0.02
X-5	-0.04	0.01	-0.01	0.03
X-6	0.03	0.03	-0.05	0.01
X-7	-0.02	-0.05	0.01	0.05

COMPLETELY STANDARDIZED EXPECTED CHANGE FOR THETA-DELTA-EPS

	Y-1	Y-2	Y-3	Y-4
X-1	-0.01	0.01	0.02	-0.03
X-2	-0.01	0.00	-0.01	0.01
X-3	0.00	0.00	0.00	0.00
X-4	0.02	0.00	0.00	-0.01
X-5	-0.02	0.01	0.00	0.01
X-6	0.02	0.02	-0.02	0.00
X-7	-0.01	-0.02	0.00	0.01

MODIFICATION INDICES FOR THETA-DELTA

	X-1	X-2	X-3	X-4	X-5	X-6	X-7
X-1	- -						
X-2	0.34	- -					
X-3	0.57	0.02	- -				
X-4	0.00	0.09	0.18	- -			
X-5	0.14	0.29	2.01	1.16	- -		
X-6	0.46	0.81	0.08	0.59	0.16	- -	
X-7	0.60	1.93	0.52	0.50	0.05	- -	- -

EXPECTED CHANGE FOR THETA-DELTA

	X-1	X-2	X-3	X-4	X-5	X-6	X-7
X-1	- -						
X-2	0.03	- -					
X-3	-0.03	0.01	- -				
X-4	0.00	0.01	-0.03	- -			
X-5	0.02	-0.03	0.11	-0.08	- -		
X-6	-0.03	0.04	-0.01	-0.03	-0.02	- -	
X-7	0.04	-0.08	0.03	0.03	-0.01	- -	- -

COMPLETELY STANDARDIZED EXPECTED CHANGE FOR THETA-DELTA

	X-1	X-2	X-3	X-4	X-5	X-6	X-7
X-1	- -						
X-2	0.02	- -					
X-3	-0.01	0.00	- -				
X-4	0.00	0.01	-0.01	- -			
X-5	0.01	-0.01	0.04	-0.05	- -		
X-6	-0.02	0.02	0.00	-0.02	-0.01	- -	
X-7	0.02	-0.03	0.01	0.02	-0.01	- -	- -

MAXIMUM MODIFICATION INDEX IS   4.21 FOR ELEMENT (1, 4) OF THETA DELTA-EPSILON

2 THE LISREL PROBLEM RUN

Next are the variances and covariances that are not parameters of the model, but are derived from them. These are produced by the MR *option on the* OU *command.*

COVARIANCES

Y - ETA

	Y-1	Y-2	Y-3	Y-4
ETA-1	2.96	2.72	3.12	3.55
ETA-2	3.12	2.87	4.72	5.37

Y - KSI

	Y-1	Y-2	Y-3	Y-4
KSI-1	0.48	0.44	-0.22	-0.25
KSI-2	0.55	0.51	-0.31	-0.35
KSI-3	0.93	0.86	1.40	1.60

X - ETA

	X-1	X-2	X-3	X-4	X-5	X-6	X-7
ETA-1	0.48	0.62	1.05	0.55	0.60	0.93	1.34
ETA-2	-0.22	-0.28	-0.54	-0.31	-0.34	1.40	2.01

X - KSI

	X-1	X-2	X-3	X-4	X-5	X-6	X-7
KSI-1	0.97	1.26	1.76	0.79	0.85	0.52	0.75
KSI-2	0.79	1.02	1.95	1.12	1.21	0.13	0.19
KSI-3	0.52	0.68	0.63	0.13	0.14	1.18	1.69

In the standardized solution, all latent variables are standardized, i.e., they have a mean of zero and a standard deviation of one.

STANDARDIZED SOLUTION

LAMBDA-Y

	ETA-1	ETA-2
Y-1	1.72	- -
Y-2	1.58	- -
Y-3	- -	2.17
Y-4	- -	2.47

LAMBDA-X

	KSI-1	KSI-2	KSI-3
X-1	0.99	- -	- -
X-2	1.27	- -	- -
X-3	0.91	1.15	- -
X-4	- -	1.06	- -
X-5	- -	1.14	- -
X-6	- -	- -	1.08
X-7	- -	- -	1.56

BETA

	ETA-1	ETA-2
ETA-1	- -	0.68
ETA-2	0.74	- -

GAMMA

	KSI-1	KSI-2	KSI-3
ETA-1	0.12	0.30	- -
ETA-2	-0.56	- -	0.50

The correlations among the latent variables presented below are often much easier to interpret than the variances and covariances calculated above.

CORRELATION MATRIX OF ETA AND KSI

	ETA-1	ETA-2	KSI-1	KSI-2	KSI-3
ETA-1	1.00				
ETA-2	0.83	1.00			
KSI-1	0.28	-0.10	1.00		
KSI-2	0.30	-0.14	0.76	1.00	
KSI-3	0.50	0.60	0.49	0.12	1.00

PSI

	ETA-1	ETA-2
ETA-1	0.16	
ETA-2	-0.02	0.03

REGRESSION MATRIX ETA ON KSI (STANDARDIZED)

	KSI-1	KSI-2	KSI-3
ETA-1	-0.51	0.61	0.68
ETA-2	-0.94	0.46	1.00

COMPLETELY STANDARDIZED SOLUTION

LAMBDA-Y

	ETA-1	ETA-2
Y-1	0.96	- -
Y-2	0.98	- -
Y-3	- -	0.99
Y-4	- -	0.98

LAMBDA-X

	KSI-1	KSI-2	KSI-3
X-1	0.85	- -	- -
X-2	0.91	- -	- -
X-3	0.47	0.59	- -
X-4	- -	0.90	- -
X-5	- -	0.86	- -
X-6	- -	- -	0.91
X-7	- -	- -	0.95

BETA

	ETA-1	ETA-2
ETA-1	- -	0.68
ETA-2	0.74	- -

GAMMA

	KSI-1	KSI-2	KSI-3
ETA-1	0.12	0.30	- -
ETA-2	-0.56	- -	0.50

CORRELATION MATRIX OF ETA AND KSI

	ETA-1	ETA-2	KSI-1	KSI-2	KSI-3
ETA-1	1.00				
ETA-2	0.83	1.00			
KSI-1	0.28	-0.10	1.00		
KSI-2	0.30	-0.14	0.76	1.00	
KSI-3	0.50	0.60	0.49	0.12	1.00

PSI

	ETA-1	ETA-2
ETA-1	0.16	
ETA-2	-0.02	0.03

THETA-EPS

	Y-1	Y-2	Y-3	Y-4
	0.08	0.05	0.03	0.03

THETA-DELTA

	X-1	X-2	X-3	X-4	X-5	X-6	X-7
	0.29	0.17	0.02	0.19	0.25	0.17	0.10

REGRESSION MATRIX ETA ON KSI (STANDARDIZED)

	KSI-1	KSI-2	KSI-3
ETA-1	-0.51	0.61	0.68
ETA-2	-0.94	0.46	1.00

The effects of one variable on another can be direct, most of which are seen in a path diagram as one-way arrows; they are parameters in the model. Others are found by computing the reduced form equations (see Equation 4.2). The total effects include the direct effects, as well as indirect effects that result from correlations among exogenous variables and circular or reciprocal effects.

The standard error (in parentheses) and t-value are listed below each effect.

TOTAL AND INDIRECT EFFECTS

TOTAL EFFECTS OF KSI ON ETA

	KSI-1	KSI-2	KSI-3
ETA-1	-0.90	1.00	1.08
	(0.43)	(0.34)	(0.22)
	-2.09	2.92	4.81
ETA-2	-2.06	0.94	2.01
	(0.52)	(0.40)	(0.27)
	-3.99	2.32	7.49

INDIRECT EFFECTS OF KSI ON ETA

	KSI-1	KSI-2	KSI-3
ETA-1	-1.11	0.50	1.08
	(0.34)	(0.24)	(0.22)
	-3.27	2.10	4.81

```
ETA-2        -0.84       0.94       1.01
             (0.47)     (0.40)     (0.31)
             -1.80       2.32       3.27
```

TOTAL EFFECTS OF ETA ON ETA

	ETA-1	ETA-2
ETA-1	1.02	1.08
	(0.41)	(0.28)
	2.48	3.85
ETA-2	1.89	1.02
	(0.72)	(0.41)
	2.64	2.48

The stability index is used in models with reciprocal or circular paths; as long as it is less than 1, there is no problem: the system is stable, and the total effects are finite.

```
LARGEST EIGENVALUE OF B*B' (STABILITY INDEX) IS    0.879
```

INDIRECT EFFECTS OF ETA ON ETA

	ETA-1	ETA-2
ETA-1	1.02	0.55
	(0.41)	(0.25)
	2.48	2.21
ETA-2	0.95	1.02
	(0.55)	(0.41)
	1.74	2.48

TOTAL EFFECTS OF ETA ON Y

	ETA-1	ETA-2
Y-1	2.02	1.08
	(0.41)	(0.28)
	4.91	3.85
Y-2	1.86	1.00
	(0.38)	(0.26)
	4.83	3.86
Y-3	1.89	2.02
	(0.72)	(0.41)
	2.64	4.91

Y-4	2.15	2.30
	(0.82)	(0.47)
	2.63	4.87

INDIRECT EFFECTS OF ETA ON Y

	ETA-1	ETA-2
Y-1	1.02	1.08
	(0.41)	(0.28)
	2.48	3.85
Y-2	0.94	1.00
	(0.38)	(0.26)
	2.47	3.86
Y-3	1.89	1.02
	(0.72)	(0.41)
	2.64	2.48
Y-4	2.15	1.16
	(0.82)	(0.47)
	2.63	2.47

TOTAL EFFECTS OF KSI ON Y

	KSI-1	KSI-2	KSI-3
Y-1	-0.90	1.00	1.08
	(0.43)	(0.34)	(0.22)
	-2.09	2.92	4.81
Y-2	-0.82	0.92	0.99
	(0.39)	(0.31)	(0.21)
	-2.09	2.92	4.84
Y-3	-2.06	0.94	2.01
	(0.52)	(0.40)	(0.27)
	-3.99	2.32	7.49
Y-4	-2.35	1.07	2.29
	(0.59)	(0.46)	(0.31)
	-3.99	2.32	7.48

STANDARDIZED TOTAL AND INDIRECT EFFECTS

STANDARDIZED TOTAL EFFECTS OF KSI ON ETA

	KSI-1	KSI-2	KSI-3
ETA-1	-0.51	0.61	0.68
ETA-2	-0.94	0.46	1.00

STANDARDIZED INDIRECT EFFECTS OF KSI ON ETA

	KSI-1	KSI-2	KSI-3
ETA-1	-0.64	0.31	0.68
ETA-2	-0.38	0.46	0.51

STANDARDIZED TOTAL EFFECTS OF ETA ON ETA

	ETA-1	ETA-2
ETA-1	1.02	1.37
ETA-2	1.50	1.02

STANDARDIZED INDIRECT EFFECTS OF ETA ON ETA

	ETA-1	ETA-2
ETA-1	1.02	0.69
ETA-2	0.75	1.02

STANDARDIZED TOTAL EFFECTS OF ETA ON Y

	ETA-1	ETA-2
Y-1	3.47	2.35
Y-2	3.19	2.17
Y-3	3.25	4.38
Y-4	3.70	4.99

COMPLETELY STANDARDIZED TOTAL EFFECTS OF ETA ON Y

	ETA-1	ETA-2
Y-1	1.94	1.32
Y-2	1.97	1.34
Y-3	1.47	1.99
Y-4	1.47	1.98

STANDARDIZED INDIRECT EFFECTS OF ETA ON Y

	ETA-1	ETA-2
Y-1	1.75	2.35
Y-2	1.61	2.17
Y-3	3.25	2.21
Y-4	3.70	2.51

COMPLETELY STANDARDIZED INDIRECT EFFECTS OF ETA ON Y

	ETA-1	ETA-2
Y-1	0.98	1.32
Y-2	0.99	1.34
Y-3	1.47	1.00
Y-4	1.47	1.00

STANDARDIZED TOTAL EFFECTS OF KSI ON Y

	KSI-1	KSI-2	KSI-3
Y-1	-0.88	1.06	1.17
Y-2	-0.81	0.97	1.08
Y-3	-2.04	0.99	2.18
Y-4	-2.32	1.13	2.48

COMPLETELY STANDARDIZED TOTAL EFFECTS OF KSI ON Y

	KSI-1	KSI-2	KSI-3
Y-1	-0.49	0.59	0.65
Y-2	-0.50	0.60	0.66
Y-3	-0.92	0.45	0.99
Y-4	-0.92	0.45	0.99

This analysis shows that the model fits the data well. In the following chapters some examples illustrate what can be done when this is not the case. For instance, detecting misspecification of a model (Example 5.3), evaluating alternative models (Examples 5.6 and 6.4) and how to deal with a nonidentified model (Example 6.6). Example 8.1 illustrates that sometimes the data are to blame, which leads to nonadmissible solutions in that case. Finally, Chapter 11 gives some hints on what can be done when everything else fails.

3

Submodel 1: Measurement models and confirmatory factor analysis

This chapter describes various types of models, all fitting the framework of Submodel 1 as defined in the section *The measurement (factor analysis) model for* x *(NX ≠ 0; NK ≠ 0)* on page 9, along with examples and sample problem command files. The submodel is

$$\mathbf{x} = \boldsymbol{\Lambda}\boldsymbol{\xi} + \boldsymbol{\delta} \,, \tag{3.1}$$

where

$\mathbf{x}' = (x_1, x_2, \ldots, x_q)$ are the observed or measured variables,

$\boldsymbol{\Lambda}$ is the matrix $\boldsymbol{\Lambda}_x$ of the general model,

$\boldsymbol{\xi}' = (\xi_1, \xi_2, \ldots, \xi_n)$ are latent or unobservable variables, and

$\boldsymbol{\delta}' = (\delta_1, \delta_2, \ldots, \delta_q)$ are error variables.

Assumptions: 1) the ξ's and δ's are random variables with zero means, 2) the δ's are uncorrelated with the ξ's, and 3) all observed variables are measured in deviations from their means.

The measurement model represents the regression of $\mathbf{x}$ on $\boldsymbol{\xi}$ and the element λ_{ij} of $\boldsymbol{\Lambda}$ is the partial regression coefficient of ξ_j in the regression of x_i on $\xi_1, \xi_2, \ldots, \xi_n$.

The assumed model implies that the covariance matrix of $\mathbf{x}$ is

$$\boldsymbol{\Sigma} = \boldsymbol{\Lambda}\boldsymbol{\Phi}\boldsymbol{\Lambda}' + \boldsymbol{\Theta} \,, \tag{3.2}$$

123

where Φ and Θ are the covariance matrices of ξ and δ, respectively.

Standardization: In the standardized solution for this submodel, the ξ-variables have unit variance and Φ is a correlation matrix. If the latent variables are assumed uncorrelated in order to make the model identifiable, Φ becomes the identity matrix, $\mathbf{I}$.

3.1 The one-factor congeneric measurement model

The most common type of measurement model is the one-factor congeneric measurement model; see Jöreskog (1971b). A path diagram of this model is shown in Figure 3.1.

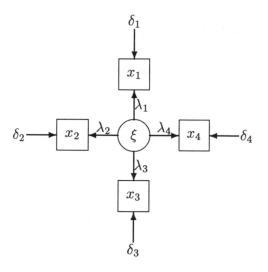

Figure 3.1   The Congeneric Measurement Model

The equations corresponding to Figure 3.1 are written in matrix form as

$$\begin{pmatrix} x_1 \\ x_2 \\ x_3 \\ x_4 \end{pmatrix} = \begin{pmatrix} \lambda_1 \\ \lambda_2 \\ \lambda_3 \\ \lambda_4 \end{pmatrix} \xi + \begin{pmatrix} \delta_1 \\ \delta_2 \\ \delta_3 \\ \delta_4 \end{pmatrix} \tag{3.3}$$

or

$$\mathbf{x} = \boldsymbol{\lambda}\xi + \boldsymbol{\delta} \, .$$

The model (3.3) is empirically not directly verifiable since there are more unobserved variables than observed. However, with the assumption that the latent variable is standardized, the equations imply that the covariance matrix of the observed variables is of the form

$$\boldsymbol{\Sigma} = \boldsymbol{\lambda}\boldsymbol{\lambda}' + \boldsymbol{\Theta} = \begin{pmatrix} \lambda_1^2 + \theta_{11} & & & \\ \lambda_2\lambda_1 & \lambda_2^2 + \theta_{22} & & \\ \lambda_3\lambda_1 & \lambda_3\lambda_2 & \lambda_3^2 + \theta_{33} & \\ \lambda_4\lambda_1 & \lambda_4\lambda_2 & \lambda_4\lambda_3 & \lambda_4^2 + \theta_{44} \end{pmatrix} \quad (3.4)$$

In this equation, $\boldsymbol{\Theta}$ is a diagonal matrix with elements θ_{ii}, the variances of δ_i $(i = 1, 2, 3, 4)$.

The hypothesis that the population covariance matrix has this form is testable from a random sample of observations. In addition, the following subhypotheses are testable.

Congeneric, parallel, and tau-equivalent measures

The above model is called the *congeneric measurement* model. The measures $x_1, x_2, \ldots, x_q$ are said to be *congeneric* if their true values $\tau_1, \tau_2, \ldots, \tau_q$ have all pair-wise correlations equal to unity. This is true of the model, since $\tau_i = \lambda_i\xi = x_i - \delta_i$ $(i = 1, 2, 3, 4)$ and all τ's are linearly related and hence have unit correlation. The true variance in x_i is λ_i^2 and the reliability of x_i is

$$\rho_{ii} = \frac{\lambda_i^2}{\sigma_{ii}} = \frac{\lambda_i^2}{\lambda_i^2 + \theta_{ii}} = 1 - \frac{\theta_{ii}}{\lambda_i^2 + \theta_{ii}} \, . \quad (3.5)$$

Strictly speaking, the error δ_i is considered to be the sum of two uncorrelated random components s_i and e_i, where s_i is a specific factor (specific to x_i) and e_i is the true measurement error. However, unless there are several replicate measures x_i with the same s_i, one cannot distinguish between these two components or separately estimate their variances. In consequence, ρ_{ii} in (3.5) is a lower bound for the true reliability.

Parallel measures have equal true score variances and equal error variances, *i.e.*,

$$\lambda_1^2 = \cdots = \lambda_4^2 \qquad \theta_{11} = \cdots = \theta_{44} \, .$$

Tau-equivalent measures have equal true score variances, but possibly different error variances.

Tests of parallelism and tau-equivalence are demonstrated in the following example.

Example 3.1: Analysis of reader reliability in essay scoring

Source: Votaw (1948).

In an experiment to establish methods of obtaining reader reliability in essay scoring, 126 examinees were given a three-part English Composition examination. Each part required the examinee to write an essay, and for each examinee, scores were obtained on the following: (1) the original part 1 essay, (2) a handwritten copy of the original part 1 essay, (3) a carbon copy of the handwritten copy in (2), and (4) the original part 2 essay. Scores were assigned by a group of readers using procedures designed to counterbalance certain experimental conditions. The investigator would like to know whether, on the basis of this sample of size 126, the four scores can be used interchangeably or whether scores on the copies (2) and (3) are less reliable than the originals (1) and (4).

The covariance matrix of the four measurements is given in the command file below. The hypotheses to be tested are that the measurements are (1) parallel, (2) tau-equivalent, and (3) congeneric, respectively. All analyses use the ML fit function.

The LISREL command file for this analysis is:

```
Analysis of Reader Reliability in Essay Scoring; Votaw's Data
Congeneric model estimated by ML
DATA       NI=4  NO=126
LABELS;  ORIGPRT1  WRITCOPY  CARBCOPY  ORIGPRT2
CMATRIX
25.0704
12.4363     28.2021
11.7257      9.2281     22.7390
20.7510     11.9732     12.0692     21.8707
MODEL      NX=4  NK=1  LX=FR  PH=ST
LKSI;    Esayabil
OUTPUT   SE ND=2
```

The DA command specifies four observed variables and a sample size of 126; the MA default is assumed, so the covariance matrix will be analyzed.

Labels for the input variables follow the LA command.

The CM command indicates that a covariance matrix is to be input. Because an external file is not specified, the matrix follows in the command file. A format statement does not appear, so the input is in free format.

The MO command specifies four x-variables and one latent variable; the elements of λ are all free (LX=FR), and the latent variable is standardized (PH=ST).

A label for the latent variable follows the LK command.

The OU command requests only standard errors (SE) as additional output, and the number of decimal places is set to two.

To obtain the input for the hypothesis of tau-equivalence, insert the command

```
EQUAL    LX(1) - LX(4)
```

before the OU command. This specifies that the elements of λ should be equal.

The hypothesis of parallel measurements is specified by adding one more EQ command:

```
EQUAL    TD(1) - TD(4)
```

Table 3.1   Essay Scoring Data: Summary of Analyses

	Hypothesis	df	χ^2	p
(1)	Parallel	8	109.12	0.000
(2)	Tau-equivalent	5	40.42	0.000
(3)	Congeneric	2	2.28	0.320

Table 3.2   Essay Scoring Data: Results for Congeneric Model

i	$\hat{\lambda}_i$	s.e.$(\hat{\lambda}_i)$	$\hat{\rho}_{ii}$
1	4.57	0.36	0.83
2	2.68	0.45	0.25
3	2.65	0.40	0.31
4	4.54	0.33	0.94

In the results of this analysis, as summarized in Table 3.1, it is seen that the hypotheses (1) and (2) are untenable, but the hypothesis (3) is acceptable.

The results under the hypothesis (3) are given in Table 3.2. The three columns of Table 3.2 can be read off directly from the output for the ML solution. The reliabilities in column 3 appear where the output says "squared multiple correlations for x-variables."

Inspecting the different λ's, it is evident that these are different even taking their respective standard errors of estimate into account. Comparing the reliabilities in the last column, one sees that they are high for scores (1) and (4) and low for scores (2) and (3). Thus, it appears that scores obtained from originals are more reliable than scores based on copies.

3.2 Several sets of congeneric measures: the multi-factor model

The previous model generalizes immediately to several sets of congeneric measures. If there are n sets of such measures, with $m_1, m_2, \ldots, m_n$ in each set, respectively, we write

$$x' = (x'_1, \ x'_2, \ldots, \ x'_n),$$

where $\mathbf{x}_g (g = 1, 2, \ldots, n,)$ is the vector of observed variables for the g-th set. Associated with the vector $\mathbf{x}_g$ there is a true score ξ_g and vectors $\boldsymbol{\lambda}_g$ and $\boldsymbol{\delta}_g$ defined as in Section 3.1 so that

$$\mathbf{x}_g = \boldsymbol{\lambda}_g \xi_g + \boldsymbol{\delta}_g . \tag{3.6}$$

As before we may assume, without loss of generality, that ξ_g is scaled to zero mean and unit variance. If the different latent variables $\xi_1, \xi_2, \ldots, \xi_n$ are all mutually uncorrelated, then each set of measures can be analyzed separately as in the previous section. However, in most cases these latent variables correlate with each other and an overall analysis of the entire set of measures must be made. Let

$$q = m_1 + m_2 + \cdots + m_n$$

be the total number of measurements. Then $\mathbf{x}$ is of order q. Let $\boldsymbol{\delta}$ be the corresponding vector of error scores. Furthermore, let

$$\boldsymbol{\xi}' = (\xi_1, \xi_2, \ldots, \xi_n)$$

and let $\boldsymbol{\Lambda}$ be the matrix of order $q \times n$, partitioned as

$$\boldsymbol{\Lambda} = \begin{pmatrix} \boldsymbol{\lambda}_1 & \mathbf{0} & \cdots & \mathbf{0} \\ \mathbf{0} & \boldsymbol{\lambda}_2 & \cdots & \mathbf{0} \\ \vdots & \vdots & \ddots & \vdots \\ \mathbf{0} & \mathbf{0} & \cdots & \boldsymbol{\lambda}_n \end{pmatrix} .$$

Then $\mathbf{x}$ is represented as

$$\mathbf{x} = \boldsymbol{\Lambda}\boldsymbol{\xi} + \boldsymbol{\delta} . \tag{3.7}$$

Let $\boldsymbol{\Phi}$ be the correlation matrix of $\boldsymbol{\xi}$. Then the covariance matrix $\boldsymbol{\Sigma}$ of $\mathbf{x}$ is

$$\boldsymbol{\Sigma} = \boldsymbol{\Lambda}\boldsymbol{\Phi}\boldsymbol{\Lambda}' + \boldsymbol{\Theta} ,$$

where $\boldsymbol{\Theta}$ is a diagonal matrix of order q containing the error variances.

Example 3.2: Ability and aspiration

Source: Calsyn & Kenny (1977).

The measured variables are

x_1 = *self-concept of ability (S-C ABIL)*
x_2 = *perceived parental evaluation (PPAREVAL)*
x_3 = *perceived teacher evaluation (PTEAEVAL)*
x_4 = *perceived friend's evaluation (PFRIEVAL)*
x_5 = *educational aspiration (EDUC ASP)*
x_6 = *college plans (COL PLAN).*

The x_1, x_2, x_3, and x_4 are assumed to be indicators of "ability" and x_5 and x_6 are assumed to be indicators of "aspiration." The problem is to estimate the correlation between true ability and true aspiration.

The path diagram for this example is given in Figure 3.2. Following the rules given in Section 1.2, the coefficients associated with each arrow are those shown in the figure. Alternatively, these same rules lead to the equations

$$\begin{pmatrix} x_1 \\ x_2 \\ x_3 \\ x_4 \\ x_5 \\ x_6 \end{pmatrix} = \begin{pmatrix} \lambda_{11} & 0 \\ \lambda_{21} & 0 \\ \lambda_{31} & 0 \\ \lambda_{41} & 0 \\ 0 & \lambda_{52} \\ 0 & \lambda_{62} \end{pmatrix} \begin{pmatrix} \xi_1 \\ \xi_2 \end{pmatrix} + \begin{pmatrix} \delta_1 \\ \delta_2 \\ \delta_3 \\ \delta_4 \\ \delta_5 \\ \delta_6 \end{pmatrix}$$

or

$$\mathbf{x} = \mathbf{\Lambda}\boldsymbol{\xi} + \boldsymbol{\delta}\, .$$

Note that the subscripts on λ correspond to the row and column of $\mathbf{\Lambda}$ where the coefficient appears.

The model includes only the three parameter matrices $\mathbf{\Lambda}$, $\mathbf{\Phi}$ and $\mathbf{\Theta}$, where $\mathbf{\Lambda}$ is a 6×2 matrix, $\mathbf{\Phi}$ is a 2×2 correlation matrix and $\mathbf{\Theta}$ is a 6×6 diagonal matrix with error variances in the diagonal. Consider first the solution in which the latent variables are in the metric of the reference variables. This is obtained by fixing a one in each column of $\mathbf{\Lambda}$.

Case 1. For an analysis in which the latent variables are unstandardized, the LISREL command file is as follows:

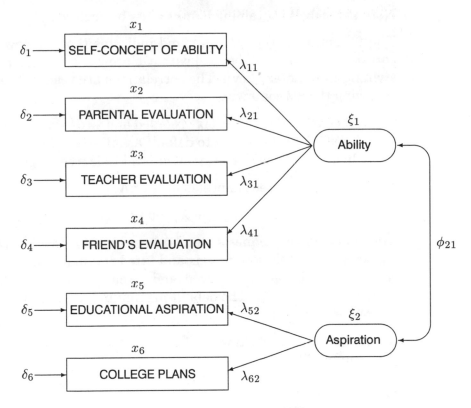

Figure 3.2   Path Diagram for Ability and Aspiration

```
ABILITY AND ASPIRATION
DATA    NI=6 NO=556 MA=KM
LABELS; 'S-C ABIL' PPAREVAL PTEAEVAL PFRIEVAL 'EDUC ASP' 'COL PLAN'
KMATRIX SYMMETRIC
(6F4.2)
 100
  73 100
  70  68 100
  58  61  57 100
  46  43  40  37 100
  56  52  48  41  72 100
MODEL   NX=6 NK=2
LK;     Ability Aspiratn
FREE    LX(2,1) LX(3,1) LX(4,1) LX(6,2);  VALUE 1  LX(1,1) LX(5,2)
OUTPUT  SE TV RS MR FS
```

Note that labels containing blanks must be enclosed in single quotes.

The SY option of the KM command indicates that the lower half of the correlation matrix will be read with each row beginning a new record (by striking the "Enter" key). The correlations are read in the fixed format following the KM command.

The MO command specifies six observed and two latent variables, but the model matrices are allowed to default as follows: all elements of Λ fixed initially at zero; Φ is free symmetric; and Θ is free diagonal.

The FR command frees four elements of Λ.

The VA command fixes λ_{11} and λ_{52} at 1.0.

The OU command requests standard errors (SE), t-values (TV), fitted covariance (or correlation) matrix and fitted residuals (RS), covariances (or correlations) between observed and latent variables (MR), and factor scores regression (FS). The default maximum likelihood method of analysis (ML) is assumed.

Case 2. For an analysis in which the two latent variables are standardized, the command file is:

```
ABILITY AND ASPIRATION
DA NI=6 NO=556 MA=KM
LA
'S-C ABIL' PPAREVAL PTEAEVAL PFRIEVAL 'EDUC ASP' 'COL PLAN'
KM SY
(6F4.2)
100
  73 100
  70  68 100
  58  61  57 100
  46  43  40  37 100
  56  52  48  41  72 100
MO NX=6 NK=2 PH=ST
LK
Ability Aspiratn
FR LX(1,1) LX(2,1) LX(3,1) LX(4,1) LX(5,2) LX(6,2)
OU SE TV RS MR FS
```

This input differs from the previous in three ways: PH=ST is added in MO, LX(1,1) and LX(5,2) have been added on the FR command, and the VA

Table 3.3

The Same Solution in Two Different Scalings of the Latent Variables

Reference Variables Solution		Standardized Solution	

$$\Lambda = \begin{pmatrix} 1 & 0 \\ .984 & 0 \\ .933 & 0 \\ .805 & 0 \\ 0 & 1 \\ 0 & 1.198 \end{pmatrix} \qquad \Lambda = \begin{pmatrix} .863 & 0 \\ .849 & 0 \\ .805 & 0 \\ .695 & 0 \\ 0 & .775 \\ 0 & .929 \end{pmatrix}$$

$$\Phi = \begin{pmatrix} .745 & \\ .446 & .601 \end{pmatrix} \qquad \Phi = \begin{pmatrix} 1 & \\ .666 & 1 \end{pmatrix}$$

command has been deleted. PH=ST fixes the scales for the latent variables so that Φ becomes a correlation matrix, $i.e.$, the two latent variables are standardized. The parameters λ_{11} and λ_{51} are now estimated instead of being fixed at 1. Note that the number of free parameters in the model remains the same.

The estimated Λ and Φ for the two solutions are shown in Table 3.3. These solutions are equivalent. They only differ in the sense that the unit of measurement in ξ_1 and ξ_2 is different.

If the scales for ξ-variables are fixed by PH=ST, the solution obtained is not unique, since each column of Λ_x may be multiplied by minus one. This means that the fit function has several minima with the same fit. Therefore, when good reference variables are available, it is better to fix the scales by assigning fixed ones in each column of Λ_x.

The results also include the correlations between the latent variables (factors) and the observed variables, shown below, and the factor scores regressions, shown thereafter (both for the standardized solution).

```
COVARIANCES
   X - KSI
          S-C ABIL   PPAREVAL   PTEAEVAL   PFRIEVAL   EDUC ASP   COL PLAN
ABILITY      .863       .849       .805       .695       .516       .619
ASPIRATN     .575       .566       .536       .463       .775       .929
```

In this case both x and ξ are standardized, and the entries above are correlations. In factor analysis terminology, they comprise the *factor structure*, as distinguished from the *factor pattern*, $\hat{\Lambda}$, in the standardized solution of Table 3.3. That is, the factor pattern is $\hat{\Lambda}$ and the factor structure is $\hat{\Lambda}\hat{\Phi}$.

It should be pointed out that the elements of the factor pattern, *i.e.*, the elements of $\hat{\Lambda}$ are not in general correlations even if both x and ξ are standardized. The elements of $\hat{\Lambda}$ are regression coefficients and, as such, they can exceed the absolute value one even though both x and ξ are standardized. The elements of the factor structure, *i.e.*, the covariances between x and ξ, on the other hand, will of course be correlations if both x and ξ are standardized.

The estimated joint covariance matrix of x and ξ is (*cf.* Sec. 1.11):

$$
\begin{pmatrix}
\hat{\Lambda}\hat{\Phi}\hat{\Lambda}' + \hat{\Theta} & \\
\hat{\Phi}\hat{\Lambda}' & \hat{\Phi}
\end{pmatrix} .
$$

The upper left part of this matrix is the estimate $\hat{\Sigma}$ of Σ in (3.2) after the model has been fitted. This matrix may be saved in a file by putting SI=*filename* on the OU command; see *output requests* in Chapter 2.

```
FACTOR SCORES REGRESSIONS
          S-C ABIL   PPAREVAL   PTEAEVAL   PFRIEVAL   EDUC ASP   COL PLAN
ABILITY      .341       .307       .230       .135       .024       .085
ASPIRATN     .043       .038       .029       .017       .205       .717
```

The coefficients above, representing the estimated bivariate regression of ξ_1 and ξ_2 on all the observed variables, are computed by the formula,

$$
\mathbf{A} = \hat{\Phi}\hat{\Lambda}'\hat{\Sigma}^{-1} .
$$

The matrix $\mathbf{A}$ may be saved in a file and used to compute estimated factor scores $\hat{\boldsymbol{\xi}}_\alpha$ for any person with observed scores $\mathbf{x}_\alpha$, say, by the formula

$$\hat{\boldsymbol{\xi}}_\alpha = \mathbf{A}\mathbf{x}_\alpha \ .$$

When the LISREL model involves both ξ- and η-variables the factor scores regression will be computed by regressing all the ξ- and η-variables on all the observed variables.

Example 3.3: Estimating the disattenuated correlation

Source: Lord (1957).

Two measures x_1 and x_2 are 15-item vocabulary tests administered under liberal time limits. Two other measures x_3 and x_4 are highly speeded 75-item vocabulary tests. The covariance matrix based on $NO{=}649$ examinees, is given in Table 3.4.

The disattenuated correlation, ϕ, between the two latent variables is estimated, and the hypothesis $\phi = 1$ is tested. In addition, the hypothesis that the measures are parallel is tested.

The measurement model is

$$
\begin{pmatrix} x_1 \\ x_2 \\ x_3 \\ x_4 \end{pmatrix} = \begin{pmatrix} \lambda_1 & 0 \\ \lambda_2 & 0 \\ 0 & \lambda_3 \\ 0 & \lambda_4 \end{pmatrix} \begin{pmatrix} \xi_1 \\ \xi_2 \end{pmatrix} + \begin{pmatrix} \delta_1 \\ \delta_2 \\ \delta_3 \\ \delta_4 \end{pmatrix},
$$

with covariance matrix

$$
\begin{aligned}
\boldsymbol{\Sigma} \; &= \; \begin{pmatrix} \lambda_1 & 0 \\ \lambda_2 & 0 \\ 0 & \lambda_3 \\ 0 & \lambda_4 \end{pmatrix} \begin{pmatrix} 1 & \phi \\ \phi & 1 \end{pmatrix} \begin{pmatrix} \lambda_1 & \lambda_2 & 0 & 0 \\ 0 & 0 & \lambda_3 & \lambda_4 \end{pmatrix} + \begin{pmatrix} \theta_1 & 0 & 0 & 0 \\ 0 & \theta_2 & 0 & 0 \\ 0 & 0 & \theta_3 & 0 \\ 0 & 0 & 0 & \theta_4 \end{pmatrix} \\[2mm]
&= \; \begin{pmatrix} \lambda_1^2 + \theta_1 & & & \\ \lambda_1\lambda_2 & \lambda_2^2 + \theta_2 & & \\ \lambda_1\lambda_3\phi & \lambda_2\lambda_3\phi & \lambda_3^2 + \theta_3 & \\ \lambda_1\lambda_4\phi & \lambda_2\lambda_4\phi & \lambda_3\lambda_4 & \lambda_2^2 + \theta_4 \end{pmatrix}.
\end{aligned}
$$

Table 3.4   Covariance Matrix for Four Vocabulary Measures

	x_1	x_2	x_3	x_4
x_1	86.3979			
x_2	57.7751	86.2632		
x_3	56.8651	59.3177	97.2850	
x_4	58.8986	59.6683	73.8201	97.8192

In this model, x_1 and x_2 are congeneric measures of ξ_1, and x_3 and x_4 are congeneric measures of ξ_2. The disattenuated correlation ϕ is the correlation between ξ_1 and ξ_2. To analyze the data, one can set up the four hypotheses

$$H_1 \quad : \quad \lambda_1 = \lambda_2, \lambda_3 = \lambda_4, \theta_1 = \theta_2, \theta_3 = \theta_4, \phi = 1$$
$$H_2 \quad : \quad \lambda_1 = \lambda_2, \lambda_3 = \lambda_4, \theta_1 = \theta_2, \theta_3 = \theta_4$$
$$H_3 \quad : \quad \phi = 1$$
$$H_4 \quad : \quad \lambda_1, \lambda_2, \lambda_3, \lambda_4, \theta_1, \theta_2, \theta_3, \theta_4, \text{ and } \phi \text{ unconstrained,}$$

and estimate the model under each of these. Under hypotheses H_1, H_2, and H_3, the model involves *equality constraints*, imposed on the parameters of the base model H_4.

All four models can be estimated in one run using stacked input. The command file analyzes the models in the order H_4, H_3, H_2, and H_1. The covariance matrix of the four variables is in the file EX33.COV, which is rewound after each problem. Because Φ is singular by definition in H_1 and H_3, AD must be set OFF in these cases.

```
ESTIMATING THE DISATTENUATED CORRELATION    HYPOTHESIS 4
DA NI=4 NO=649
CM FI=EX33.COV RE
MO NX=4 NK=2 PH=FI
FR LX 1 1 LX 2 1 LX 3 2 LX 4 2
FR PH 2 1
VA 1 PH 1 1 PH 2 2
OU SE
```

Table 3.5 Four Vocabulary Measures: Summary of Analyses

Hypothesis	No.par.	χ^2	df	p
H_1	4	37.33	6	0.00
H_2	5	1.93	5	0.86
H_3	8	36.21	2	0.00
H_4	9	0.70	1	0.40

```
ESTIMATING THE DISATTENUATED CORRELATION     HYPOTHESIS 3
DA NI=4 NO=649
CM FI=EX33.COV RE
MO NX=4 NK=2 PH=FI
FR LX 1 1 LX 2 1 LX 3 2 LX 4 2
VA 1 PH 1 1 PH 2 1 PH 2 2
OU SE AD=OFF
ESTIMATING THE DISATTENUATED CORRELATION     HYPOTHESIS 2
DA NI=4 NO=649
CM FI=EX33.COV RE
MO NX=4 NK=2 PH=FI
FR LX 1 1 LX 2 1 LX 3 2 LX 4 2
FR PH 2 1
VA 1 PH 1 1 PH 2 1 PH 2 2
EQ LX 1 1 LX 2 1
EQ TD 1 TD 2
EQ LX 3 2 LX 4 2
EQ TD 3 TD 4
OU SE
ESTIMATING THE DISATTENUATED CORRELATION     HYPOTHESIS 1
DA NI=4 NO=649
CM FI=EX33.COV
MO NX=4 NK=2 PH=FI
FR LX 1 1 LX 2 1 LX 3 2 LX 4 2
VA 1 PH 1 1 PH 2 1 PH 2 2
EQ LX 1 1 LX 2 1
EQ TD 1 TD 2
EQ LX 3 2 LX 4 2
EQ TD 3 TD 4
OU SE AD=OFF
```

Table 3.6   Four Vocabulary Measures: Test of Hypotheses

	Parallel	Congeneric	
$\varphi = 1$	$\chi_6^2 = 37.33$	$\chi_2^2 = 36.21$	$\chi_4^2 = 1.12$
$\varphi \neq 1$	$\chi_5^2 = 1.93$	$\chi_1^2 = 0.70$	$\chi_4^2 = 1.23$
	$\chi_1^2 = 35.40$	$\chi_1^2 = 35.51$	

The results are shown in Table 3.5. Each hypothesis is tested against the general alternative that Σ is unconstrained. To consider various hypotheses that can be tested, the four χ^2 values of Table 3.5 are recorded in a 2×2 table as in Table 3.6. Test of H_1 against H_2 gives $\chi^2 = 35.40$ with one degree of freedom. An alternative test is H_3 against H_4, which gives $\chi^2 = 35.51$ with one degree of freedom. Thus, regardless of whether we treat the two pairs of measures as parallel or congeneric, the hypothesis $\phi = 1$ is rejected. There is strong evidence that the unspeeded and speeded measures do not measure the same trait. The hypothesis that the two pairs of measures are parallel can also be tested by means of Table 3.6. This gives $\chi^2 = 1.12$ or $\chi^2 = 1.23$ with four degrees of freedom, depending on whether we assume $\phi = 1$ or $\phi \neq 1$. Thus we cannot reject the hypothesis that the two pairs of measures are parallel. It appears that H_2 is the most reasonable of the four hypotheses. The maximum likelihood estimate of ϕ under H_2 is $\hat{\phi} = 0.899$ with a standard error of 0.019. An approximate 95% confidence interval for ϕ is $0.86 < \phi < 0.94$.

3.3   Confirmatory factor analysis

In exploratory factor analysis, the objective is to find, for a given set of response variables $x_1, \ldots, x_q$, a set of underlying latent factors $\xi_1, \ldots, \xi_n$, fewer in number than the observed variables. These factors are supposed to account for the intercorrelations of the response variables in the sense that when the factors are partialed out no correlation between variables should remain. The assumed model is

$$x = \Lambda \xi + \delta ,\tag{3.8}$$

where $E(\xi) = 0$ and $E(\delta) = 0$, δ being uncorrelated with ξ.

If $\Phi = E(\xi \xi')$ is taken as a correlation matrix and $\Theta = E(\delta \delta')$ is diagonal, the covariance Σ of x is

$$\Sigma = \Lambda \Phi \Lambda' + \Theta .\tag{3.9}$$

If $(q-n)^2 < q+n$, this relationship can be tested statistically, unlike (3.8), which involves hypothetical variables and cannot be verified directly.

When $n > 1$ there is an indeterminacy in (3.9) arising from the fact that a nonsingular linear transformation of ξ changes Λ and in general also Φ but leaves Σ unchanged. The usual way to deal with this indeterminacy in exploratory factor analysis is to choose $\Phi = I$ and $\Lambda' \Theta \Lambda$ or $\Lambda' \Lambda$ to be diagonal and to estimate the parameters in Λ and Θ subject to these conditions. This leads to an arbitrary set of factors, which may then be subjected to a rotation or a linear transformation to another set of factors that may be given a more meaningful interpretation. Thurstone's principle of simple structure or Kaiser's varimax criterion are often used in these rotations.

In a confirmatory factor analysis, the investigator has such knowledge about the factorial nature of the variables that he or she is able to specify at least n^2 independent conditions on Λ and Φ. The most common way of doing this, assuming that Φ is an unconstrained correlation matrix, is to set at least $n - 1$ zeros in each column of Λ. This is a necessary condition but it is not sufficient. When there are many variables it usually suffices that the zeros are distributed over the rows of Λ in such a way that Λ has full column rank. The following example illustrates confirmatory factor analysis, including in particular the assessment of model fit and the use of the model modification index.

Table 3.7   Correlation Matrix for Nine Psychological Variables

VIS-PERC	1.000								
CUBES	0.318	1.000							
LOZENGES	0.436	0.419	1.000						
PAR-COMP	0.335	0.234	0.323	1.000					
SEN-COMP	0.304	0.157	0.283	0.722	1.000				
WORDMEAN	0.326	0.195	0.350	0.714	0.685	1.000			
ADDITION	0.116	0.057	0.056	0.203	0.246	0.170	1.000		
COUNTDOT	0.314	0.145	0.229	0.095	0.181	0.113	0.585	1.000	
S-C-CAPS	0.489	0.239	0.361	0.309	0.345	0.280	0.408	0.512	1.000

Example 3.4: Nine psychological variables – A confirmatory factor analysis

Source: Holzinger & Swineford (1939).

Table 3.7 shows correlations based on data for nine psychological tests administered to 145 seventh- and eighth-grade children. For this example, three common factors are hypothesized: visual perception, verbal ability, and speed. The first three variables are assumed to measure Visual, the next three to measure Verbal, and the last three to measure Speed. A path diagram of the assumed factor model is shown in Figure 3.3.

The LISREL input for this analysis is:

```
NINE PSYCHOLOGICAL VARIABLES - A CONFIRMATORY FACTOR ANALYSIS
DA NI=9 NO=145 MA=KM
LA
VIS-PERC CUBES LOZENGES PAR-COMP SEN-COMP WORDMEAN ADDITION
COUNTDOT S-C-CAPS
KM FI=EX34.COR
MO NX=9 NK=3 PH=ST
LK
Visual Verbal Speed
PA LX
3(1 0 0) 3(0 1 0) 3(0 0 1)
PL LX(9,1)
OU SE TV MI
```

The first nine lines of the command file are similar to Example 3.2. Both labels and correlations are read in free format without format lines. The

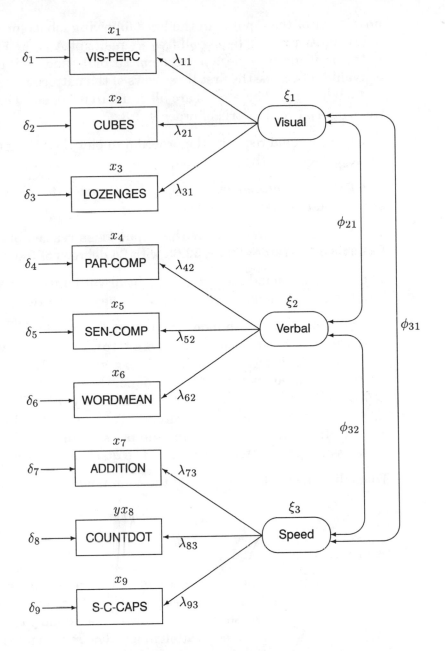

Figure 3.3
Confirmatory Factor Analysis Model for Nine Psychological Variables

novel part of the input is in the lines following labels for the latent variables. Rather than a listing all free elements of Λ on an FR command, as in the previous example, a pattern matrix of 0's and 1's is entered. This is convenient because the first three rows of the pattern matrix are all equal to 1 0 0, the next three rows are all equal to 0 1 0, etc. One line contains the whole pattern matrix of order 9×3.

The PL command requests the program to plot the fitting function (ML in this case) against the parameter λ_{91}.

The OU command requests modification indices (MI) as well as standard errors and t-statistics.

The ML solution produced by this input looks reasonable except for the fact that χ^2 is rather large: 52.63 with 24 degrees of freedom.

The modification indices give a straightforward answer to the question of how the model should be modified to fit the data better.

The largest modification index is 24.74 and occurs for λ_{91}. This is highly significant. The modification index is approximately a χ^2 with one degree of freedom. This modification index suggests directly that λ_{91} should be set free and predicts that, if this is done, the overall χ^2 will decrease by about 24.74 and that λ_{91} will be approximately 0.57. This result is also shown in a plot of the concentrated fit function printed in the program output. If the model is true, the sample size large, and the asymptotic theory valid, the plotted curve should be quadratic around the minimum.

To modify the model, merely add the command

```
FR LX(9,1)
```

before the OU command.

The overall goodness-of-fit measure for the modified model is $\chi^2 = 28.86$ with 23 degrees of freedom. The difference between the previous χ^2 and this one is $52.63 - 28.86 = 23.77$, which is reasonably close to the value 24.74 predicted by the modification index. The reason for the discrepancy is that the fit function is not quite quadratic in a region of the parameter space around the first solution. The modification index is based on a quadratic approximation of the fit function.

4

Submodel 2: Causal models for directly observed variables

The class of LISREL models in which dependent variables and explanatory variables are directly observed is called Submodel 2. In this model there are no latent variables, only directly observed or measured variables: y's and x's. The y's are to be explained by the model; *i.e.*, variation and co-variation among the y-variables is to be accounted for by the x-variables. The x-variables may be random variables or a set of fixed values.

The general form of the submodel is the *structural equation*

$$\mathbf{y} = \boldsymbol{\alpha} + \mathbf{B}\mathbf{y} + \boldsymbol{\Gamma}\mathbf{x} + \boldsymbol{\zeta} \,, \tag{4.1}$$

where

$$
\begin{aligned}
\mathbf{y}' &= (y_1, y_2, \ldots, y_p) \text{ are the jointly dependent variables} \\
\mathbf{x}' &= (x_1, x_2, \ldots, x_q) \text{ are the explanatory variables} \\
\boldsymbol{\zeta}' &= (\zeta_1, \zeta_2, \ldots, \zeta_p) \text{ are equation errors.}
\end{aligned}
$$

The $(p \times 1)$ vector $\boldsymbol{\alpha}$ contains the intercept terms of the equations. If a covariance or correlation matrix is analyzed, $\boldsymbol{\alpha}$ in (4.1) may be omitted. See Chapter 10 on how to analyze the structure of $\boldsymbol{\alpha}$.

The analysis of Submodel 2 is based on the following assumptions:

(i) $(\mathbf{I} - \mathbf{B})$ is nonsingular,

(ii) $E(\boldsymbol{\zeta}) = \mathbf{0}$, where E is the expected value operator,

(iii) $\boldsymbol{\zeta}$ is uncorrelated with $\mathbf{x}$.

The ζ-variables are random *disturbance terms*, sometimes called *errors in equations*. They represent an aggregate of all known and unknown influences of the y's that are uncorrelated with the x's.

The parameter matrices involved in this model are

$$\mathbf{B}, \ \boldsymbol{\Gamma}, \ \text{and} \ \boldsymbol{\Psi} \ = \text{Cov}(\zeta) \,.$$

In this submodel, the matrix $\boldsymbol{\Phi} = \text{Cov}(\mathbf{x})$ is assumed to be an unconstrained free covariance matrix. If $\mathbf{x}$ is fixed, $\boldsymbol{\Phi}$ is to be interpreted as the usual matrix of mean sums of squares and cross products formed from the set of fixed values of $\mathbf{x}$.

The estimate of $\boldsymbol{\Phi}$, under all estimation methods, is set equal to $\mathbf{S}_{xx}$, the observed covariance matrix of $\mathbf{x}$.

The structural equation (4.1) should be distinguished from the *reduced form equation*

$$\mathbf{y} = \mathbf{A}\boldsymbol{\alpha} + \mathbf{A}\boldsymbol{\Gamma}\mathbf{x} + \mathbf{A}\zeta \qquad (4.2)$$

where $\mathbf{A} = (\mathbf{I} - \mathbf{B})^{-1}$. Equation (4.2) is obtained from (4.1) by solving for $\mathbf{y}$.

The reduced form equation (4.2) is the regression of $\mathbf{y}$ on $\mathbf{x}$. In contrast, the structural equations in (4.1) are not necessarily regression equations because the random disturbance term ζ_i in the i-th equation is not necessarily uncorrelated with all the y-variables appearing on the right in that equation.

On these assumptions, the covariance matrix of the observations is

$$\boldsymbol{\Sigma} = \text{Cov}\begin{pmatrix} \mathbf{y} \\ \mathbf{x} \end{pmatrix} = \begin{pmatrix} \mathbf{A}\boldsymbol{\Gamma}\boldsymbol{\Phi}\boldsymbol{\Gamma}'\mathbf{A}' + \mathbf{A}\boldsymbol{\Psi}\mathbf{A}' & \\ \boldsymbol{\Phi}\boldsymbol{\Gamma}'\mathbf{A}' & \boldsymbol{\Phi} \end{pmatrix} \,. \qquad (4.3)$$

Special Cases.

1. When $\mathbf{B} = \mathbf{0}$, which is the default value for $\mathbf{B}$ in LISREL, the structural and reduced form equations are identical and each equation represents an actual **regression equation** (see Sec. 4.1).

   Diagrams of univariate and bivariate regression models are shown in Figures 4.1 and 4.2.

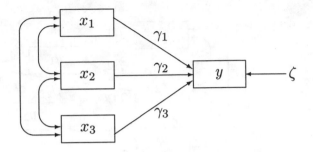

Figure 4.1   A Single Regression Equation

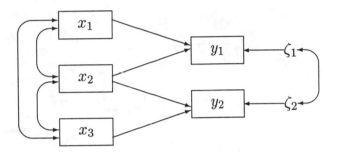

Figure 4.2   Bivariate Regression

2. When **B** is *sub-diagonal* (or when the y-variables can be ordered so that **B** becomes sub-diagonal) and $\mathbf{\Psi}$ is diagonal, the structural equation is a **recursive system**. The application of recursive system models is usually called path analysis. (See Section 4.2).

   A diagram of a recursive system is shown in Figure 4.3.

3. When the structural equations cannot be ordered such that **B** becomes subdiagonal, the system is called **non-recursive**. These models are common in econometrics, where they are referred to as *interdependent systems* or *simultaneous equations*. Examples of such models are presented in Section 4.3.

   A diagram of a non-recursive system is shown in Figure 4.4.

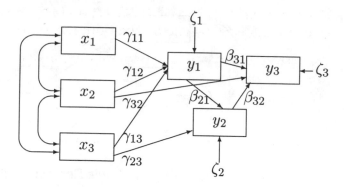

Figure 4.3   Recursive System

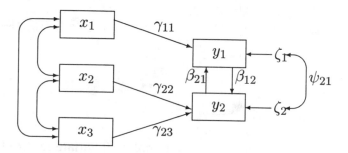

Figure 4.4   Non-recursive System

4.1 Regression models

Regression models that describe the relationship between a single dependent variable and several explanatory variables are called *univariate multiple regression* or often just *multiple regression*. Those that describe relationships between several dependent and several independent variable are called *multivariate multiple regression*.

A single regression equation

In the univariate regression equation,

$$y = \alpha + \gamma_1 x_1 + \gamma_2 x_2 + \cdots + \gamma_q x_q + \zeta , \qquad (4.4)$$

the x-variables are considered fixed, and it is assumed that the distribution of ζ does not depend on the values of $x_1, x_2, \ldots, x_q$.

Expressed for the i-th case (observation, individual, sample unit), the regression equation is

$$y_i = \alpha + \gamma_1 x_{i1} + \gamma_2 x_{i2} + \cdots + \gamma_q x_{iq} + \zeta_i \, ,$$

and the assumptions of regression analysis can be stated as

$$E(\zeta_i \mid \mathbf{X}) = 0 \quad E(\zeta_i \zeta_j \mid \mathbf{X}) = \begin{cases} \psi & \text{if } i = j \\ 0 & \text{if } i \neq j \end{cases} \quad \text{rank}(\mathbf{X}) = q < N \, ,$$

where $\mathbf{X}$ is the matrix of order $N \times q$ formed from the observed values $x_{im}(i = 1, 2, \ldots, N; m = 1, 2, \ldots, q)$ and E denotes conditional expectation. For formal tests of hypotheses, an additional assumption is usually made, namely that ζ_i is normally distributed.

The error term ζ is an aggregate of all variables influencing y that are not included in the relationship. The uncorrelatedness between ζ and the x-variables is a crucial assumption. Studies should be planned and designed so that this assumption is met. Failure to observe this may lead to considerable bias in estimated γ-coefficients. This is sometimes called *omitted variables bias*.

The following example shows how to use LISREL to estimate a single regression equation.

Example 4.1: Regression of the GNP on economic factors

Source: Goldberger (1964).

The data in Table 4.1 give values for gross national product in billions of dollars (y), labor inputs in millions of man-years (x_1), real capital in billions of dollars (x_2), and the time in years measured from 1928 (x_3). The data consist of 23 annual observations for the United States during 1929–1941 and 1946–1955.

The command file for this problem is:

Table 4.1   Data for Regression of GNP

Year	x_1	x_2	x_3	y	Year	x_1	x_2	x_3	y
1929	47	54	1	142	1946	51	9	18	209
1930	43	59	2	127	1947	53	25	19	214
1931	39	57	3	118	1948	53	39	20	225
1932	34	48	4	98	1949	50	51	21	221
1933	34	36	5	94	1950	52	62	22	243
1934	36	24	6	102	1951	54	75	23	257
1935	38	19	7	116	1952	54	94	24	265
1936	41	18	8	128	1953	55	108	25	276
1937	42	22	9	140	1954	52	118	26	271
1938	37	24	10	131	1955	54	124	27	291
1939	40	23	11	143					
1940	42	27	12	157					
1941	47	36	13	182					

```
Regression of GNP
DA NI=4 NO=0
LA
GNP LABOR CAPITAL TIME
RA FI=EX41.RAW
MO NY=1 NX=3
OU SE TV
```

Note that the raw data are read from an external file, EX41.RAW, and, because NO=0 on the DA command, the program reads and counts cases from this file until an end-of-file is encountered.

The output file reveals that the TSLS solution and the ML solution produced by LISREL are identical. In fact, all methods in LISREL will produce the same solution — namely, the classical ordinary least-squares (OLS) solution.

This is a consequence of the fact that, as a LISREL model, a single regression equation is a just-identified model that fits the data in the same way regardless which of the LISREL fit functions are minimized. To examine the fit of the model to the individual observations, it is necessary to inspect the estimated error terms ζ_i for each case to see if there are indications of outliers or other forms of non-normality. This cannot be done with LISREL, however.

To determine the significance of each explanatory variable, the estimated regression coefficients must be examined in relation to their standard errors. This is done by looking at the t-values.

A formal test of the significance of the whole regression equation, *i.e.*, a test of the hypothesis that all γ's are zero, can be obtained by computing

$$ F = \frac{R^2/q}{(1 - R^2)/(N - q - 1)}, \tag{4.5} $$

where R^2 is the squared multiple correlation listed in the output file, N is the total sample size and q is the number of genuine x-variables. F is used as an F-statistic with q and $N - q - 1$ degrees of freedom. In this example, $R^2 = 0.997$ and $F = 2104.8$ with 3 and 19 degrees of freedom. All regression coefficients are highly significant.

Stepwise regression

Regression analysis can be used as a part of a model building process. To determine an equation for y in which only the most significant determinants of $x_1, x_2, \ldots, x_q$ are included, some form of stepwise procedure for choosing the x-variables may be used. But there is no unique statistical method for making these choices; personal judgment may be necessary.

A way to do stepwise regression with LISREL is to start with an equation in which all γ's are zero and add successively the one particular x-variable that improves fit maximally. The fit can be measured either by χ^2 or the improvement in fit by the modification index (MI). If a correlation matrix is analyzed and the GLS fit function is used, the MI's will be exact χ^2-differences.

Although it is often a good idea to run each step separately and inspect the results after each step, the procedure can be made fully automatic using the automatic model modification option (AM). Each MI is then used as a χ^2 with one degree of freedom and variables are added to the regression equation until the largest MI is no longer significant. The significance level in percent is specified with the SL keyword. The default value for SL is 1.

Table 4.2   Covariance Matrix for Werner Blood Chemistry Data

	y	x_1	x_2	x_3	x_4	x_5	x_6	x_7
CHOLEST	1857.015							
AGE	154.514	97.978						
HEIGHT	1.220	2.192	6.161					
WEIGHT	128.106	51.804	24.093	420.242				
BIRTHPIL	1.965	0.279	0.204	0.823	0.251			
ALBUMIN	0.882	-0.280	-0.005	-1.725	-0.042	0.129		
CALCIUM	5.149	-0.040	0.168	0.627	-0.015	0.077	0.224	
URICACID	13.130	2.314	0.349	6.977	0.009	0.012	0.088	1.257

Example 4.2: Stepwise regression

Source: Dixon (1981).

Table 4.2 gives the covariance matrix for the Werner Blood Chemistry Data based on NO=180. The variables are:

$$y = Cholesterol \quad x_1 = Age \quad x_2 = Height \quad x_3 = Weight$$
$$x_4 = Birthpill \quad x_5 = Albumin \quad x_6 = Calcium \quad x_7 = Uric\ Acid$$

The following command file will perform a stepwise regression analysis on the summary statistics of Table 4.2.

```
Stepwise Regression for Werner Blood Chemistry Data
Using GLS on Correlation Matrix
DA NI=8 NO=180 MA=KM
LA
CHOLEST AGE HEIGHT WEIGHT BIRTHPIL ALBUMIN CALCIUM
URICACID
CM FI=EX42.COV
MO NY=1 NX=7 GA=FI
OU ME=GLS TV SE MI AM
```

The results are shown in Table 4.3. The modification indices for x-variables 1 and 6 are equal to the drop in the GLS χ^2 statistics. After the addition of x_6, the largest remaining modification index, for x_7, is not significant.

Table 4.3   Stepwise Regression for Werner Blood Chemistry Data

Step	Parameter to free	MI	χ^2	df	p-value
0	γ_1	30.82	55.89	7	0.000
1	γ_6	15.34	25.07	6	0.000
2	γ_7	5.95	9.73	5	0.083

Analysis of variance and covariance

Suppose there are G groups and we want to compare their means on a response variable y. We may also wish to know if the sensitivity of the analysis can be increased by the use of the covariates, $x_1, x_2, \ldots, x_q$. These analyses are usually done by one-way analysis of variance (ANOVA) or analysis of covariance (ANCOVA), respectively.

The essential results of analysis of variance can be obtained from LISREL by forming dummy variables $d_1, d_2, \ldots, d_{G-1}$ and regressing y on these dummy variables. Those of analysis of covariance are obtained by regressing y on the covariates and the dummy variables.

The dummy variables represent group memberships such that $d_{ig} = 1$ if case i belongs to group g and $d_{ig} = 0$ otherwise. The raw data is of the form:

Case	y	x	d_1	d_2	$\cdots$	d_G
1	y_1	x_{11}	d_{11}	d_{12}	$\cdots$	d_{1G}
2	y_2	x_{21}	d_{21}	d_{22}	$\cdots$	d_{2G}
$\vdots$	$\vdots$	$\vdots$	$\vdots$	$\vdots$	$\ddots$	$\vdots$
N	y_N	x_N	d_{N1}	d_{N2}	$\cdots$	d_{NG}

It is not necessary that the number of cases per group is the same.

The hypothesis that all group means are equal is the same as the hypothesis that $\gamma_1 = \gamma_2 = \cdots = \gamma_{G-1} = 0$. For the analysis of variance a formal

F statistic can be computed as

$$F = \frac{R^2/(G-1)}{(1-R^2)/(N-G)} , \qquad (4.6)$$

where R^2 is the squared multiple correlation in the regression of y on $d_1, d_2, \ldots, d_{G-1}$. Each γ_i measures the mean difference $\mu_i - \mu_G$, the significance of which can be tested with the corresponding t-value used as a t-statistic.

The analysis of covariance (ANCOVA) can be done in a similar way. First, regress the response variable y on one or more covariates, $x_1, x_2, \ldots, x_q$, to obtain the squared multiple correlation R_{yx}^2.

Second, regress y on $x_1, x_2, \ldots, x_q$ and $d_1, d_2, \ldots, d_{G-1}$ to obtain the squared multiple correlation R_{yxd}^2. Then

$$F = \frac{R_{yxd}^2 - R_{yx}^2/(G-1)}{(1 - R_{yxd}^2)/(N-G-1)} \qquad (4.7)$$

can be used as an F statistic with $(G-1)$ and $(N-G-1)$ degrees of freedom for testing the hypothesis that the group means, adjusted for mean differences in the covariates, are zero.

Both the ANOVA and the ANCOVA considered above assume that the within-group variances of y are equal. In addition, ANCOVA assumes that the regressions of y on $x_1, x_2, \ldots, x_q$ are the same for each group. These assumptions can be tested using multi-group analysis in LISREL (see Chapter 10).

The following example, adapted from Huitema (1980), illustrates both ANOVA and ANCOVA.

Example 4.3: ANOVA and ANCOVA

Source: Simulation based on Huitema (1980).

An experiment is performed to investigate the effects of three different types of study objectives on student achievement in freshman biology. The students are randomly assigned to three different groups and instructed as follows.

1. *General: Students are told to know and understand everything in the text.*
2. *Specific: Students are provided with a clear specification of the terms and concepts they are expected to master and of the testing format.*
3. *Specific with study time allocations: The amount of time that should be spent on each topic is provided in addition to specific objectives that describe the type of behavior expected on examinations.*

The dependent variable is a biology achievement test administered at the end of the course.

In addition, an academic aptitude test score, to serve as a covariate, was obtained before the the students were assigned to the treatment groups.

Simulated data for this study are shown in Table 4.4. The dummy variables indicating each student's group assignment have been inserted.

For the ANOVA part of the problem, regress the Biology score (y) on d_1 and d_2. The command file for this analysis is:

Table 4.4   Fictitious Data for ANOVA and ANCOVA (N=30)

Biology Score	Aptitude Score	Dummy Variables	Biology Score	Aptitude Score	Dummy Variables
15	29	1 0 0	44	43	0 1 0
19	49	1 0 0	46	64	0 1 0
21	48	1 0 0	47	61	0 1 0
27	35	1 0 0	40	55	0 1 0
35	53	1 0 0	54	54	0 1 0
39	47	1 0 0	14	33	0 0 1
23	46	1 0 0	20	45	0 0 1
38	74	1 0 0	30	35	0 0 1
33	72	1 0 0	32	39	0 0 1
50	67	1 0 0	34	36	0 0 1
20	22	0 1 0	42	48	0 0 1
34	24	0 1 0	40	63	0 0 1
28	49	0 1 0	38	57	0 0 1
35	46	0 1 0	54	56	0 0 1
42	52	0 1 0	56	78	0 0 1

```
ANOVA
DA NI=5
LA
Y X D1 D2 D3
RA FI=EX43.RAW
SE
1 3 4 /
MO NY=1 NX=2
OU SE TV
```

The squared multiple correlation, R^2, is 0.106. The hypothesis that the three group means are equal (equivalent to the hypothesis that γ_1 and γ_2 are both zero) is tested with the F statistic (4.6) with 2 and 27 degrees of freedom. F becomes:

$$F = \frac{0.106/2}{(1 - 0.106)/27} = 1.60 \ .$$

As this value is not significant, no differences in group means of the Biology score are detected.

For the ANCOVA, first regress the Biology scores on the Aptitude scores. The command file is:

```
ANCOVA, Part 1
DA NI=5
LA
Y X D1 D2 D3
RA FI=EX43.RAW
SE
1 2 /
MO NY=1 NX=1; OU SE TV
```

The result is: $R^2 = 0.396$.

Next, run the regression of y on x, d_1, and d_2 using the following command file:

```
ANCOVA, Part 2
DA NI=5
LA
Y X D1 D2 D3
RA FI=EX43.RAW
SE
1 2 3 4/
MO NY=1 NX=3; OU SE TV
```

Now the strength of the regression has increased to $R^2 = 0.575$.

The F statistic (4.7) with 2 and 26 degrees of freedom for testing the equality of means, adjusted by the covariate, is

$$\frac{(0.575 - 0.396)/2}{(1 - 0.575)/26} = 5.48 \; .$$

Thus, the result of the more sensitive analysis of covariance is significant at the 5 percent level. There is some evidence that the group means of the Biology Achievement Score are different when they are adjusted for difference in the Aptitude Test Score. By controlling for the covariate, we get a more powerful test of the group differences than when using the response variable alone in the analysis of variance.

Multivariate regression

As an example of a multivariate multiple regression analysis, the following small study illustrates the case of two dependent variables y_1 and y_2 and three explanatory variables x_1, x_2, and x_3.

Example 4.4: Bivariate regression

Source: Finn (1974).

The data in Table 4.5 represent the scores of fifteen freshmen at a large midwestern university on five educational measures. The five measures are:

$y_1 = $ *grade average for required courses taken [GRAVEREQ]*
$y_2 = $ *grade average for elective courses taken [GRAVELEC]*
$x_1 = $ *high-school general knowledge score from previous year [KNOWL-EDG]*
$x_2 = $ *IQ score from previous year [IQPREVYR]*
$x_3 = $ *educational motivation score from previous year [ED MOTIV]*

The purpose of the analysis is to examine the predictive value of x_1, x_2, and x_3 for the grade averages y_1 and y_2.

Table 4.5
Scores for Fifteen College Freshmen on Five Educational Measures

Case	y_1	y_2	x_1	x_2	x_3
1	.8	2.0	72	114	17.3
2	2.2	2.2	78	117	17.6
3	1.6	2.0	84	117	15.0
4	2.6	3.7	95	120	18.0
5	2.7	3.2	88	117	18.7
6	2.1	3.2	83	123	17.9
7	3.1	3.7	92	118	17.3
8	3.0	3.1	86	114	18.1
9	3.2	2.6	88	114	16.0
10	2.6	3.2	80	115	16.4
11	2.7	2.8	87	114	17.6
12	3.0	2.4	94	112	19.5
13	1.6	1.4	73	115	12.7
14	.9	1.0	80	111	17.0
15	1.9	1.2	83	112	16.1

With the variables measured from their means and intercept terms omitted, the bivariate regression of y_1 and y_2 on x_1, x_2, and x_3 may be written

$$y_1 = \gamma_{11}x_1 + \gamma_{12}x_2 + \gamma_{13}x_3 + \zeta_1$$
$$y_2 = \gamma_{21}x_1 + \gamma_{22}x_2 + \gamma_{23}x_3 + \zeta_2 \,,$$

or in matrix form

$$\underline{\underline{y}} = \Gamma x + \zeta \,,$$

where Γ is the regression matrix of order 2×3. This is a LISREL model of the form (4.1) with $\mathbf{B}$ zero, Γ a full free matrix, and Ψ a symmetric free matrix. Figure 4.5 shows the path diagram of this model.

The LISREL command file for such a model is extremely simple:

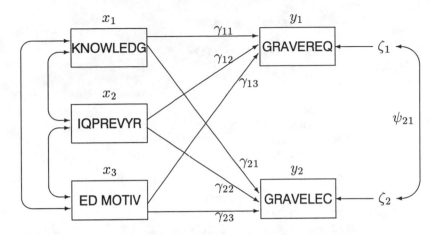

Figure 4.5   Path Diagram for Prediction of Grade Averages

```
PREDICTION OF GRADE AVERAGES
DA  NI=5 NO=15;  RA  FI=EX44.RAW
LA; GRAVEREQ GRAVELEC KNOWLEDG IQPREVYR 'ED MOTIV'
MO  NY=2 NX=3
OU  TV SE
```

As in the case of a single regression equation, the initial estimates produced by the program are identical to the maximum likelihood estimates. The model of the covariance structure for these data is just-identified. The measures of overall fit have zero degrees of freedom and indicate perfect fit. The model is only useful to the extent that it gives information about the relative importance of the x-variables as predictors of the two grade averages.

The estimated regression coefficients appear in the Γ matrix of the LISREL estimates, and the covariances of the residuals, ζ_1 and ζ_2, in the Ψ matrix. These estimates, with their corresponding t-statistics, are shown below.

```
LISREL ESTIMATES (MAXIMUM LIKELIHOOD)
```

	GAMMA		
	KNOWLEDG	IQPREVYR	ED MOTIV
GRAVEREQ	.085	.008	−.015
GRAVELEC	.047	.145	.126

```
        PSI
             GRAVEREQ    GRAVELEC
GRAVEREQ        .257
GRAVELEC        .169        .237
```

T-VALUES

```
        GAMMA
             KNOWLEDG    IQPREVYR    ED MOTIV
GRAVEREQ       3.168        .169       -.134
GRAVELEC       1.823       3.117       1.170
```

```
        PSI
             GRAVEREQ    GRAVELEC
GRAVEREQ       2.345
GRAVELEC       1.875       2.345
```

The t-values reveal that only x_1 is a significant predictor of y_1 and only x_2 is a significant predictor of y_2. The variable x_3 is not significant for either purpose. It should be noted, however, that the sample size is too small to draw any safe conclusions.

The maximum likelihood estimate of $\mathbf{\Psi}$ is:

$$\hat{\mathbf{\Psi}} = \begin{pmatrix} 0.257 & \\ 0.169 & 0.237 \end{pmatrix} .$$

This is the partial covariance matrix of y for given x. The partial covariance 0.169 has a t-value of 1.875 and is therefore not significant, despite the fact that the partial correlation between y_1 and y_2,

$$r_{y_1 y_2 . x_1 x_2 x_3} = 0.169/(0.257 \times 0.237)^{\frac{1}{2}} = 0.685 ,$$

is quite large. This seemingly contradictory result occurs because the sample size is so small.

4.2 Path analysis

The technique of path analysis originated by Sewell Wright in the 1930s. It can be used to test the plausibility of putative causal relationships between one variable and another in non-experimental conditions. In general, the procedure can be formulated as one of estimating the coefficients of a set of linear structural equations representing the cause and effect relationships hypothesized by the investigator.

The system of relationships involves variables of two kinds: independent or cause variables $x_1, x_2, \ldots, x_q$ and dependent or effect variables $y_1, y_2, \ldots, y_p$.

The classical approach to path analysis consists of solving the structural equations for the dependent variables in terms of the independent and the random disturbance terms $\zeta_1, \zeta_2, \ldots, \zeta_p$. The object is to obtain the reduced form equations, to estimate the regression of the dependent variables on the independent variables and then to solve for the structural parameters in terms of the regression coefficients. The last step is not always possible.

Estimating a path analysis model for directly observed variables with LIS-REL is, in contrast, entirely straightforward. Rather than estimating each equation separately, LISREL considers the model as a system of equations and estimates all the structural coefficients directly. The reduced form is obtained as a by-product. The following example illustrates the procedure.

Example 4.5: Ambition and attainment

Source: Kerchoff (1974); Kenny (1979).

Table 4.6 gives the correlations between a number of attainment and background variables for 767 twelfth-grade males. The variables, in the order in which they appear in the table, are:

$$
\begin{aligned}
x_1 &= \text{\textit{intelligence [INTELLNC]}} \\
x_2 &= \text{\textit{number of siblings [SIBLINGS]}} \\
x_3 &= \text{\textit{father's education [FATHEDUC]}} \\
x_4 &= \text{\textit{father's occupation [FATHOCCU]}} \\
y_1 &= \text{\textit{grades [GRADES]}} \\
y_2 &= \text{\textit{educational expectation [EDUCEXP]}} \\
y_3 &= \text{\textit{occupational aspiration [OCCUASP]}}
\end{aligned}
$$

Table 4.6
Correlations for Background, Ambition and Attainment Variables

	x_1	x_2	x_3	x_4	y_1	y_2	y_3
INTELLNC	1.000						
SIBLINGS	−.100	1.000					
FATHEDUC	.277	−.152	1.000				
FATHOCCU	.250	−.108	.611	1.000			
GRADES	.572	−.105	.294	.248	1.000		
EDUCEXP	.489	−.213	.446	.410	.597	1.000	
OCCUASP	.335	−.153	.303	.331	.478	.651	1.000

Figure 4.6 is a possible path diagram to explain these correlations. The model is a *complete recursive system* with *exogenous variables* x_1, x_2, x_3, and x_4, and *jointly dependent variables* y_1, y_2, and y_3. The path coefficients have been omitted in Figure 4.6. The structural equations are:

$$y_1 = \gamma_{11}x_1 + \gamma_{12}x_2 + \gamma_{13}x_3 + \gamma_{14}x_4 + \zeta_1$$
$$y_2 = \beta_{21}y_1 + \gamma_{21}x_1 + \gamma_{22}x_2 + \gamma_{23}x_3 + \gamma_{24}x_4 + \zeta_2$$
$$y_3 = \beta_{31}y_1 + \beta_{32}y_2 + \gamma_{31}x_1 + \gamma_{32}x_2 + \gamma_{33}x_3 + \gamma_{34}x_4 + \zeta_3$$

These equations have the same matrix form as (4.1) with $\mathbf{B}$ free below the diagonal, $\boldsymbol{\Gamma}$ full and free, and $\boldsymbol{\Psi}$ diagonal (and $\boldsymbol{\alpha}$ omitted).

The LISREL command file for fitting this model is as follows:

```
Ambition and attainment
DATA     NI=7 NO=767
LABELS;  INTELLNC SIBLINGS FATHEDUC FATHOCCU GRADES EDUCEXP OCCUASP
KMATRIX
 1
-.100  1
 .277 -.152  1
 .250 -.108 .611 1
 .572 -.105 .294 .248 1
 .489 -.213 .446 .410 .597 1
 .335 -.153 .303 .331 .478 .651 1
```

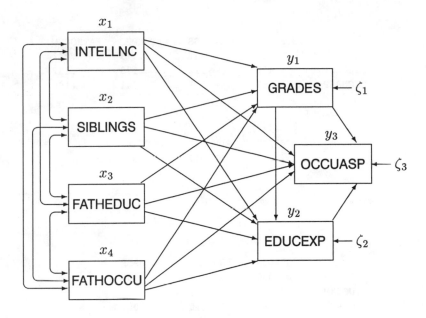

Figure 4.6
Path Diagram for Recursive Model of Ambition and Attainment

```
SELECT;   5 6 7 1 2 3 4
MODEL     NY=3 NX=4 BE=SD PS=DI
OUTPUT    SE TV EF
```

When there are no *a priori* fixed elements among the β's or γ's, the model is just identified and fits the data perfectly. The initial estimates are identical to the maximum likelihood estimates. The ML estimates and the t-values are shown below.

```
LISREL ESTIMATES (MAXIMUM LIKELIHOOD)

        BETA

              GRADES    EDUCEXP    OCCUASP
    GRADES     .000       .000       .000
   EDUCEXP     .405       .000       .000
   OCCUASP     .158       .550       .000
```

GAMMA

	INTELLNC	SIBLINGS	FATHEDUC	FATHOCCU
GRADES	.526	-.030	.119	.041
EDUCEXP	.160	-.112	.173	.152
OCCUASP	-.039	-.019	-.041	.100

PSI

GRADES	EDUCEXP	OCCUASP
.651	.517	.557

T-VALUES

BETA

	GRADES	EDUCEXP	OCCUASP
GRADES	.000	.000	.000
EDUCEXP	12.554	.000	.000
OCCUASP	4.291	14.616	.000

GAMMA

	INTELLNC	SIBLINGS	FATHEDUC	FATHOCCU
GRADES	17.161	-1.011	3.164	1.093
EDUCEXP	4.986	-4.232	5.123	4.587
OCCUASP	-1.162	-.679	-1.161	2.858

PSI

GRADES	EDUCEXP	OCCUASP
19.519	19.519	19.519

Direct and indirect effects. Figure 4.6 shows that there are both direct and indirect effects of the the x-variables on y_2 and y_3. These effects can be calculated from the estimated parameters of the model. For example, the direct effect of x_1 on y_2 is $\gamma_{21} = 0.160$ and the indirect effect of x_1 on y_2 via y_1 is $\gamma_{11}\beta_{21} = 0.526 \times 0.405 = 0.213$.

The sum of the direct effect and all indirect effects is called total effects. These total effects are given by LISREL when EF appears on the OU command. The total and indirect effects for the present example are shown below.

```
TOTAL AND INDIRECT EFFECTS

    TOTAL EFFECTS OF X ON Y

            INTELLNC   SIBLINGS   FATHEDUC   FATHOCCU
    GRADES     .526      -.030       .119       .041
   EDUCEXP     .373      -.124       .221       .168
   OCCUASP     .249      -.092       .099       .198

    INDIRECT EFFECTS OF X ON Y

            INTELLNC   SIBLINGS   FATHEDUC   FATHOCCU
    GRADES     .000       .000       .000       .000
   EDUCEXP     .213      -.012       .048       .016
   OCCUASP     .288      -.073       .140       .099

    TOTAL EFFECTS OF Y ON Y

             GRADES    EDUCEXP    OCCUASP
    GRADES     .000       .000       .000
   EDUCEXP     .405       .000       .000
   OCCUASP     .381       .550       .000

    INDIRECT EFFECTS OF Y ON Y

             GRADES    EDUCEXP    OCCUASP
    GRADES     .000       .000       .000
   EDUCEXP     .000       .000       .000
   OCCUASP     .223       .000       .000
```

The total effect of x_1 on y_2 is 0.373. This is the sum of the direct effect of 0.160 and the indirect effect 0.213 computed above.

The t-values for the solution of Example 4.5 reveal that the effects γ_{12}, γ_{14}, γ_{31}, γ_{32}, and γ_{33} may not be significant. A formal test of the hypothesis that these five γ's are zero should be based on an independent sample. This can be obtained by running the model again, inserting a command

```
FIX GA(1,2) GA(1,4) GA(3,1)-GA(3,3)
```

after the MO command.

4.3 Econometric models

Unlike the previous example, where the system of equations was recursive, *econometric models* are usually *non-recursive* or so-called *"interdependent systems."* Data for econometric models are often in the form of *time series* and the models are usually *dynamic* in the sense that elements of time play important roles in the model. Another characteristic of econometric models is that they often contain definitional equations or *identities*. These are exact relationships without disturbance terms and with no unknown parameters to be estimated.

Although the identities are not subject to estimation, they must nevertheless be specified in the command file in order to define which variables are *independent (exogenous)* and which are *jointly dependent (endogenous)*. If the identities are omitted, the program will estimate the behavioral equations by ordinary least squares (OLS), yielding inconsistent (biased) estimates.

The following example illustrates the formulation of a non-recursive econometric model, including the identity relations. LISREL is then used to fit the model, subject to the identities, to a sample of time series data.

Example 4.6: Klein's model I of US economy

Source: Klein (1950); Goldberger (1964); Theil (1971).

Klein's Model I illustrates a classical econometric model that has been used extensively as a benchmark problem for studying econometric methods. It is an eight-equation system based on annual business data for the United States in the period between the two world wars.

The endogenous variables are:

$$
\begin{aligned}
C_t &= \textit{Aggregate Consumption } (y_1) \\
I_t &= \textit{Net Investment } (y_2) \\
W_t^* &= \textit{Private Wage Bill } (y_3) \\
P_t &= \textit{Total Profits } (y_4) \\
Y_t &= \textit{Total Income } (y_5)
\end{aligned}
$$

$$
\begin{aligned}
K_t &= \text{End-of-Year Capital Stock } (y_6) \\
W_t &= \text{Total Wage Bill } (y_7) \\
E_t &= \text{Total Production of Private Industry } (y_8)
\end{aligned}
$$

The predetermined variables are the exogenous variables:

$$
\begin{aligned}
W_t^{**} &= \text{Government Wage Bill } (x_1) \\
T_t &= \text{Taxes } (x_2) \\
G_t &= \text{Government Non-Wage Expenditures } (x_3) \\
A_t &= \text{Time in Years From 1931 } (x_4)
\end{aligned}
$$

In addition, the lagged endogenous variables are:

$$
P_{t-1}(x_5), \quad K_{t-1}(x_6) \text{ and } E_{t-1}(x_7).
$$

All variables except A_t are in billions of 1934 dollars.

The three behavioral equations of Klein's Model I are:

$$
\begin{aligned}
C_t &= a_1 P_t + a_2 P_{t-1} + a_3 W_t + \xi_1 \\
I_t &= b_1 P_t + b_2 P_{t-1} + b_3 K_{t-1} + \zeta_2 \\
W_t^* &= c_1 E_t + c_2 E_{t-1} + c_3 A_t + \zeta_3 \,.
\end{aligned}
$$

In addition to these stochastic equations the model includes five identities:

$$
\begin{aligned}
P_t &= Y_t - W_t \\
Y_t &= C_t + I_t + G_t - T_t \\
K_t &= K_{t-1} + I_t \\
W_t &= W_t^* + W_t^{**} \\
E_t &= Y_t + T_t - W_t^{**}
\end{aligned}
$$

The model can be formulated as a LISREL model of the form (4.1) with $p = 8$ and $q = 7$ and with $\mathbf{B}$, $\mathbf{\Gamma}$, and $\mathbf{\Psi}$ as:

$$\mathbf{B} = \begin{pmatrix} 0 & 0 & 0 & a_1 & 0 & 0 & a_3 & 0 \\ 0 & 0 & 0 & b_1 & 0 & 0 & 0 & 0 \\ 0 & 0 & 0 & 0 & 0 & 0 & 0 & c_1 \\ 0 & 0 & 0 & 0 & 1 & 0 & -1 & 0 \\ 1 & 1 & 0 & 0 & 0 & 0 & 0 & 0 \\ 0 & 1 & 0 & 0 & 0 & 0 & 0 & 0 \\ 0 & 0 & 1 & 0 & 0 & 0 & 0 & 0 \\ 0 & 0 & 0 & 0 & 1 & 0 & 0 & 0 \end{pmatrix}$$

$$\mathbf{\Gamma} = \begin{pmatrix} 0 & 0 & 0 & 0 & a_2 & 0 & 0 \\ 0 & 0 & 0 & 0 & b_2 & b_3 & 0 \\ 0 & 0 & 0 & c_3 & 0 & 0 & c_2 \\ 0 & 0 & 0 & 0 & 0 & 0 & 0 \\ 0 & -1 & 1 & 0 & 0 & 0 & 0 \\ 0 & 0 & 0 & 0 & 0 & 1 & 0 \\ 1 & 0 & 0 & 0 & 0 & 0 & 0 \\ -1 & 1 & 0 & 0 & 0 & 0 & 0 \end{pmatrix}$$

$$\mathbf{\Psi} = \begin{pmatrix} \psi_{11} & & & & & & & \\ \psi_{21} & \psi_{22} & & & & & & \\ \psi_{31} & \psi_{32} & \psi_{33} & & & & & \\ 0 & 0 & 0 & 0 & & & & \\ 0 & 0 & 0 & 0 & 0 & & & \\ 0 & 0 & 0 & 0 & 0 & 0 & & \\ 0 & 0 & 0 & 0 & 0 & 0 & 0 & \\ 0 & 0 & 0 & 0 & 0 & 0 & 0 & 0 \end{pmatrix}$$

As a consequence of the identities in the model, the last five rows of $\mathbf{B}$, $\mathbf{\Gamma}$, and $\mathbf{\Psi}$ do not contain any parameters to be estimated. Another consequence of the identities is that both $\mathbf{\Sigma}$ and $\mathbf{S}$ will be singular if all the 15 variables are included in the model. As a result it is impossible to use the ML method or GLS method, since they require either $\mathbf{\Sigma}$ or $\mathbf{S}$ to be positive definite. However, by eliminating the five redundant y-variables, ML estimation is possible as shown below, after a preliminary IV and ULS analysis. Ridge estimation is also illustrated.

Unweighted least squares. The following command file performs the ULS fitting and gives the IV estimates as a by-product. The labels and the raw data with their formats are stored in the file EX46.DAT.

```
KLEIN'S MODEL I ESTIMATED BY IV AND ULS
DA NI=15 NO=21
LA FI=EX46.DAT
RA FI=EX46.DAT
SE
1 4 3 10 14 11 13 12 7 8 15 9 2 5 6
MO NY=8 NX=7 BE=FU GA=FI PS=FI
FR BE(1,4) BE(1,7) BE(2,4) BE(3,8)
FR GA(1,5) GA(2,5) GA(2,6) GA(3,4) GA(3,7)
FR PS(1,1)-PS(3,3)
VA 1 BE(4,5) BE(5,1) BE(5,2) BE(6,2) BE(7,3) BE(8,5) GA(5,3) GA(6,6) C
GA(7,1) GA(8,2)
VA -1 BE(4,7) GA(5,2) GA(8,1)
OU ME=UL AD=OFF
```

The variables in the data file are not in the same order as in the model. The selection command puts them in the order $y_1, y_2, \ldots, y_8, x_1, x_2, \ldots, x_7$. The only parameter matrices needed are $\mathbf{B}$, $\mathbf{\Gamma}$, and $\mathbf{\Psi}$. $\mathbf{B}$ is declared full on the MO command and is fixed by default. $\mathbf{\Gamma}$ is declared fixed on the MO command and is full by default. $\mathbf{\Psi}$ is declared fixed on the MO command and is symmetric by default. After the MO command the free elements and the values of the non-zero fixed elements in $\mathbf{B}$ and $\mathbf{\Gamma}$ are defined. The FR and VA commands contain these definitions. The admissibility check is set to OFF in the OU command because $\mathbf{\Psi}$ has fixed diagonal zeros.

The results of the ULS run give two different sets of estimates for the structural parameters: IV and ULS estimates. The estimates are shown in Table 4.7.

Ridge estimates. To obtain *ridge estimates* of the model parameters, merely delete ME=UL from the OU command. The program will then attempt to perform the default maximum likelihood estimation. However, the covariance matrix is singular, so ML estimation is not possible. The program will therefore automatically invoke the ridge option with ridge constant 0.001; see the section *The ridge option in LISREL 7* on page 24. This gives the estimates shown in Table 4.7 (MLR).

Table 4.7 Parameter Estimates for Klein's Model I

Parameter	IV	TSLS	ULS	MLR	ML
a_1	0.04	0.02	0.04	−0.04	−0.23
a_2	0.19	0.22	0.21	0.29	0.39
a_3	0.82	0.81	0.81	0.79	0.80
b_1	0.04	0.15	0.05	−0.45	−0.80
b_2	0.69	0.62	0.68	0.98	1.05
b_3	−0.17	−0.16	−0.17	−0.18	−0.15
c_1	0.39	0.44	0.39	0.31	0.23
c_2	0.20	0.15	0.20	0.25	0.29
c_3	0.14	0.13	0.15	0.19	0.24

Maximum likelihood estimation. As already noted, the covariance matrices Σ and S as well as the data matrix itself are singular because of the five identities in the model. The rank of these matrices is not 15 but 10. It is possible to solve the identities for the redundant variables P_t, Y_t, K_t, W_t, and E_t in terms of the other 10 variables and substitute these solutions into the behavioral equations. This results in a system with three y-variables and seven x-variables and with coefficients which are linear combinations of the structural parameters.

Although it is possible to estimate the model in this form, this rather complicated approach is not necessary. LISREL will estimate the model directly if all the y-variables are treated as η-variables, of which only the first 3 are observed. The LISREL specification for this purpose is:

$$
\begin{aligned}
\mathbf{y}' &= (C_t,\ I_t,\ W_t^*) \\
\boldsymbol{\eta}' &= (C_t,\ I_t,\ W_t^*,\ P_t,\ Y_t,\ K_t,\ W_t,\ E_t) \\
\mathbf{x}' \equiv \quad' &= (W,\ T_t,\ G_t,\ A_t,\ P_{t-1},\ K_{k-1},\ E_{t-1})\ .
\end{aligned}
$$

The Λ_y-matrix is:

$$
\Lambda_y = \begin{pmatrix}
1 & 0 & 0 & 0 & 0 & 0 & 0 & 0 \\
0 & 1 & 0 & 0 & 0 & 0 & 0 & 0 \\
0 & 0 & 1 & 0 & 0 & 0 & 0 & 0
\end{pmatrix}.
$$

This is the matrix form called IZ in Table 1.2. The matrices $\mathbf{B}$, $\mathbf{\Gamma}$, and $\mathbf{\Psi}$ are the same as before. The command file for the ML solution is as follows:

```
KLEIN'S MODEL I ESTIMATED BY TSLS AND ML
DA NI=15 NO=21
LA FI=EX46.DAT
RA FI=EX46.DAT
SE
1 4 3 7 8 15 9 2 5 6 /
MO NY=3 NE=8 NX=7 FI LY=IZ BE=FU GA=FI PS=FI TE=ZE
FR BE(1,4) BE(1,7) BE(2,4) BE(3,8)
FR GA(1,5) GA(2,5) GA(2,6) GA(3,4) GA(3,7)
FR PS(1,1)-PS(3,3)
VA 1 BE(4,5) BE(5,1) BE(5,2) BE(6,2) BE(7,3) BE(8,5) GA(5,3) GA(6,6) C
GA(7,1) GA(8,2)
VA -1 BE(4,7) GA(5,2) GA(8,1)
ST 5 PS(1,1) PS(2,2) PS(3,3)
OU NS AD=OFF IT=80
```

The input data are the same as before. But in this case NY=3 and NX=7, so only 10 variables are selected (note that the data on P_t, Y_t, K_t, W_t and E_l are not used). The MO command specifies NE=8.

Since only NK is default on the MO command one must use FI to specify FIxed-x and LY=IZ and TE=ZE to specify that $\mathbf{y}' = (\eta_1, \eta_2, \eta_3)$. Otherwise, the MO, FR, and VA commands are the same as in the previous run.

One further complication arises. Since there are more η-variables than y-variables the, assumption for the starting value algorithm is not fulfilled (see the section *Instrumental variables (IV) and two-stage least squares (TSLS)* on page 17). The user must therefore provide such starting values that $\mathbf{\Sigma}$ becomes positive definite initially. This is accomplished simply by putting positive values in the first three diagonal elements of $\mathbf{\Psi}$, as shown by the ST command in the command file above. It is also recommended that the option NS be inserted on the OU command. This tells the program to use the steepest descent method to improve the starting point before the actual minimization of the fit function begins.

This run gives the TSLS and ML estimates of the structural parameters shown in columns 3 and 6 of Table 4.7. It is apparent that ML and ridge estimates are considerably different from the IV, TSLS, and ULS estimates, which are closer to each other.

The ML estimates for econometric models of the form considered in this section are sometimes called FIML (Full Information Maximum Likelihood) estimates or FILGRV (Full Information Least Generalized Residual Variance) estimates. It has been shown that these estimates minimize the generalized variance of the reduced form residuals, *i.e.*, the determinant of the reduced form residual covariance matrix (see Jöreskog, 1973). The ML estimates can therefore be justified without the assumption of normality. The user should be warned not to rely heavily on the standard errors and/or the χ^2-measure of fit, since they depend on both the assumption of normality and a large sample. Also, because autocorrelation is often present in time series data, the assumption of independent observations is questionable.

5 Structural equation models for latent variables

5.1 The full LISREL model

The full LISREL model combines Submodel 1, the measurement model of Chapter 3, with Submodel 2, the model designed to estimate "causal" relationships among directly observed explanatory variables and dependent variables. The full model permits these relationships to be studied when both types of variables are subject to measurement error.

As outlined in Chapter 1, the full LISREL model is a combination of a structural equation system among *latent* variables η's and ξ's (*cf.* 4.1),

$$\boldsymbol{\eta} = \mathbf{B}\boldsymbol{\eta} + \boldsymbol{\Gamma}\boldsymbol{\xi} + \boldsymbol{\zeta} \,, \tag{5.1}$$

and measurement models for observed y's and x's (*cf.* 3.1),

$$\mathbf{y} = \boldsymbol{\Lambda}_y \boldsymbol{\eta} + \boldsymbol{\epsilon} \tag{5.2}$$

$$\mathbf{x} = \boldsymbol{\Lambda}_x \boldsymbol{\xi} + \boldsymbol{\delta} \,, \tag{5.3}$$

where all variables, observed and latent, are assumed measured in deviations from their means.

The full model therefore involves the following variables:

Observed Variables:	$\mathbf{y}' = (y_1, y_2, \dots, y_p)$	$\mathbf{x}' = (x_1, x_2, \dots, x_q)$
Latent Variables:	$\boldsymbol{\eta}' = (\eta_1, \eta_2, \dots, \eta_m)$	$\boldsymbol{\xi}' = (\xi_1, \xi_2, \dots, \xi_n)$
Error Variables:	$\boldsymbol{\epsilon}' = (\epsilon_1, \epsilon_2, \dots, \epsilon_p)$	$\boldsymbol{\delta}' = (\delta_1, \delta_2, \dots, \delta_q)$
	$\boldsymbol{\zeta}' = (\zeta_1, \zeta_2, \dots, \zeta_m)$	

Figure 5.1   Path Diagram for Observed y and x and True ξ

The ϵ's and δ's are called *errors in variables* or measurement errors, and the ζ's are called *errors in equations* or structural disturbance terms.

In addition to the four matrices $\mathbf{\Lambda}_y$, $\mathbf{\Lambda}_x$, $\mathbf{B}$, and $\mathbf{\Gamma}$, the model involves the four covariance matrices $\mathbf{\Phi}$, $\mathbf{\Psi}$, $\mathbf{\Theta}_\epsilon$, and $\mathbf{\Theta}_\delta$, the covariance matrices of $\boldsymbol{\xi}$, $\boldsymbol{\zeta}$, $\boldsymbol{\epsilon}$, and $\boldsymbol{\delta}$, respectively.

5.2 Measurement errors in regression models

Simple regression

In the regression of y on x,

$$y = \gamma_{y.x} x + z \, , \tag{5.4}$$

suppose x is measured with error:

$$x = \xi + \delta \, , \tag{5.5}$$

where δ is the measurement error and ξ is the true value.

Then the true relationship between y and ξ is

$$y = \gamma \xi + \zeta \, . \tag{5.6}$$

Note that the $\gamma_{y.x}$ in (5.4) is a *regression parameter* , whereas the γ in (5.6) is a *structural parameter*. The mechanism that generates the observed variables is shown in Figure 5.1.

If the ξ, ζ, and δ are mutually uncorrelated, the covariance matrix Σ of (y, x) is

$$\Sigma = \begin{pmatrix} \gamma^2 \phi + \psi \\ \gamma \phi & \phi + \theta \end{pmatrix}$$

where $\phi = \mathsf{Var}(\xi)$, $\psi = \mathsf{Var}(\zeta)$, and $\theta = \mathsf{Var}(\delta)$.

It is possible to estimate γ from the elements of the corresponding sample covariance matrix if the relative sizes of the error variances, ϕ and θ, are known or can be estimated. The regression coefficient $\gamma_{y.x}$ in (5.4) is given by

$$\gamma_{y.x} = \frac{\mathsf{Cov}(y,x)}{\mathsf{Var}(x)} = \frac{\gamma\phi}{\phi + \theta} = \gamma\frac{\phi}{\phi + \theta} = \gamma\rho_{xx} \tag{5.7}$$

where ρ_{xx} is the reliability of x.

It is apparent that the regression parameter, $\gamma_{y.x}$, is not equal to the structural parameter, γ, if $\theta > 0$. The sample regression coefficient, $\hat{\gamma}_{y.x}$, is therefore *not a consistent estimator* of γ.

If ρ_{xx} of x is known, the structural parameter may be estimated by

$$\hat{\gamma} = \hat{\gamma}_{y.x}/\rho_{xx} . \tag{5.8}$$

In this context, $\hat{\gamma}_{y.x}$ is referred to as the *attenuated* coefficient and $\hat{\gamma}$ as the *disattenuated* coefficient.

In practice, ρ_{xx} is not known but has to be estimated from data. If r_{xx} is a consistent estimate of ρ_{xx},

$$\hat{\gamma} = \hat{\gamma}_{y.x}/r_{xx} \tag{5.9}$$

can be used to estimate γ. This reduces the bias in $\hat{\gamma}_{y.x}$ at the expense of an increased sampling variance.

If the reliability of the measure is unknown, it can be estimated by administering two similar measures to the same respondents. The following example illustrates the calculations in the case of a known and an unknown reliability coefficient.

Example 5.1: Verbal ability in grades 4 and 5

Source: Härnqvist (1962).

The sample covariance matrix computed from data on a 40-item similarities test for 262 boys who were tested first in grade 4 (x) and later in grade 5 (y) is:

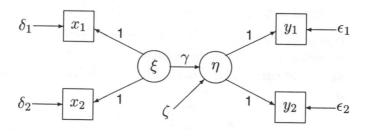

Figure 5.2   Path Diagram for Verbal Ability in Grades 4 and 5

$$S = \begin{pmatrix} \overset{y}{46.886} & \\ 45.889 & \overset{x}{59.890} \end{pmatrix}.$$

The reliability of the test is given as $r_{xx} = 0.896$. The regression estimate (5.7) is

$$\hat{\gamma}_{y.x} = \frac{45.889}{59.890} = 0.766 .$$

Corrected for attenuation, this becomes

$$\hat{\gamma} = \frac{0.766}{0.896} = 0.855 .$$

One way to estimate ρ_{xx} is to split the test into two random 20-item tests and use the score to estimate γ directly using the LISREL model shown in Figure 5.2.

Let x_1 and x_2 be random split-halves 20-item tests in grade 4 and let y_1 and y_2 be the same measures in grade 5. The covariance matrix is:

$$S = \begin{pmatrix} \overset{y_1}{12.522} & & & \\ \overset{}{10.405} & \overset{y_2}{13.554} & & \\ 11.723 & 11.494 & \overset{x_1}{16.684} & \\ 10.988 & 11.684 & 13.560 & \overset{x_2}{16.086} \end{pmatrix}.$$

The two split-halves are treated as parallel measures; see Sec. 3.1.

The LISREL command file is:

Table 5.1   Bias, Variance and MSE of Three Estimates of γ

Estimate	Bias	Variance	MSE
$\hat{\gamma}_{y.x}$	−0.080	0.000747	0.007147
$\hat{\gamma}$	0.009	0.001010	0.001091
$\hat{\gamma}_{ML}$	0.000	0.001034	0.001034

```
Verbal Ability in Grades 4 and 5
DATA     NI=4 NO=262
CMATRIX FI=EX51.COV
MODEL    NY=2 NX=2 NE=1 NK=1
VALUE    1 LY(1) LY(2) LX(1) LX(2)
EQUAL    TD(1) TD(2)
EQUAL    TE(1) TE(2)
OUTPUT   SE
```

The ML estimate of γ obtained by LISREL is

$$\hat{\gamma}_{\mathsf{ML}} = 0.846(0.032) \ .$$

Assuming that this contains no bias, we can summarize the relative advantages and disadvantages of the three estimates as in Table 5.1. The ordinary regression estimate $\hat{\gamma}_{y.x}$ has the largest bias and the smallest variance. The ML estimate from LISREL has no bias but a larger variance. Because the reliability of x, 0.896, is quite large and because the corrected estimate $\hat{\gamma}$ has a small bias, the MSE of this estimate is comparable to the MSE of the ML estimator in this example.

Multiple regression

The above principle can be extended to the case of multiple regression with several explanatory variables $x_1, x_2, \ldots, x_n$. Let the regression relationship be

$$y = \gamma_1 \xi_1 + \gamma_2 \xi_2 + \cdots + \gamma_n \xi_n + \zeta \ .$$

The estimator of γ corresponding to (5.9) is

$$\hat{\gamma} = (\mathbf{S}_{xx} - \hat{\mathbf{\Theta}}_{\delta})^{-1} \mathbf{s}_{y.x} \ , \tag{5.10}$$

where $\mathbf{S}_{xx}$ is the sample covariance matrix of the x's, $\hat{\mathbf{\Theta}}_\delta$ is a diagonal matrix of estimated error variances in the x's, and $\mathbf{s}_{y.x}$ is a vector of sample covariances between y and the x's.

In practice, (5.10) may fail because $\mathbf{S}_{xx} - \hat{\mathbf{\Theta}}_\delta$ is often not positive definite. A better approach is to read $\hat{\mathbf{\Theta}}_\delta$ into LISREL as fixed quantities, and let LISREL estimate γ from the information provided in the covariance matrix and $\hat{\mathbf{\Theta}}_\delta$. This approach is illustrated in the following example.

Example 5.2A: Role behavior of farm managers, part A

Source: Warren, White, & Fuller (1974).

In a study of a random sample of 98 managers of farmer cooperatives in Iowa, their role performance, as measured by a role behavior scale [ROL-BEHAV], was assumed to be linearly related to four variables:

x_1: *Knowledge of economic phases of management directed toward profit making in a business and product knowledge [KNOWLEDG]*

x_2: *Value Orientation: tendency to rationally evaluate means to an economic end [VALORIEN]*

x_3: *Role Satisfaction: gratification obtained by the manager from performing the managerial role [ROLSATIS]*

x_4: *Past Training: amount of formal education [TRAINING]*

The covariance matrix of the five variables is given in Table 5.2.

The ordinary least squares (OLS) regression estimates are, with standard errors below,

$$\hat{\gamma}'_{\mathbf{y.x}} = \begin{matrix} 0.230 & 0.120 & 0.056 & 0.110 \\ (0.053 & 0.036 & 0.037 & 0.039) \end{matrix}.$$

For the reliabilities of the x-variables given as

$$0.60, \quad 0.64, \quad 0.81, \quad 1.00,$$

it is possible to re-estimate γ to reduce or eliminate the effects of measurement errors by using a LISREL model of the form

$$\mathbf{x} = \boldsymbol{\xi} + \boldsymbol{\delta} \qquad y = \boldsymbol{\gamma}'\boldsymbol{\xi} + \zeta \,,$$

i.e., we take $\boldsymbol{\Lambda}_y(1 \times 1) = 1$, $\boldsymbol{\Lambda}_x(4 \times 4) = \mathbf{I}$, $\mathbf{B}(1 \times 1) = 0$, $\boldsymbol{\Gamma}(1 \times 4) = \boldsymbol{\gamma}'$, $\boldsymbol{\Phi} = \mathsf{Cov}(\boldsymbol{\xi})$, unconstrained, $\boldsymbol{\Psi}(1 \times 1) = \mathsf{Var}(\zeta)$, $\boldsymbol{\Theta}_\epsilon(1 \times 1) = 0$ and $\boldsymbol{\Theta}_\delta =$ diagonal with fixed values 0.0208, 0.0436, 0.0171, 0.0000. These values are obtained by taking 1 minus the reliabilities above times the observed variance.

The LISREL command file for this analysis is:

```
Role Behavior of Farm Managers, Part A
DATA      NI=4  NO=98
CMATRIX   FI=EX52A.COV
LABELS;  ROLBEHAV  KNOWLEDG  VALORIEN  ROLSATIS  TRAINING
MODEL     NY=1  NE=1  NX=4  NK=4  LY=ID  LX=ID  TE=ZE  TD=FI
MATRIX    TD; 0.0208   0.0436   0.0171   0
MATRIX    PH
0.0312
0.0280   0.0776
0.0044  -0.0063   0.0730
0.0192   0.0353  -0.0066   0.0946
OUTPUT    SE  AD=OFF
```

The specification AD=OFF on the OU command is necessary because of the fixed zero in TD(4), *i.e.*, because it is assumed that x_4 has no measurement error.

The disattenuated estimates of γ and standard errors are

Table 5.2   Covariance Matrix for Example 5.2A

	y	x_1	x_2	x_3	x_4
ROLBEHAV	0.0209				
KNOWLEDG	0.0177	0.0520			
VALORIEN	0.0245	0.0280	0.1212		
ROLSATIS	0.0046	0.0044	−0.0063	0.0901	
TRAINING	0.0187	0.0192	0.0353	−0.0066	0.0946

Table 5.3   Covariance Matrix for Example 5.2B

	y_1	y_2	x_{11}	x_{12}	x_{21}	x_{22}	x_{31}	x_{32}	x_4
y_1	.0271								
y_2	.0172	.0222							
x_{11}	.0219	.0193	.0876						
x_{12}	.0164	.0130	.0317	.0568					
x_{21}	.0284	.0294	.0383	.0151	.1826				
x_{22}	.0217	.0185	.0356	.0230	.0774	.1473			
x_{31}	.0083	.0011	−.0001	.0055	−.0087	−.0069	.1137		
x_{32}	.0074	.0015	.0035	.0089	−.0007	−.0088	.0722	.1024	
x_4	.0180	.0194	.0203	.0182	.0563	.0142	−.0056	−.0077	.0946

$$\hat{\gamma}'_{\mathbf{y\cdot x}} = \begin{array}{cccc} 0.380 & 0.152 & 0.059 & 0.068 \\ (0.127 & 0.079 & 0.050 & 0.044) \end{array} \ .$$

Some of these estimates and standard errors differ considerably from the OLS estimates.

If there are two or more *indicators* for each ξ, the measurement errors as well as the structural parameters can be estimated directly from the data. The procedure is illustrated in the following continuation of the previous example.

Example 5.2B: Role behavior of farm managers, part B

Source: Rock, *et al.* (1977).

Because multiple-item scales where used to measure y, x_1, x_2, and x_3, responses to the items could be assigned randomly into two parallel halves. The full covariance matrix of these split-halves is given in Table 5.3.

The values in Table 5.3 can be used to estimate the true regression equation

$$\eta = \gamma_1 \xi_1 + \gamma_2 \xi_2 + \gamma_3 \xi_3 + \gamma_4 \xi_4 + \zeta , \qquad (5.11)$$

using the following measurement models.

$$\begin{pmatrix} y_1 \\ y_2 \end{pmatrix} = \begin{pmatrix} 1 \\ 1 \end{pmatrix} \eta + \begin{pmatrix} \epsilon_1 \\ \epsilon_2 \end{pmatrix} \tag{5.12}$$

$$\begin{pmatrix} x_{11} \\ x_{12} \\ x_{21} \\ x_{22} \\ x_{31} \\ x_{32} \\ x_4 \end{pmatrix} = \begin{pmatrix} 1 & 0 & 0 & 0 \\ 1 & 0 & 0 & 0 \\ 0 & 1 & 0 & 0 \\ 0 & 1 & 0 & 0 \\ 0 & 0 & 1 & 0 \\ 0 & 0 & 1.2 & 0 \\ 0 & 0 & 0 & 1 \end{pmatrix} \begin{pmatrix} \xi_1 \\ \xi_2 \\ \xi_3 \\ \xi_4 \end{pmatrix} + \begin{pmatrix} \delta_{11} \\ \delta_{12} \\ \delta_{21} \\ \delta_{22} \\ \delta_{31} \\ \delta_{32} \\ 0 \end{pmatrix} \tag{5.13}$$

The value 1.2 in the last equation reflects the fact that x_{32} has six items whereas x_{31} has only five.

The latent variables are:

η = *role behavior*
ξ_1 = *knowledge*
ξ_2 = *value orientation*
ξ_3 = *role satisfaction*
ξ_4 = *past training*

The observed variables are (the number of items in each split-half is given in parentheses):

y_1 = *a split-half measure of role behavior (12)*
y_2 = *a split-half measure of role behavior (12)*
x_{11} = *a split-half measure of knowledge (13)*
x_{12} = *a split-half measure of knowledge (13)*
x_{21} = *a split-half measure of value orientation (15)*
x_{22} = *a split-half measure of value orientation (15)*
x_{31} = *a split-half measure of role satisfaction (5)*
x_{32} = *a split-half measure of role satisfaction (6)*
x_4 = ξ_4 = *a measure of past training*

The LISREL command file is:

```
Role Behavior of Farm Managers, Part B
DA NI=9 NO=98
CM FI=EX52B.COV
LA
Y1 Y2 X11 X12 X21 X22 X31 X32 X4
MO NY=2 NE=1 NX=7 NK=4
FI TD 7
VA 1 LY 1 LY 2 LX 1 1 LX 2 1 LX 3 2 LX 4 2 LX 5 3 LX 7 4
VA 1.2 LX 6 3
OU SE AD=OFF
```

The fit of the model is $\chi^2 = 26.97$ with 22 degrees of freedom, which represents a rather good fit. The ML estimates of the γ's and their standard errors (below) are

$$\hat{\gamma}'_{\mathbf{y.x}} = \begin{array}{cccc} 0.350 & 0.168 & 0.045 & 0.071 \\ (0.133) & (0.079) & (0.054) & (0.045) \end{array} .$$

When compared to the ordinary least squares (OLS) estimates, previously given for the regression of y on x_1, x_2, x_3, and x_4, considerable bias in the OLS estimates is evident, even though their standard errors are smaller.

Estimates of the true and error score variances for each observed measure are also obtained. The reliability of the measures as computed from these estimates are

y	x_1	x_2	x_3
0.82	0.60	0.64	0.81

The model defined by (5.11)–(5.13) can be generalized directly to the case when there are several jointly dependent variables η. The only differences will be that λ and γ will be replaced by matrices Λ_y and Γ, respectively, and ψ by a full symmetric positive-definite matrix Ψ.

5.3 Measurement errors in path analysis

Problems with measurement errors in the observed variables in path analysis can be dealt with in much the same way as in the preceding section. If the reliability or error variance in a variable y or x is known, the error

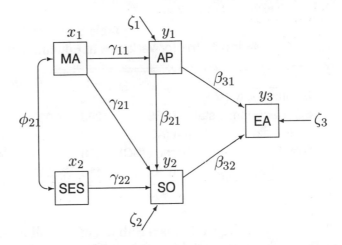

Figure 5.3   Path Diagram for Educational Attainment

variance can be used as a fixed quantity in Θ_ϵ or Θ_δ and the structural parameters in $\mathbf{B}$ and Γ estimated directly with LISREL.

If there are two or more observed indicators for each latent variable of η and/or ξ, the measurement errors can be estimated from the data. Sometimes it is possible to estimate the measurement error in an observed variable even though only a single measure is available. This is illustrated in the following example. The example also illustrates how to use the modification index to determine whether a parameter is identified or not.

Example 5.3: Educational attainment

Source: Sewell, Haller, & Ohlendorf (1970); Wiley (1973).

The structural equation model to be estimated is:

$$y_1 = \gamma_{11}x_1 + \zeta_1$$
$$y_2 = \beta_{21}y_1 + \gamma_{21}x_1 + \gamma_{22}x_2 + \zeta_2$$
$$y_3 = \beta_{31}y_1 + \beta_{32}y_2 + \zeta_3$$

The variables and their intercorrelations ($N \approx 3500$) are given in Table 5.4. The path diagram is shown in Figure 5.3.

Table 5.4

Correlation Matrix for Variables in Educational Attainment Model

	x_1	x_2	y_1	y_2	y_3
Mental ability (MA)	1.000				
Socioeconomic status (SES)	.288	1.000			
Academic performance (AP)	.589	.194	1.000		
Significant others' influence (SO)	.438	.359	.473	1.000	
Educational aspiration (EA)	.418	.380	.459	.611	1.000

The model in Figure 5.3 is a Submodel 2. Following Example 4.5 in Section 4.2, the set up of the command file is straightforward:

```
Educational Attainment Problem A
DA NI=5 NO=3500 MA=KM
LA
MA SES AP SO EA
KM FI=EX53.COR
SE
3 4 5 1 2
MO NY=3 NX=2 BE=SD PS=DI
FI GA(1,2) GA(3,1) GA(3,2)
OU SE TV MI
```

The output file reveals very large modification indices for β_{23} and γ_{32}, suggesting that they be set free. However, suppose there is measurement error in the SO variable and write

$$SO = y_2 = \eta_2 + \epsilon_2 \, ,$$

where η_2 is "true SO" and ϵ_2 is the measurement error. The path diagram for this modified model is given in Figure 5.4.

Despite the single observed measure of SO, $\theta_{22}^{(\epsilon)}$ (the variance of ϵ_2) is an identified parameter because of the overidentifying constraints in the model in this case. In principle, this statement should be proved algebraically, but the LISREL program can be used to determine whether $\theta_{22}^{(\epsilon)}$ is identified or not. The specification of the model is:

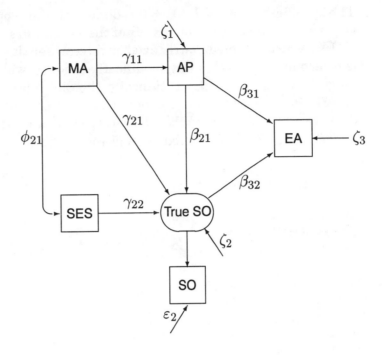

Figure 5.4　Model with Measurement Error in SO

$$
\begin{array}{llll}
x_1 & = & \text{MA} & \equiv \; \xi_1 & \delta_1 & = & 0 \\
x_2 & = & \text{SES} & \equiv \; \xi_2 & \delta_2 & = & 0 \\
y_1 & = & \text{AP} & \equiv \; \eta_1 & \epsilon_1 & = & 0 \\
y_2 & = & \text{SO} & \equiv \; \eta_2 & \epsilon_2 & = & 0 \\
y_3 & = & \text{EA} & \equiv \; \eta_3 & \epsilon_3 & = & 0 \;,
\end{array}
$$

i.e., $\mathbf{\Lambda}_y = \mathbf{I}$, $\mathbf{\Lambda}_x = \mathbf{I}$, $\mathbf{\Theta}_\epsilon = \mathbf{0}$, $\mathbf{\Theta}_\delta = \mathbf{0}$, $\mathbf{\Psi} = \text{diag}(\psi_{11}, \psi_{22}, \psi_{33})$,

$$
\mathbf{B} = \begin{pmatrix} 0 & 0 & 0 \\ \beta_{21} & 0 & 0 \\ \beta_{31} & \beta_{32} & 0 \end{pmatrix}, \; \mathbf{\Gamma} = \begin{pmatrix} \gamma_{11} & 0 \\ \gamma_{21} & \gamma_{22} \\ 0 & 0 \end{pmatrix}.
$$

Formally this model is identical to the previous one. The difference is that it is now formulated as a full LISREL model rather than as a Submodel 2.

The specification $\mathbf{\Lambda}_x = \mathbf{I}$, $\mathbf{\Theta}_\delta = \mathbf{0}$ is done with the FI option. This will also set $\hat{\mathbf{\Phi}} = \mathbf{S}_{xx}$ the correlation matrix of the x-variables. The trick is to specify $\mathbf{\Theta}_\epsilon$ to be a diagonal matrix fixed at zero rather than specifying that $\mathbf{\Theta}_\epsilon$ is a zero matrix. In this way, modification indices will be obtained for the diagonal elements of $\mathbf{\Theta}_\epsilon$. Technically, the difference is as follows. When TE=ZE, $\mathbf{\Theta}_\epsilon$ is not stored in computer memory so that no modification indices can be computed. When TE=FI, space is allocated for the diagonal elements of $\mathbf{\Theta}_\epsilon$, so that modification indices can be computed for these elements.

The LISREL command file is:

```
Educational Attainment Problem B
DA NI=5 NO=3500 MA=KM
LA
MA SES AP SO EA
KM FI=EX53.COR
SE
3 4 5 1 2
MO NY=3 NX=2 FI NE=3 BE=SD PS=DI LY=ID TE=FI
FI GA(1,2) GA(3,1) GA(3,2)
OU SE TV MI AD=OFF ND=2
```

AD=OFF on the OU command is essential because $\mathbf{\Theta}_\epsilon$ is a fixed zero matrix by intention.

The resulting output file shows a χ^2 of overall fit equal to 193.53 with three degrees of freedom. The modification indices should be inspected to determine the identification of the model.

The modification index for $\theta_{22}^{(\epsilon)}$ is 176.97. This means that $\theta_{22}^{(\epsilon)}$ will be identified if it is set free. The modification index for β_{23} is identical to that of $\theta_{22}^{(\epsilon)}$. This means that these two models are equivalent; see Chapter 8. However, the model with β_{23} free does not make sense.

To run the model with $\theta_{22}^{(\epsilon)}$ free, all that needs to be done is to add the following command to the LISREL command file:

```
FR TE(2)
```

The resulting solution has $\chi^2 = 7.14$ with two degrees of freedom. Thus, adding the single parameter $\theta_{22}^{(\epsilon)}$, gives a reduction in χ^2 of 186.39 which is close to the value predicted by the modification index. The estimated value of $\theta_{22}^{(\epsilon)}$ is 0.40 with a standard error of 0.02. Thus, if the model is correct, the reliability of SO is only 0.60. The example demonstrates that one possible source of specification error in the model of Figure 5.3 may be that there is measurement error in the SO-variable.

5.4 MIMIC models

The term MIMIC stands for Multiple Indicators and Multiple Causes. The simplest form of a MIMIC model involves a single unobserved latent variable "caused" by several observed x-variables and indicated by several observed y-variables. The model equations are

$$\mathbf{y} = \boldsymbol{\lambda}\eta + \boldsymbol{\epsilon}\,, \qquad\qquad (5.14)$$

$$\eta = \boldsymbol{\gamma}'\mathbf{x} + \zeta\,, \qquad\qquad (5.15)$$

where $\mathbf{y}' = (y_1, y_2, \ldots, y_p)$ are indicators of the latent variable η, and $\mathbf{x}' = (x_1, x_2, \ldots, x_q)$ are the "causes" of η. From the LISREL point of view one can regard (5.14) as the measurement model for η and (5.15) as the structural equation for η. The ϵ's and ζ are assumed to be mutually uncorrelated. Equation (5.14) says that the y's are congeneric measures of η and (5.15) says that η is linear in the x's plus a random disturbance term. The model can also be viewed as a multivariate regression model with two specific constraints:

- ☐ The regression matrix must have rank 1.
- ☐ The residual covariance matrix must satisfy the congeneric measurement model.

This can be seen by substituting (5.15) into (5.14), yielding

$$\begin{aligned} \mathbf{y} &= \boldsymbol{\lambda}\boldsymbol{\gamma}'\mathbf{x} + \boldsymbol{\lambda}\zeta + \boldsymbol{\epsilon}\,, \\ &= \boldsymbol{\Pi}\mathbf{x} + \mathbf{z}\,, \end{aligned}$$

which shows that $\boldsymbol{\Pi} = \boldsymbol{\lambda}\boldsymbol{\gamma}'$ and $\mathrm{Cov}(\mathbf{z}) = \boldsymbol{\lambda}\boldsymbol{\lambda}'\psi + \boldsymbol{\Theta}_\epsilon$, where $\psi = \mathrm{Var}(\zeta)$ and $\boldsymbol{\Theta}_\epsilon$ is the diagonal covariance matrix of $\boldsymbol{\epsilon}$.

Table 5.5   Correlations for Variables in MIMIC Model

	x_1	x_2	x_3	y_1	y_2	y_3
Income	1.000					
Occupation	.304	1.000				
Education	.305	.344	1.000			
Church attendance	.100	.156	.158	1.000		
Memberships	.284	.192	.324	.360	1.000	
Friends seen	.176	.136	.226	.210	.265	1.000

To estimate a MIMIC model with LISREL is straightforward. Equations (5.14) and (5.15) correspond to (5.2) and (5.1), respectively. Equation (5.3) in this case says simply that $\mathbf{x} \equiv \boldsymbol{\xi}$, *i.e.*, $\boldsymbol{\Lambda}_x = \mathbf{I}$ and $\boldsymbol{\Theta}_\delta = \mathbf{0}$. The latter specification is handled by the FI option which also implies that $\boldsymbol{\Phi} = \mathrm{Cov}(\boldsymbol{\xi})$ will be estimated by $\mathbf{S}_{xx}$, the sample covariance matrix of $\mathbf{x}$.

Example 5.4: Social status and social participation

Source: Hodge & Treiman (1968).

In a study of the relationship between social status and social participation in a sample of 530 women, six social status variables were measured. Their names and correlations are given in Table 5.5.

All variables are standardized. A path diagram is given in Figure 5.5. The y's may be viewed as independent indicators of a latent variable η (social participation), which is caused by the x's. Thus,

$$\eta = \gamma_1 x_1 + \gamma_2 x_2 + \gamma_3 x_3 + \zeta \,,$$

$$y_1 = \lambda_1 \eta + \epsilon_1, \quad y_2 = \lambda_2 \eta + \epsilon_2, \quad y_3 = \lambda_3 \eta + \epsilon_3 \,.$$

From a substantive viewpoint, it may be helpful to view the x's as determining

$$\xi = \gamma_1 x_1 + \gamma_2 x_2 + \gamma_3 x_3 = social\ status \,,$$

which in turn determines

$$\eta = \xi + \epsilon = social\ participation\ .$$

The LISREL command file for the analysis is:

```
Social Status and Participation
DA NI=6 NO=530 MA=KM
LA
INCOME OCCUPATION EDUCATION CHURCHAT MEMBERSH FRIENDS
KM FI=EX54.COR
SE
4 5 6 1 2 3
MO N=3 NE=1 NX=3 FI LY=FR
LE
SOCIALPR
FI LY(1)
VA 1 LY(1)
OU SE TV
```

Although the overall fit of the model is not too bad ($\chi^2 = 12.5$ with 6 degrees of freedom), most of the relationships in the model are poorly determined as revealed by the low squared multiple correlation. The t-values reveal that occupation may not be a significant determinant of social participation, although income and education are.

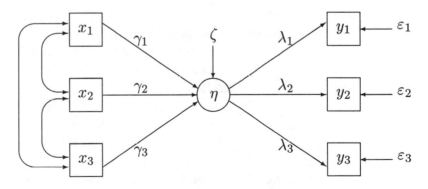

Figure 5.5   Path Diagram for MIMIC Model

5.5 Path analysis with latent variables

Path analysis may be formulated for latent variables as well as for directly observed variables (discussed in Section 4.2). In its most general form, there is a structural equation system of the form (5.1) for a set of latent variables η's and ξ's. In most applications, the system is recursive but models with non-recursive systems have also been proposed. A recursive system based on longitudinal data is considered in Example 6.4. In the present section, a non-recursive system for latent variables and various alternative models are considered sequentially.

Example 5.5: Peer influences on ambition

Source: Duncan, Haller, & Portes (1968).

Figure 5.6 is meant to represent the way in which a person's peers (e.g., best friends) influence his or her decisions (e.g., choice of occupation). The paths between RESPONDENT'S AMBITION and BEST FRIEND'S AMBITION recognize that the relation must be reciprocal. As a test of this model, a sample of Michigan high-school students were paired with their best friends and measured on a number of background variables. In addition, scaled measures of occupational and educational aspiration were obtained to serve as indicators of a latent variable AMBITION.

The observed measures in the study are:

$x_1 = $ *respondent's parental aspiration [REPARASP]*
$x_2 = $ *respondent's intelligence [REINTGCE]*
$x_3 = $ *respondent's socioeconomic status [RESOCIEC]*
$x_4 = $ *best friend's socioeconomic status [BFSOCIEC]*
$x_5 = $ *best friend's intelligence [BFINTGCE]*
$x_6 = $ *best friend's parental aspiration [BFPARASP]*
$y_1 = $ *respondent's occupational aspiration [REOCCASP]*
$y_2 = $ *respondent's educational aspiration [REEDASP]*
$y_3 = $ *best friend's educational aspiration [BFEDASP]*
$y_4 = $ *best friend's occupational aspiration [BFOCCASP]*
$\eta_1 = $ *respondent's ambition [REAMBITN]*
$\eta_2 = $ *best friend's ambition [BFAMBITN]*

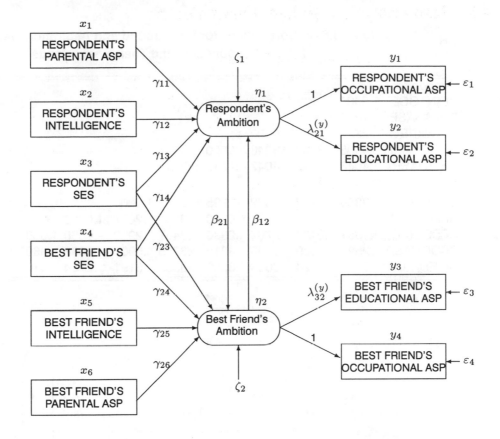

Figure 5.6   Path Diagram for Peer Influences on Ambition

The correlation[1] *matrix based on 329 observations is shown in Table 5.6.*

The specifications for the LISREL model are as follows.

Let $\xi_i \equiv x_i$, or $\Lambda_x(6 \times 6) = \mathbf{I}$ and $\Theta_\delta = \mathbf{0}$ (specified by the FI option). And let $\lambda_2 = \lambda_{21}^{(y)}$, $\lambda_3 = \lambda_{32}^{(y)}$, $\beta_1 = \beta_{12}$, $\beta_2 = \beta_{21}$, $\gamma_1 = \gamma_{11}$, $\gamma_2 = \gamma_{12}$, $\gamma_3 = \gamma_{13}$, $\gamma_4 = \gamma_{14}$, $\gamma_5 = \gamma_{23}$, $\gamma_6 = \gamma_{24}$, $\gamma_7 = \gamma_{25}$, $\gamma_8 = \gamma_{26}$.

Then the structural equations are

---

[1]For correct standard errors and chi-squares, the covariances should be analyzed.

Table 5.6 Correlations for Background and Aspiration Measures for 329 Respondents and Their Best Friends

Respondent										
REINTGCE	1.0000									
REPARASP	.1839	1.0000								
RESOCIEC	.2220	.0489	1.0000							
REOCCASP	.4105	.2137	.3240	1.0000						
RE EDASP	.4043	.2742	.4047	.6247	1.0000					
Best Friend										
BFINTGCE	.3355	.0782	.2302	.2995	.2863	1.0000				
BFPARASP	.1021	.1147	.0931	.0760	.0702	.2087	1.0000			
BFSOCIEC	.1861	.0186	.2707	.2930	.2407	.2950	−.0438	1.0000		
BFOCCASP	.2598	.0839	.2786	.4216	.3275	.5007	.1988	.3607	1.0000	
BF EDASP	.2903	.1124	.3054	.3269	.3669	.5191	.2784	.4105	.6404	1.0000

$$\begin{pmatrix} \eta_1 \\ \eta_2 \end{pmatrix} = \begin{pmatrix} 0 & \beta_1 \\ \beta_2 & 0 \end{pmatrix} \begin{pmatrix} \eta_1 \\ \eta_2 \end{pmatrix} + \begin{pmatrix} \gamma_1 & \gamma_2 & \gamma_3 & \gamma_4 & 0 & 0 \\ 0 & 0 & \gamma_5 & \gamma_6 & \gamma_7 & \gamma_8 \end{pmatrix} \begin{pmatrix} \xi_1 \\ \xi_2 \\ \xi_3 \\ \xi_4 \\ \xi_5 \\ \xi_6 \end{pmatrix} + \begin{pmatrix} \zeta_1 \\ \zeta_2 \end{pmatrix},$$

and the equations relating the η's to the y's are

$$\begin{pmatrix} y_1 \\ y_2 \\ y_3 \\ y_4 \end{pmatrix} = \begin{pmatrix} 1 & 0 \\ \lambda_2 & 0 \\ 0 & \lambda_3 \\ 0 & 1 \end{pmatrix} \begin{pmatrix} \eta_1 \\ \eta_2 \end{pmatrix} + \begin{pmatrix} \epsilon_1 \\ \epsilon_2 \\ \epsilon_3 \\ \epsilon_4 \end{pmatrix}.$$

In Λ_y the scales for η_1 and η_2 are fixed the same as in y_1 and y_4, respectively. Since y_1 and y_4 are on the same scale, η_1 and η_2 are also on the same scale, as is necessary to make meaningful comparisons between the respondent and the best friend. Since $\boldsymbol{\xi} \equiv \mathbf{x}$ and there are no constraints on $\boldsymbol{\Phi}$, $\boldsymbol{\Phi} = \boldsymbol{\Sigma}_{xx}$, which is estimated as $\mathbf{S}_{xx}$. The matrix $\boldsymbol{\Psi}$ (2×2) is

$$\boldsymbol{\Psi} = \begin{pmatrix} \psi_{11} & \\ \psi_{21} & \psi_{22} \end{pmatrix}$$

with $\psi_{ii} = \mathsf{Var}(\zeta_i)$ (for $i = 1, 2$) and $\psi_{21} = \mathsf{Cov}(\zeta_1, \zeta_2)$. The matrix $\boldsymbol{\Theta}_\epsilon$ is diagonal with diagonal elements $\theta_{ii}^{(\epsilon)} = \mathsf{Var}(\epsilon_i)$. Since $\boldsymbol{\xi} \equiv \mathbf{x}$, the structural equations are equivalent to

$$\boldsymbol{\eta} = \mathbf{B}\boldsymbol{\eta} + \boldsymbol{\Gamma}\mathbf{x} + \boldsymbol{\zeta}$$

with reduced form

$$\boldsymbol{\eta} = (\mathbf{I} - \mathbf{B})^{-1}\boldsymbol{\Gamma}\mathbf{x} + (\mathbf{I} - \mathbf{B})^{-1}\boldsymbol{\zeta} \ . \qquad (5.16)$$

In addition,

$$\mathbf{y} = \boldsymbol{\Lambda}_y\boldsymbol{\eta} + \boldsymbol{\epsilon} = \boldsymbol{\Lambda}_y(\mathbf{I} - \mathbf{B})^{-1}\boldsymbol{\Gamma}\mathbf{x} + \boldsymbol{\Lambda}_y(\mathbf{I} - \mathbf{B})^{-1}\boldsymbol{\zeta} + \boldsymbol{\epsilon} = \mathbf{P}\mathbf{x} + \mathbf{z} \ , \quad (5.17)$$

where

$$\mathbf{P} = \boldsymbol{\Sigma}_{yx}\boldsymbol{\Sigma}_{xx}^{-1} = \boldsymbol{\Lambda}_y(\mathbf{I} - \mathbf{B})^{-1}\boldsymbol{\Gamma} = \boldsymbol{\Lambda}_y\boldsymbol{\Pi}$$

and

$$\mathbf{z} = \boldsymbol{\Lambda}_y(\mathbf{I} - \mathbf{B})^{-1}\boldsymbol{\zeta} + \boldsymbol{\epsilon} \ .$$

Identification

Because $\boldsymbol{\Psi}$ is unconstrained, it follows from (5.16) that, for any given $\mathbf{B}$ and $\boldsymbol{\Gamma}$, there is a one-to-one correspondence between $\boldsymbol{\Psi}$ and the covariance matrix of $\boldsymbol{\eta}$, $\boldsymbol{\Omega}$ say, where

$$\boldsymbol{\Omega} = \begin{pmatrix} \omega_{11} & \\ \omega_{21} & \omega_{22} \end{pmatrix} \ .$$

From (5.17),

$$\begin{aligned}
\boldsymbol{\Sigma}_{yy} &= \boldsymbol{\Lambda}_y\boldsymbol{\Omega}\boldsymbol{\Lambda}_y{}' + \boldsymbol{\Theta}_\epsilon \\
&= \begin{pmatrix}
\omega_{11} + \theta_{11}^{(\epsilon)} & & & \\
\lambda_2\omega_{11} & \lambda_2^2\omega_{11} + \theta_{22}^{(\epsilon)} & & \\
\lambda_3\omega_{21} & \lambda_2\lambda_3\omega_{21} & \lambda_3^2\omega_{22} + \theta_{33}^{(\epsilon)} & \\
\omega_{21} & \lambda_2\omega_{21} & \lambda_3\omega_{22} & \omega_{22} + \theta_{44}^{(\epsilon)}
\end{pmatrix} \ .
\end{aligned}$$

In addition,

$$(\mathbf{I} - \mathbf{B})^{-1} = (1 - \beta_1\beta_2)^{-1} \begin{pmatrix} 1 & \beta_1 \\ \beta_2 & 1 \end{pmatrix}$$

$$\mathbf{\Pi} = (1 - \beta_1\beta_2)^{-1} \begin{pmatrix} \gamma_1 & \gamma_2 & \gamma_3 + \beta_1\gamma_5 & \gamma_4 + \beta_1\gamma_6 & \beta_1\gamma_7 & \beta_1\gamma_8 \\ \beta_2\gamma_1 & \beta_2\gamma_2 & \gamma_5 + \beta_2\gamma_3 & \gamma_6 + \beta_2\gamma_4 & \gamma_7 & \gamma_8 \end{pmatrix}.$$

The first and last rows of $\mathbf{P}$ are identical to the first and second row of $\mathbf{\Pi}$ $= (\mathbf{I} - \mathbf{B})^{-1}\mathbf{\Gamma}$, respectively. The second row of $\mathbf{P}$ is λ_2 times the first row of $\mathbf{\Pi}$ and the third row of $\mathbf{P}$ is λ_3 times the second row of $\mathbf{\Pi}$. Hence it is clear that λ_2 and λ_3 are identified and that

$$\lambda_2 = \frac{p_{2i}}{p_{1i}} \quad \text{and} \quad \lambda_3 = \frac{p_{3i}}{p_{4i}}, \qquad i = 1, 2, \ldots, 6.$$

Since $\mathbf{\Pi}$ consists of two rows of $\mathbf{P}$, $\mathbf{\Pi}$ is identified. From $\mathbf{\Pi}$ it follows that $\gamma_1, \gamma_2, \gamma_7, \gamma_8, \beta_1,$ and β_2 are determined as

$$\gamma_1 = \pi_{11}, \quad \gamma_2 = \pi_{12}, \quad \gamma_7 = \pi_{25}, \quad \gamma_8 = \pi_{26}$$

$$\beta_1 = (\pi_{15}/\pi_{25}) = (\pi_{16}/\pi_{26}), \qquad \beta_2 = (\pi_{21}/\pi_{11}) = (\pi_{22}/\pi_{12}).$$

Then $\gamma_3, \gamma_4, \gamma_5$ and γ_6 are obtained from $\pi_{13}, \pi_{14}, \pi_{23}$ and π_{24}. With λ_2 and λ_3 determined we can now obtain $\omega_{11}, \omega_{21},$ and ω_{22} from the off-diagonal elements of $\mathbf{\Sigma}_{yy}$. Finally, the $\theta_{ii}^{(\epsilon)}$ $(i = 1, 2, 3, 4)$ can be determined from the diagonal elements of $\mathbf{\Sigma}_{yy}$.

This analysis shows that all parameters are identified. Altogether there are 19 parameters (2 β's, 8 γ's, 3 ω's, 2 λ's, and 4 $\theta^{(\epsilon)}$'s) if $\mathbf{x}$ is fixed. When $\mathbf{x}$ is random there will be an additional 21 parameters in $\mathbf{\Phi} = \mathbf{\Sigma}_{xx}$. In both cases the degrees of freedom will be 15.

Analysis

The LISREL command file for the analysis is:

```
Peer Influences on Ambition: Model with BE(2,1) = BE(1,2) and PS(2,1) = 0
DA NI=10 NO=329
LA FI=EX55.LAB; KM FI=EX55.COR
SELECT
```

```
   4  5 10 9  2  1 3  8 6 7
MO NY=4 NE=2 NX=6 FIXED-X PS=DI BE=FU
LE; REAMBITN BFAMBITN
FR LY(2,1) LY(3,2) BE(1,2); FI GA(5) - GA(8)
VA 1 LY(1) LY(8); EQ BE(1,2) BE(2,1)
OU SE TV EF SS
```

The labels and correlations are read from the files EX55.LAB and EX55.COR, respectively. The variables in the correlation matrix are in the order x_2, x_1, x_3, y_1, y_2, x_5, x_6, x_4, y_4, and y_3. The SE command is necessary to order the variables to correspond to the model. The MO command specifies FIXED-X which takes care of NK=6, LX=ID, TD=ZE, and PH=$\mathbf{S}_{xx}$. The other parameter matrices are default except PS=DI and BE=FU. The FR command specifies the free elements in LY and BE and the FI command specifies the four fixed zeros in GA. Note that these four zeros are consecutive elements in GA and we specify these by their linear index. The VA command sets the scale for the two η's. Finally, the EQ command specifies that the two β's are equal.

The overall goodness-of-fit measure is $\chi^2 = 26.70$ with 15 degrees of freedom. A test of the hypothesis $\psi_{21} = 0$ gives $\chi^2 = 0.19$ with one degree of freedom and a test of $\beta_1 = \beta_2$, given $\psi_{21} = 0$, gives $\chi^2 = 0.01$ with one degree of freedom. Hence, it is clear that these hypotheses cannot be rejected. The overall goodness-of-fit of the model with $\psi_{21} = 0$ and $\beta_1 = \beta_2$ is given by $\chi^2 = 26.90$ with 17 degrees of freedom. The probability level is 0.06.

The TSLS estimates and the maximum likelihood estimates with their standard errors are given in Table 5.7. The standardized solution in which η_1 and η_2 are scaled to unit variance is also given in Table 5.7. It is seen in Table 5.7 that the corresponding parameters for the respondent and his best friend are very close. There are good reasons to suggest that the whole model should be completely symmetric between the respondent and his best friend so that not only $\beta_1 = \beta_2$ but also

$$\lambda_2 = \lambda_3, \gamma_1 = \gamma_8, \gamma_2 = \gamma_7, \gamma_3 = \gamma_6, \gamma_4 = \gamma_5, \psi_{11} = \psi_{22},$$

$$\theta_{11}^{(\epsilon)} = \theta_{44}^{(\epsilon)}, \quad \text{and} \quad \theta_{22}^{(\epsilon)} = \theta_{33}^{(\epsilon)}.$$

The overall χ^2 for this model is 30.76 with 25 degrees of freedom. This has a probability level of 0.20. Thus, this model is more parsimonious and

Table 5.7   Estimates for the Model in Figure 5.6

Table 5.7   Estimates for the Model in Figure 5.6 with $\psi_{21} = 0$ and $\beta_1 = \beta_2$

Parameter	TSLS Estimates	Unscaled Solution (ML)	Standardized Solution (ML)
λ_1	1.000	1.000	0.767
λ_2	1.122	1.061 (0.089)	0.813
λ_3	1.120	1.074 (0.081)	0.828
λ_4	1.000	1.000	0.771
β_1	0.210	0.180 (0.039)	0.181
β_2	0.210	0.180 (0.039)	0.179
γ_1	0.156	0.164 (0.039)	0.214
γ_2	0.242	0.254 (0.042)	0.331
γ_3	0.208	0.221 (0.042)	0.288
γ_4	0.072	0.077 (0.041)	0.101
γ_5	0.058	0.068 (0.039)	0.089
γ_6	0.208	0.218 (0.039)	0.283
γ_7	0.314	0.331 (0.041)	0.429
γ_8	0.150	0.152 (0.036)	0.197
ψ_{11}	0.266	0.281 (0.046)	0.478
ψ_{22}	0.220	0.229 (0.039)	0.385
$\theta_{11}^{(\epsilon)}$	0.443	0.412 (0.051)	0.412
$\theta_{22}^{(\epsilon)}$	0.299	0.338 (0.052)	0.338
$\theta_{33}^{(\epsilon)}$	0.283	0.313 (0.046)	0.313
$\theta_{44}^{(\epsilon)}$	0.428	0.404 (0.046)	0.404

has a better fit than the other models. The command file for this model is the same as the previous one but with the following commands added before the OU command:

```
EQ LY(2,1) LY(3,2)
EQ GA(1,1) GA(2,6); EQ GA(1,2) GA(2,5)
EQ GA(1,3) GA(2,4); EQ GA(1,4) GA(2,3)
EQ PS(1)   PS(2)
EQ TE(1)   TE(4);   EQ TE(2)   TE(3)
```

The resulting stability index for the model, and the total and indirect effects of η on η are given below.

```
TOTAL AND INDIRECT EFFECTS

       TOTAL EFFECTS OF ETA ON   ETA

          REAMBITN    BFAMBITN
REAMBITN     .034        .186
BFAMBITN     .186        .034

      LARGEST EIGENVALUE OF B*B' (STABILITY INDEX) IS    .032

       STANDARD ERRORS FOR TOTAL EFFECTS OF ETA ON   ETA

          REAMBITN    BFAMBITN
REAMBITN     .015        .043
BFAMBITN     .043        .015

       INDIRECT EFFECTS OF ETA ON   ETA

          REAMBITN    BFAMBITN
REAMBITN     .034        .006
BFAMBITN     .006        .034

       STANDARD ERRORS FOR INDIRECT EFFECTS OF ETA ON   ETA

          REAMBITN    BFAMBITN
REAMBITN     .015        .004
BFAMBITN     .004        .015
```

Example 5.6: Performance and satisfaction

Source: Bagozzi (1980).

For a study in an industrial sales force, a structural equation model was designed specifically to answer such questions as: "Is the relationship between performance and job satisfaction myth or reality? Does performance influence satisfaction, or does satisfaction influence performance?"

The variables included in the study are as shown in Figure 5.7 (note that the abbreviations in the observed variables are spelled out for the latent variables).

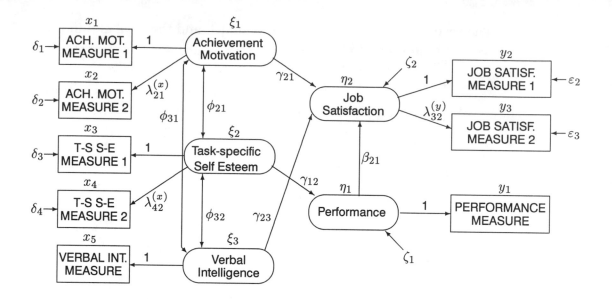

Figure 5.7   Modified Model for Performance and Satisfaction

Table 5.8 gives the means, standard deviations, and product moment correlations of the observed variables based on a sample of N = 122.

The analysis of these data shown here differs slightly from that of the original source:

1. The performance measure y_1 is scaled to measure in hundreds of dollars rather than in dollars. Otherwise no scaling of the variables is used, and the analysis is based on the covariance matrix rather than the correlation matrix. When constraints are imposed on Θ_ϵ or Θ_δ, the normal theory standard errors in LISREL are valid only when the covariance matrix is analyzed.

2. Although no replicate measure is available for ξ_3 (verbal intelligence), this variable must be considered a fallible measure. A reliability of 0.85 is therefore assumed for x_5 on the grounds that a typical value of 0.85 is a better assumption than an arbitrary value of 1.00. The assumed value of the reliability will affect parameter estimates as well as standard errors. To specify a reliability 0.85 for x_5, assign the fixed value 0.15 times the variance of x_5 to the element $\theta_{55}^{(\epsilon)}$. Then the variance is held fixed at $0.15 \times 3.65^2 = 1.998$.

5 MODELS FOR LATENT VARIABLES

Table 5.8 Means, Standard Deviations and Correlations for the Observed Variables in Bagozzi's Model

Variable	y_1	y_2	y_3	x_1	x_2	x_3	x_4	x_5
PERFORMM	1.000							
JBSATIS1	.418	1.000						
JBSATIS2	.394	.627	1.000					
ACHMOT1	.129	.202	.266	1.000				
ACHMOT2	.189	.284	.208	.365	1.000			
T-S S-E1	.544	.281	.324	.201	.161	1.000		
T-S S-E2	.507	.225	.314	.172	.174	.546	1.000	
VERBINTM	−.357	−.156	−.038	−.199	−.277	−.294	−.174	1.000
Mean	720.86	15.54	18.46	14.90	14.35	19.57	24.16	21.36
St. Dev.	2.09	3.43	2.81	1.95	2.06	2.16	2.06	3.65

The correlations between y_1 and y_2 and between y_1 and y_3 are 0.418 and 0.394, respectively, and are both very significant. Once a correlation between η_1 and η_2 has been established, four rival hypotheses may be considered to account for it, namely:

The latent variables η_1 and η_2 are correlated because

   H_1: they have ξ_1, ξ_2, and ξ_3 as common causes (spurious correlation)
   H_{2a}: η_2 influences η_1
   H_{2b}: η_1 influences η_2
   H_3: η_1 and η_2 influence each other reciprocally

H_1 is tested with $\mathbf{B} = 0$, $\mathbf{\Gamma}(2 \times 3) = $ FU,FR and $\mathbf{\Psi}(2 \times 2) = $ SY,FR. This hypothesis is rejected because $\hat{\psi}_{21}$ is significant. To test H_{2a}, set $\psi_{21} = 0$ and free β_{12}. To test H_{2b}, fix ψ_{21} and free β_{21}. In both models the freed $\mathbf{B}$ element is significant, so neither hypothesis can be rejected, nor can one be preferred over the other on statistical grounds.

The H_3 model can only be identified if one of the three ξ-variables in each equation is excluded. A good choice is the effect of ξ_1 on η_1, least significant in H_{2a}, and the effect of ξ_2 on η_2, least significant in H_{2b}. Then, the following structural equations are estimated in the H_3 model.

$$\eta_1 = -0.136(0.151)\eta_2 + 0.931(0.220)\xi_2 - 0.090(0.062)\xi_3 + \zeta_1 \quad R^2 = 0.444$$
$$\eta_2 = 0.748(0.220)\eta_1 + 1.113(0.452)\xi_1 + 0.243(0.109)\xi_3 + \zeta_2 \quad R^2 = 0.447$$

This model has an overall χ^2 of 10.31, the same value as for the previous models, but it has one parameter less. The probability level of this χ^2 is 0.668.

In the first equation the effect of η_2 on η_1 is not significant, indicating the causal relationship between η_1 and η_2 is indeed one way rather than reciprocal. Also, in the first equation, the effect of ξ_3 is not significant. In the second equation all included variables are significant. It we clean up the model by eliminating the direct paths which are insignificant, we obtain a model estimated as follows.

$$\eta_1 = 0.923(0.140)\xi_2 + \zeta_1 \quad R^2 = 0.533$$
$$\eta_2 = 0.594(0.140)\eta_1 + 1.228(0.477)\xi_1 + 0.213(0.107)\xi_3 + \zeta_2$$
$$R^2 = 0.478$$

This model has a χ^2 of 14.19 with 15 degrees of freedom, which still represents a very good fit. The sum of the two R^2's, 1.011, is now higher than for all previous models. The effect of ξ_3 on η_2 is barely significant but this effect is likely to be larger in a larger sample.

A path diagram for the final model is shown in Figure 5.7. The specification for the model is:

$$LY = \begin{pmatrix} 1 & 0 \\ 0 & 1 \\ 0 & * \end{pmatrix} \qquad TE = \begin{pmatrix} 0 \\ * \\ * \end{pmatrix} \text{(diag)}$$

$$LX = \begin{pmatrix} 1 & 0 & 0 \\ * & 0 & 0 \\ 0 & 1 & 0 \\ 0 & * & 0 \\ 0 & 0 & 1 \end{pmatrix} \qquad TD = \begin{pmatrix} * \\ * \\ * \\ * \\ 1.998 \end{pmatrix} \text{(diag)}$$

$$\text{BE} = \begin{pmatrix} 0 & 0 \\ * & 0 \end{pmatrix} \quad \text{GA} = \begin{pmatrix} 0 & * & 0 \\ * & 0 & * \end{pmatrix} \quad \text{PS} = \begin{pmatrix} * \\ * \end{pmatrix} \text{(diag)} ,$$

where $*$ means a free parameter to be estimated and all other values are fixed. As before, the fixed ones in Λ_y and Λ_x set the scales for the η's and the ξ's.

The LISREL command file is:

```
! Modified Model for Performance and Satisfaction
! References
! Bagozzi, R.P. Performance and satisfaction in an industrial sales force:
! An examination of their antecedents and simultaneity.
! Journal of Marketing, 1980, 44, 65-77.
!
! Joreskog, K.G. and Sorbom, D. Recent developments in structural equation
! modeling. Journal of Marketing Research, 1982, 19, 404-416.
Da ni=8 no=122
La
(8A8)
performmjbsatis1jbsatis2 achmot1 achmot2t-s s-e1t-s s-e2verbintm
km file=ex56.dat
sd file=ex56.dat
mo ny=3 nx=5 ne=2 nk=3 be=fu ps=di
le
perform jobsatis
lk
achmot 't-s s-e' 'verb int'
fr ly 3 2 lx 2 1 lx 4 2 be 2 1
fi te 1 td 5 ga 1 1 ga 2 2 ga 1 3
va 1 ly 1 1 ly 2 2 lx 1 1 lx 3 2 lx 5 3;va 1.998 td 5
ou se tv rs ef mi ss ad=off
```

This command file illustrates the following features:

☐ Upper case or lower case characters may be used freely on all lines.

☐ Several title lines are allowed, as long as they do not begin with DA. Here, the exclamation mark (!) is used to avoid that problem. It indicates that the line is a title or comment.

☐ Blank lines are allowed between title lines as well as between command lines.

☐ Labels are enclosed with single quotes if they contain blank spaces.

6 The LISREL submodel 3

The LISREL Submodel 3A is defined by the two equations:

$$\mathbf{y} = \boldsymbol{\Lambda}_y \boldsymbol{\eta} + \boldsymbol{\epsilon} \tag{6.1}$$

$$\boldsymbol{\eta} = \mathbf{B}\boldsymbol{\eta} + \boldsymbol{\Gamma}\boldsymbol{\xi} + \boldsymbol{\zeta} \tag{6.2}$$

There are no x-variables in this submodel; the variables involved are:

Observed variables:	$\mathbf{y}'$	=	$(y_1, y_2, \ldots, y_p)$
Latent variables:	$\boldsymbol{\eta}'$	=	$(\eta_1, y_2, \ldots, \eta_m)$
	$\boldsymbol{\xi}'$	=	$(\xi_1, \xi_2, \ldots, \xi_n)$
Error variables:	$\boldsymbol{\epsilon}'$	=	$(\epsilon_1, \epsilon_2, \ldots, \epsilon_p)$
	$\boldsymbol{\zeta}'$	=	$(\zeta_1, \zeta_2, \ldots, \zeta_m)$

Although it may seem strange that there are ξ-variables but no x-variables, this is formally possible. Solving (6.2) for $\boldsymbol{\eta}$ and substituting into (6.1) gives the single defining equation

$$\mathbf{y} = \boldsymbol{\Lambda}_y (\mathbf{I} - \mathbf{B})^{-1} (\boldsymbol{\Gamma}\boldsymbol{\xi} + \boldsymbol{\zeta}) + \boldsymbol{\epsilon} \,. \tag{6.3}$$

A special case is the so-called "ACOVS" model, in which $\mathbf{B} = \mathbf{0}$ (default):

$$\mathbf{y} = \boldsymbol{\Lambda}_y (\boldsymbol{\Gamma}\boldsymbol{\xi} + \boldsymbol{\zeta}) + \boldsymbol{\epsilon} \,, \tag{6.4}$$

with covariance matrix

$$\boldsymbol{\Sigma} = \boldsymbol{\Lambda}_y (\boldsymbol{\Gamma}\boldsymbol{\Phi}\boldsymbol{\Gamma}' + \boldsymbol{\Psi}) \boldsymbol{\Lambda}_y' + \boldsymbol{\Theta}_\epsilon \,. \tag{6.5}$$

201

Another special case is when there are no ξ-variables. This is called Submodel 3B. In this case, (6.2) and (6.3) reduce to:

$$\eta = \mathbf{B}\eta + \zeta \tag{6.6}$$

$$\mathbf{y} = \boldsymbol{\Lambda}_y(\mathbf{I} - \mathbf{B})^{-1}\zeta + \epsilon \tag{6.7}$$

Equations (6.1) and (6.6) define the Submodel 3B, which has only four parameter matrices — namely, $\boldsymbol{\Lambda}_y, \mathbf{B}, \boldsymbol{\Psi}$, and $\boldsymbol{\Theta}_\epsilon$.

Under Submodel 3B, the covariance matrix of $\mathbf{y}$ is

$$\boldsymbol{\Sigma} = \boldsymbol{\Lambda}_y(\mathbf{I} - \mathbf{B})^{-1}\boldsymbol{\Psi}(\mathbf{I} - \mathbf{B}')^{-1}\boldsymbol{\Lambda}_y' + \boldsymbol{\Theta}_\epsilon . \tag{6.8}$$

Paradoxically, Submodel 3B is more general than the full LISREL model. To see this, write (1.1), (1.2), and (1.3) in the form:

$$\begin{pmatrix} \mathbf{y} \\ \mathbf{x} \end{pmatrix} = \begin{pmatrix} \boldsymbol{\Lambda}_y & \mathbf{0} \\ \mathbf{0} & \boldsymbol{\Lambda}_x \end{pmatrix} \begin{pmatrix} \eta \\ \xi \end{pmatrix} + \begin{pmatrix} \epsilon \\ \delta \end{pmatrix} \tag{6.9}$$

$$\begin{pmatrix} \eta \\ \xi \end{pmatrix} = \begin{pmatrix} \mathbf{B} & \boldsymbol{\Gamma} \\ \mathbf{0} & \mathbf{0} \end{pmatrix} \begin{pmatrix} \eta \\ \xi \end{pmatrix} + \begin{pmatrix} \zeta \\ \xi \end{pmatrix} \tag{6.10}$$

Equations (6.9) and (6.10) are in the form of (6.1) and (6.6), respectively. The lower part of (6.10) is just a tautology which says that $\xi \equiv \xi$.

The conclusion is:

> *Every LISREL model can be written as a LISREL model with only y- and η-variables.*

There are two advantages of using this submodel rather than the full model.

1. It may be preferred because it has fewer parameter matrices, although each one is larger.
2. More important, this model provides for correlations between δ's and ϵ's, which are not possible in the full LISREL model. Examples of models with such correlated error terms appear in Section 6.4.

Important Note: Since Submodel 3A has ξ-variables but no x-variables, the LISREL method of computing TSLS and IV estimates will not work because there are no reference variables for the ξ's. Starting values must be provided by the user. The NS parameter on the OU command tells the program to use these starting values instead of TSLS and IV estimates.

Table 6.1   Various Test Theory Models

Model	Covariance Structure	No. of Parameters
Parallel	$\Sigma = \lambda^2 \mathbf{jj'} + \theta\mathbf{I}$	2
Tau-equivalent	$\Sigma = \lambda^2 \mathbf{jj'} + \Theta$	$p + 1$
Variable-length	$\Sigma = \mathbf{D}_\lambda(\boldsymbol{\lambda\lambda'} + \psi\mathbf{I})\mathbf{D}_\lambda$	$p + 1$
Congeneric	$\Sigma = \boldsymbol{\lambda\lambda'} + \Theta$	$2p$

6.1   A model for tests that differ in length only

This model assumes that there is a length parameter λ_i associated with observed test score y_i in such a way that the true score variance is proportional to λ_i^4 and that the error variance is proportional to λ_i^2. It can be shown that the covariance structure for this model is of the form

$$\boldsymbol{\Sigma} = \mathbf{D}_\lambda(\boldsymbol{\lambda\lambda'} + \psi\mathbf{I})\mathbf{D}_\lambda \, ,$$

where $\mathbf{D}_\lambda = \mathrm{diag}(\lambda_1, \lambda_2, \ldots, \lambda_p)$ and $\boldsymbol{\lambda'} = (\lambda_1, \lambda_2, \ldots, \lambda_p)$. This is of the form (6.5) with $\boldsymbol{\Lambda}_y = \mathbf{D}_\lambda$, $\boldsymbol{\Gamma} = \boldsymbol{\lambda}$, $\boldsymbol{\Phi} = 1$, $\boldsymbol{\Psi} = \psi\mathbf{I}$, and $\boldsymbol{\Theta}_\epsilon = \mathbf{0}$. The model specifies equality constraints between the diagonal elements of $\boldsymbol{\Lambda}_y$ and the elements of the column vector $\boldsymbol{\Gamma}$, and also the equality of all the diagonal elements of $\boldsymbol{\Psi}$. The model has $p + 1$ parameters and is less restrictive than the parallel model but more restrictive than the congeneric model. A summary of various test theory models and their number of parameters is given in Table 6.1. In this table, $\mathbf{j}$ denotes a column vector with all elements equal to one.

Example 6.1: Three subtests of SAT

Source: Kristof (1971).

The covariance matrix shown below, based on candidates (N = 900) who took the January, 1969, administration of the Scholastic Aptitude Test (SAT), represents the following variables:

1. *Verbal Omnibus, containing 40 items administered in 30 minutes.*
2. *Reading Comprehension, containing 50 items administered in 45 minutes.*
3. *An additional section of the SAT administered experimentally.*

$$S = \begin{pmatrix} 54.85 & & \\ 60.21 & 99.24 & \\ 48.42 & 67.00 & 63.81 \end{pmatrix}$$

The following LISREL analysis tests whether the three tests can be considered to differ only in length.

```
Kristof's Model Estimated for Three Subtests of SAT
DA NI=3 NO=900
CM
54.85 60.21 99.24 48.42 67.00 63.81
MO NY=3 NE=3 NK=1 LY=DI,FR PH=ST PS=DI TE=ZE
EQ LY 1 GA 1
EQ LY 2 GA 2
EQ LY 3 GA 3
EQ PS 1 - PS 3
ST 2 ALL
OU SE TV SO NS MI RS
```

There are some important differences between this example and all previous examples:

□ The scales for the three η's are defined by the particular constraints imposed in the model. *They are not defined in the usual way by fixing elements of* Λ_y. The SO option on the OU command tells the program *not* to check that scales have been defined in the usual way.

□ Starting values must be specified and the NS parameter must be set on the OU command (as already stated just before Section 6.1).

The following ML estimates are obtained:

$$\hat{\lambda}_1 = 2.58, \ \hat{\lambda}_2 = 3.03, \ \hat{\lambda}_3 = 2.69, \ \hat{\psi}_1 = 1.60 \ .$$

The χ^2 goodness-of-fit measure is 4.91 with two degrees of freedom. The p-value is 0.086 and the output file shows that no standardized residuals and modification indices are significant. It appears that this model fits the data reasonably well.

6.2 Second-order factor analysis

Equation (6.1) is in the form of a factor analysis model for **y** with first-order factors η and measurement errors ϵ; compare with (3.1). Now suppose that the variables η in turn can be accounted for by a set of factors ξ, so-called second-order factors, so that

$$\eta = \Gamma\xi + \zeta, \tag{6.11}$$

where Γ is a matrix of second-order factor loadings and ζ is a vector of unique variables for η. Combining (6.1) and (6.11) gives (6.4) with covariance matrix (6.5). A path diagram for second-order factor analysis is shown in Figure 6.1.

Example 6.2: Second-order factor analysis.

To illustrate the model, we use data on some cognitive ability tests. The standard deviations and correlations of two forms of each of five tests are given in Table 6.2. The sample size is: $N = 267$.

We shall examine the hypothesis that the two forms of each test are tau-equivalent, except for the two-word fluency tests "Things Round" and "Things Blue" which are only assumed to be congeneric. The five true scores are postulated to depend on two factors, the first, "Speed of Closure," being measured by the first three tests and the second, "Vocabulary," being measured by the last two tests.

The model specification is:

$$
\Lambda_y =
\begin{pmatrix}
1 & 0 & 0 & 0 & 0 \\
1 & 0 & 0 & 0 & 0 \\
0 & 1 & 0 & 0 & 0 \\
0 & 1 & 0 & 0 & 0 \\
0 & 0 & 1 & 0 & 0 \\
0 & 0 & 1 & 0 & 0 \\
0 & 0 & 0 & 1 & 0 \\
0 & 0 & 0 & * & 0 \\
0 & 0 & 0 & 0 & 1 \\
0 & 0 & 0 & 0 & 1
\end{pmatrix},
\Gamma =
\begin{pmatrix}
* & 0 \\
* & 0 \\
* & 0 \\
0 & * \\
0 & *
\end{pmatrix},
\Phi =
\begin{pmatrix}
1 & \\
* & 1
\end{pmatrix},
$$

$$\Psi = \text{diagonal}, \qquad \Theta_\epsilon = \text{diagonal}.$$

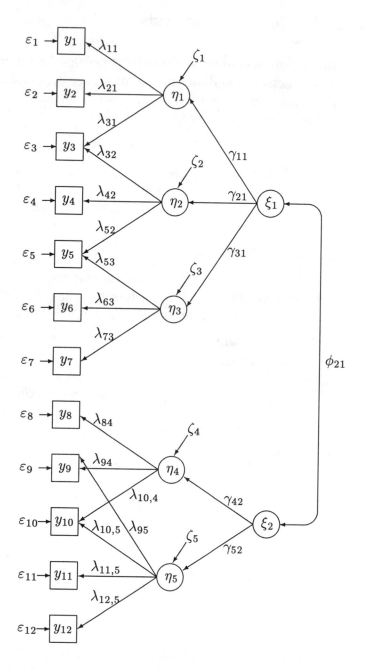

Figure 6.1   Path Diagram for Second-Order Factor Analysis

Table 6.2

Correlations and Standard Deviations for Some Cognitive Tests

Tests	Stand. Dev.	Correlations									
GESCOM - A	2.42	1									
GESCOM - B	2.80	.74	1								
CONWOR - A	3.40	.33	.42	1							
CONWOR - B	3.19	.34	.39	.65	1						
HIDPAT - A	1.94	.26	.21	.15	.18	1					
HIDPAT - B	1.79	.23	.24	.22	.21	.77	1				
THIROUND	5.63	.15	.12	.14	.11	.17	.20	1			
THIBLUE	3.10	.14	.14	.14	.15	.06	.09	.42	1		
VOCABU - A	3.05	−.04	−.03	.09	.16	.06	.09	.19	.21	1	
VOCABU - B	2.25	.02	.02	.10	.23	.04	.07	.09	.21	.72	1

The LISREL command file is:

```
Second Order Factor Analysis
DA NI=10 NO=267
LA FI=EX62.DAT
KM FI=EX62.DAT
SD FI=EX62.DAT
MO NY=10 NE=5 NK=2 GA=FI PH=ST PS=DI
LE
GESCOM CONWOR HIDPAT THINGS VOCABU
LK
SPEEDCLO VOCABUL
VA 1 LY 1 1 LY 2 1 LY 3 2 LY 4 2 LY 5 3 LY 6 3 LY 7 4 LY 9 5 LY 10 5
FR LY 8 4 GA 1 1 GA 2 1 GA 3 1 GA 4 2 GA 5 2
ST 1 ALL
OU SE TV SS NS
```

The goodness-of-fit statistic $\chi^2 = 53.06$ with 33 degrees of freedom, which does not represent a particularly good fit. The lack of fit may be due to either the assumption of tau-equivalence for the four pairs of test forms

Table 6.3   Variance Components for Cognitive Tests

	Error	Specific	Common
GESCOM - A	0.193	0.428	0.379
GESCOM - B	0.338	0.351	0.311
CONWOR - A	0.386	0.279	0.335
CONWOR - B	0.313	0.313	0.374
HIDPAT - A	0.291	0.587	0.122
HIDPAT - B	0.163	0.694	0.144
THIROUND	0.682	0.145	0.172
THIBLUE	0.445	0.254	0.301
VOCABU - A	0.468	0.465	0.067
VOCABU - B	0.044	0.835	0.121

or the hypothesized second-order structure. When the assumption of tau-equivalence is relaxed, χ^2 drops to 41.69 with 29 degrees of freedom. The difference in χ^2, 11.37, with 4 degrees of freedom, has a probability level of 0.025. This suggests that the lack of fit is probably due to both assumptions.

By computing the diagonal elements of $\hat{\Lambda}_y \hat{\Gamma} \hat{\Phi} \hat{\Gamma}' \hat{\Lambda}'_y$, $\hat{\Lambda}_y \hat{\Psi} \hat{\Lambda}'_y$, and $\hat{\Theta}_\epsilon$ and relating these to the total variance in $\hat{\Sigma}$, one gets a variance decomposition of each test form into common, specific and error components, respectively. These variance components are given in Table 6.3.

6.3   Variance and covariance components

Covariance structure analysis may be used to study differences in test performance when the tests have been constructed by assigning items or subtests according to objective features of content or format to subclasses of a factorial or hierarchical classification.

Bock (1960) suggested that the scores of N subjects on a set of tests classified in a 2^q factorial design may be viewed as data from an $N \times 2^q$ experimental design, where the subjects represent a random mode of classification and the tests represent n fixed modes of classification. Bock pointed out that conventional mixed-model analysis of variance gives useful information about the psychometric properties of the tests. In particular, the presence of non-zero variance components for the random mode of classification and for the interaction of the random and fixed modes of classification provides information about the number of dimensions in which the tests are able to discriminate among subjects. The relative size of these components measures the power of the tests to discriminate among subjects along the respective dimensions.

Example 6.3: The rod and frame test

Source: Browne (1970).

The Rod and Frame (RF) test is used as a measure of field dependence. A subject is seated in a darkened room on a chair which may be tilted to the left or to the right. In front of him is a luminous rod located in a luminous square frame. The chair, frame, and rod are tilted to pre-specified positions. By operating push buttons connected to an electric motor, the subject should move the rod to the vertical position. The score on the trial is the angle of the rod from the vertical, so positive and negative values are possible. Each subject undergoes 12 trials. The last two columns of the design matrix $\mathbf{A}$ *below give initial positions of the frame and chair for each trial.*

$$
\mathbf{A} = \begin{pmatrix}
1 & 1 & 1 \\
1 & -1 & -1 \\
1 & 1 & 1 \\
1 & -1 & -1 \\
1 & -1 & 1 \\
1 & 1 & -1 \\
1 & -1 & 1 \\
1 & 1 & -1 \\
1 & 1 & 0 \\
1 & -1 & 0 \\
1 & 1 & 0 \\
1 & -1 & 0
\end{pmatrix}
$$

Table 6.4 **Inter-Trial Covariance Matrix for the Rod and Frame Test**

1	2	3	4	5	6	7	8	9	10	11	12
51.6											
−27.7	72.1										
38.9	−41.1	69.9									
−36.4	40.7	−39.1	75.8								
13.8	−5.2	17.9	1.9	84.8							
−13.6	10.9	9.5	17.8	−37.4	91.1						
21.5	−9.4	8.5	−13.1	59.7	−54.4	79.9					
−12.8	−17.2	−3.1	22.0	−43.3	52.7	−49.9	87.2				
11.0	−8.9	19.2	−11.2	−12.6	21.9	−10.6	17.5	27.6			
−4.5	10.2	−7.6	12.7	20.4	−11.5	16.5	−14.8	−8.8	19.9		
9.2	−.3	18.9	−13.6	−3.9	19.0	−8.3	13.1	17.7	−2.8	27.3	
−3.7	7.5	−4.5	12.8	19.9	−8.8	15.5	−8.6	−5.4	13.3	−1.0	16.0

A value of +1 denotes that the position of the frame or chair was at +28° from the vertical, a value of −1 denotes that the angle was −28° and a value of 0 denotes that the initial position was vertical.

The covariance matrix between trials of the RF test obtained from a sample of 107 eighteen-year-old males is given in Table 6.4.

We want to estimate the variance components associated with general bias, frame effect, chair effect, and error.

Let a, b, and c be uncorrelated random components associated with general bias, frame effect, and chair effect, respectively, and let e denote an error component uncorrelated with a, b, and c and uncorrelated over trials. Let

$$\mathbf{u}'_\nu = (a_\nu, b_\nu, c_\nu)$$

be the values of a, b, and c for subject ν. Then the scores on the twelve trials for subject ν is

$$\mathbf{x}_\nu = \mathbf{A}\mathbf{u}_\nu + \mathbf{e}_\nu$$

with covariance matrix

$$\mathbf{\Sigma} = \mathbf{A}\mathbf{\Phi}\mathbf{A}' + \sigma_e^2\mathbf{I}\,, \tag{6.12}$$

where

$$\mathbf{\Phi} = \text{diag}(\sigma_a^2, \sigma_b^2, \sigma_c^2)\,.$$

Equation (6.12) shows that all the 78 variances and covariances in Σ are *linear* functions of the four parameters σ_a^2, σ_b^2, σ_c^2, and σ_e^2. To see this explicitly, consider the covariance matrix generated by trials 1, 2, 5, and 9:

$$\Sigma = \begin{pmatrix} \sigma_a^2 + \sigma_b^2 + \sigma_c^2 + \sigma_e^2 & & & \\ \sigma_a^2 - \sigma_b^2 - \sigma_c^2 & \sigma_a^2 + \sigma_b^2 + \sigma_c^2 + \sigma_e^2 & & \\ \sigma_a^2 - \sigma_b^2 + \sigma_c^2 & \sigma_a^2 + \sigma_b^2 - \sigma_c^2 & \sigma_a^2 + \sigma_b^2 + \sigma_c^2 + \sigma_e^2 & \\ \sigma_a^2 + \sigma_b^2 & \sigma_a^2 - \sigma_b^2 & \sigma_a^2 - \sigma_b^2 & \sigma_a^2 + \sigma_b^2 + \sigma_e^2 \end{pmatrix}$$

This is an example of *a linear covariance structure*. If this structure holds, the four parameters can be solved in terms of the elements of Σ. For example, $\sigma_a^2 = \frac{1}{2}(\sigma_{41}+\sigma_{42})$, $\sigma_b^2 = \frac{1}{2}(\sigma_{41}+\sigma_{42}-\sigma_{21}-\sigma_{31})$, $\sigma_c^2 = \sigma_{31}-\sigma_{42}$, etc. There are many ways in which the four parameters can be solved in terms of the σ's. If the ten equations are consistent, however, all solutions are identical. In this case the parameters are *overidentified*.

Consider the covariance structure Σ, generated by the first four rows of $\mathbf{A}$:

$$\begin{pmatrix} \sigma_a^2 + \sigma_b^2 + \sigma_c^2 + \sigma_e^2 & & & \\ \sigma_a^2 - \sigma_b^2 - \sigma_c^2 & \sigma_a^2 + \sigma_b^2 + \sigma_c^2 + \sigma_e^2 & & \\ \sigma_a^2 + \sigma_b^2 + \sigma_c^2 & \sigma_a^2 - \sigma_b^2 - \sigma_c^2 & \sigma_a^2 + \sigma_b^2 + \sigma_c^2 + \sigma_e^2 & \\ \sigma_a^2 - \sigma_b^2 - \sigma_c^2 & \sigma_a^2 + \sigma_b^2 + \sigma_c^2 & \sigma_a^2 - \sigma_b^2 - \sigma_c^2 & \sigma_a^2 + \sigma_b^2 + \sigma_c^2 + \sigma_e^2 \end{pmatrix}$$

In this case we can solve for $\sigma_a^2 = \frac{1}{2}(\sigma_{21} + \sigma_{31})$, say, but it is impossible to solve for σ_b^2 and σ_c^2 separately. Only the sum $\sigma_b^2 + \sigma_c^2$ is identified. This is an example of a *non-identified model* in which some parameters are identified and others are not. The reason for this is that the matrix $\mathbf{A}$ has rank 2 and not rank 3 as in the previous case.

Estimation of the variance components according to model (6.12) gives

$$\sigma_a^2 = 3.52 \qquad \sigma_b^2 = 14.23 \qquad \sigma_c^2 = 27.45 \qquad \sigma_e^2 = 22.56 \ .$$

However, examination of the fit of the model to the data reveals that the fit is very poor: $\chi^2 = 464.3$ with 74 degrees of freedom. We shall therefore seek an alternative model that better accounts for the data. This is obtained by structuring the error component $\mathbf{e}$.

There are six distinct experimental conditions among the twelve trials, each one repeated twice. Let τ_i $(i = 1, 2, \ldots, 6)$ be random components associated with these experimental conditions. Then

$$x_{i\alpha} = \tau_i + e_{i\alpha} \, ,$$

where $\alpha = 1, 2$ indexes the two replications. This simply means that one should allow the error variances to be different for different experimental conditions but still equal within replications of the same condition. An analysis according to this model gives $\chi^2 = 311.2$ with 69 degrees of freedom. The reduction in χ^2 clearly indicates that the error variances depend on the experimental condition.

The LISREL command file for this analysis is:

```
The Rod and Frame Test
DA   NI = 12   NO = 107
CM   FI = EX63.COV
MO   NX = 12   NK = 3   LX = FI   PH = DI
MA   LX
1    1    1
1   -1   -1
1    1    1
1   -1   -1
1   -1    1
1    1   -1
1   -1    1
1    1   -1
1    1    0
1   -1    0
1    1    0
1   -1    0
EQ   TD(1)   TD(3)
EQ   TD(2)   TD(4)
EQ   TD(5)   TD(7)
EQ   TD(6)   TD(8)
EQ   TD(9)   TD(11)
EQ   TD(10)  TD(12)
OU   SE   TV
```

The ML estimates of the variance components are now, with standard errors below the estimates:

$$\sigma_a^2 = 4.08 \quad \sigma_b^2 = 11.27 \quad \sigma_c^2 = 26.19$$
$$(0.74) \qquad\quad (1.73) \qquad\quad (4.13)$$

$$\sigma_{e_1}^2 = 22.03 \quad \sigma_{e_2}^2 = 37.63 \quad \sigma_{e_3}^2 = 28.57 \quad \sigma_{e_4}^2 = 40.50 \quad \sigma_{e_5}^2 = 11.63 \quad \sigma_{e_6}^2 = 5.07$$
$$(2.69) \qquad\quad (4.20) \qquad\quad (3.29) \qquad\quad (4.63) \qquad\quad (1.41) \qquad\quad (.66)$$

The results indicate that most of the variance in the trials is associated with the chair effect. The variance due to the frame effect is less than half of this and the variance due to general bias is still smaller. The error variances are generally quite large, except for the two experimental conditions in which the chair is already vertical.

Since the fit of the model is still not satisfactory one could allow the variance components to be correlated. However, an analysis with Φ free reveals that none of the covariances in Φ is significant.

6.4 Two-wave models

LISREL may be useful in analyzing data from longitudinal studies. The characteristic feature of a longitudinal research design is that the same measurements are obtained from the same people at two or more occasions. The purpose of a longitudinal or panel study is to assess the changes that occur between the occasions and to attribute these changes to certain background characteristics and events existing or occurring before the first occasion and/or to various treatments and developments that occur after the first occasion.

Suppose that two variables are used on two occasions, si i.e., in a two-wave longitudinal design. Assume that the two variables measure the same latent variable η on two different occasions, si i.e., y_1 and y_2 measure η_1 on the first occasion and y_3 and y_4 measure η_2 on the second occasion.

The equations defining the measurement relations are:

$$\left. \begin{array}{l} y_1 = \eta_1 + \epsilon_1 \\ y_2 = \lambda_1 \eta_1 + \epsilon_2 \\ y_3 = \eta_2 + \epsilon_3 \\ y_4 = \lambda_2 \eta_2 + \epsilon_4 \end{array} \right\} \tag{6.13}$$

The main interest is in the stability of η over time. This can be studied by means of the structural relationship

$$\eta_2 = \beta \eta_1 + \zeta \, .$$

In particular, one is interested in whether β is close to one and ζ is small.

Let Ω be the covariance matrix of (η_1, η_2) and let Θ be the covariance matrix of $(\epsilon_1, \epsilon_2, \epsilon_3, \epsilon_4)$. If all the ϵ's are uncorrelated, so that Θ is diagonal, the covariance matrix of (y_1, y_2, y_3, y_4) is

$$\Sigma = \begin{pmatrix} \omega_{11} + \theta_{11} & & & \\ \lambda_1 \omega_{11} & \lambda_1^2 \omega_{11} + \theta_{22} & & \\ \omega_{21} & \lambda_1 \omega_{21} & \omega_{22} + \theta_{33} & \\ \lambda \omega_{21} & \lambda_1 \lambda_2 \omega_{21} & \lambda_2 \omega_{22} & \lambda_2^2 \omega_{22} + \theta_{44} \end{pmatrix} .$$

The matrix Σ has 10 variances and covariances which are functions of 9 parameters. It is readily verified that all 9 parameters are identified so the model has one degree of freedom.

Often when the same variables are used repeatedly, there is a tendency for the corresponding errors (the ϵ's) to correlate over time because of memory or other retest effects. Hence there is a need to generalize the above model to allow for correlations between ϵ_1 and ϵ_3 and also between ϵ_2 and ϵ_4. This means that there will be two non-zero covariances θ_{31} and θ_{42} in Θ. The covariance matrix of the observed variables changes to

$$\Sigma = \begin{pmatrix} \omega_{11} + \theta_{11} & & & \\ \lambda_1 \omega_{11} & \lambda_1^2 \omega_{11} + \theta_{22} & & \\ \omega_{21} + \theta_{31} & \lambda_1 \omega_{21} & \omega_{22} + \theta_{33} & \\ \lambda_2 \omega_{21} & \lambda_1 \lambda_2 \omega_{21} + \theta_{42} & \lambda_2 \omega_{22} & \lambda_2^2 \omega_{22} + \theta_{44} \end{pmatrix} .$$

This Σ has its 10 independent elements expressed in terms of 11 parameters. Hence it is clear that the model is not identified. In fact, none of the 11 parameters is identified without further conditions imposed. The loadings λ_1 and λ_2 may be multiplied by a constant and the ω's divided by the same constant. This does not change σ_{21}, σ_{32}, σ_{41} and σ_{43}. The change in the other σ's may be compensated by adjusting the θ's additively. Hence to make the model identified one must fix one λ or one ω at a non-zero value or one θ at some arbitrary value. However, the *correlation* between η_1 and η_2 is identified without any restrictions, since

$$\text{Corr}(\eta_1, \eta_2) = (\omega_{21}^2 / \omega_{11} \omega_{22})^{\frac{1}{2}} = [(\sigma_{32} \sigma_{41})/(\sigma_{21} \sigma_{43})]^{\frac{1}{2}} \, .$$

The model may therefore be used to estimate this correlation coefficient and to test whether this is one. The maximum likelihood estimate of the correlation coefficient is $[(s_{32}s_{41})/(s_{21}s_{43})]^{\frac{1}{2}}$. To make further use of the model it is necessary to make some assumption about the nature of the variables. For example, if it can be assumed that the two variables on each occasion are tau-equivalent, we can set both λ_1 and λ_2 equal to one. Then the model can be estimated and tested with one degree of freedom. If $\lambda_1 = \lambda_2$ the model is just identified.

While the above model is not identified as it stands, it becomes so as soon as there is information about one or more background variables affecting η_1 or η_2 or both.

Example 6.4: Stability of alienation

Source: Wheaton, *et al.* (1977).

Data on attitude scales were collected from 932 persons in two rural regions in Illinois at three points in time: 1966, 1967, and 1971. The variables used for the present example are the Anomia subscale and the Powerlessness subscale, taken to be indicators of Alienation. This example uses data from 1967 and 1971 only. The background variables are the respondent's education (years of schooling completed) and Duncan's Socioeconomic Index (SEI). These are taken to be indicators of the respondent's socioeconomic status (SES). The sample covariance matrix of the six observed variables is given in Table 6.5.

Four models will be considered:

Model A is given in Figure 6.2

Model D is given in Figure 6.3

Model C is equal to D with $\theta_{42}^{(\epsilon)} = 0$.

Model B is equal to C with $\theta_{31}^{(\epsilon)} = 0$.

In these path diagrams we have abandoned our tradition to label the coefficients with two subscripts according to the rules given in Chapter 1, we have simply labeled the coefficients with one index instead.

Table 6.5
Covariance Matrix for Variables in the Stability of Alienation Example

	y_1	y_2	y_3	y_4	x_1	x_2
ANOMIA67	11.834					
POWERL67	6.947	9.364				
ANOMIA71	6.819	5.091	12.532			
POWERL71	4.783	5.028	7.495	9.986		
EDUCATIN	−3.839	−3.889	−3.841	−3.625	9.610	
SOCIOIND*	−2.190	−1.883	−2.175	−1.878	3.552	4.503

* The variable SOCIOIND has been scaled down by a factor 10.

The variables in the models are:

$y_1 = $ Anomia 67
$y_2 = $ Powerlessness 67
$y_3 = $ Anomia 71
$y_4 = $ Powerlessness 71
$x_1 = $ Education
$x_2 = $ SEI
$\xi = $ SES
$\eta_1 = $ Alienation 67
$\eta_2 = $ Alienation 71

In the first model we use only the y's and η's and the model (6.13) with all ϵ's uncorrelated. This is a Submodel 3A with $\mathbf{B} = 0$. The command file is:

```
Stability of Alienation, Model A (uncorrelated error terms)
DAta    NI=4 NO=932
LAbels; ANOMIA67 POWER67 ANOMIA71 POWER71 EDUCATIN SOCIOIND
CMatrix FI=EX64.COV
SElect; 1 2 3 4 /
MOdel   NY=4 NE=2 BE=SD PS=DI TE=SY
LEs;    ALIEN67 ALIEN71
FRee    LY(2,1) LY(4,2)
VAlue 1 LY(1,1) LY(3,2)
OUtput  SE TV MI ND=2
```

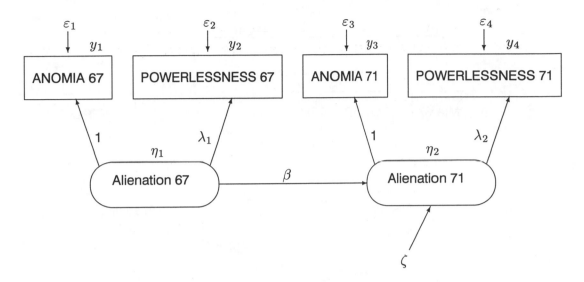

Figure 6.2   Path Diagram for Stability and Alienation: Model A

The file EX64.COV contains a covariance matrix for 6 variables but only four of them are used in Model A. No SE command is necessary, however, because the four variables in the model are the *first four* variables in the file. The specification TE=SY on the MO command does the same thing as if TE is the default. The only difference is that when TE=SY, the entire lower half of Θ_ϵ is stored in the computer. The off-diagonal elements of Θ_ϵ are still fixed zeroes but, with TE=SY, any such element can be declared free. Also, with this specification, one can get modification indices for the off-diagonal elements of Θ_ϵ which is important in this example.

The results are summarized in Table 6.6, column 2. The overall χ^2 is 61.11 with one degree of freedom. The model suffers from two kinds of specification errors: there is bias in β due to omitted variables and the error terms are correlated for the same variables. The modification indices for Θ_ϵ indicate that ϵ_1, ϵ_2 and ϵ_3, ϵ_4 should be correlated between sets but not within sets. However, as the model has only one degree of freedom, only one parameter can be relaxed. The modification indices show that any one of the four correlations can be relaxed yielding a model with perfect fit. This is an example of a case when the modification indices reveal

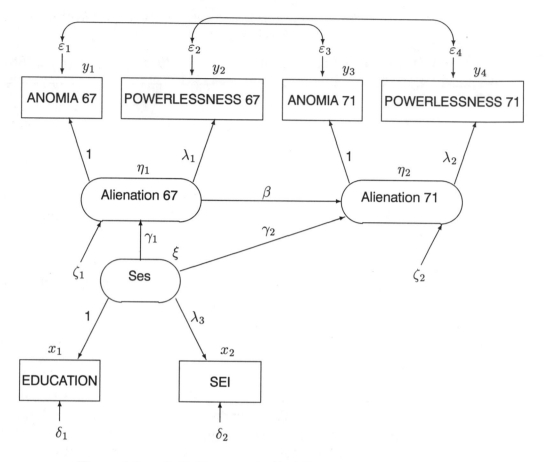

Figure 6.3   Path Diagram for Stability and Alienation: Model D

several equivalent models in the sense defined in Chapter 8.

To deal with the omitted variables bias, one must include the education measures in the model. Consider first Model B.

This model is specified as:

$$\begin{pmatrix} y_1 \\ y_2 \\ y_3 \\ y_4 \end{pmatrix} = \begin{pmatrix} 1 & 0 \\ \lambda_1 & 0 \\ 0 & 1 \\ 0 & \lambda_2 \end{pmatrix} \begin{pmatrix} \eta_1 \\ \eta_2 \end{pmatrix} + \begin{pmatrix} \epsilon_1 \\ \epsilon_2 \\ \epsilon_3 \\ \epsilon_4 \end{pmatrix} \qquad (6.14)$$

Table 6.6   Maximum Likelihood Estimates for the Models A–D
(Standard Errors in Parentheses)

Parameter	Model A	Model B	Model C	Model D
λ_1	.85(.04)	.89(.04)	1.03(.05)	.98(.06)
λ_2	.82(.04)	.85(.04)	.97(.05)	.92(.06)
λ_3		.53(.04)	.52(.04)	.52(.04)
β	.79(.04)	.70(.05)	.62(.05)	.61(.05)
γ_1		−.61(.06)	−.55(.05)	−.58(.06)
γ_2		−.17(.05)	−.21(.05)	−.23(.05)
ϕ		6.67(.64)	6.88(.66)	6.80(.65)
ψ_{11}	8.20(.62)	5.31(.47)	4.71(.43)	4.85(.47)
ψ_{22}	4.09(.43)	3.74(.39)	3.87(.34)	4.09(.40)
$\theta_{11}^{(\epsilon)}$	3.63(.37)	4.02(.34)	5.07(.37)	4.74(.45)
$\theta_{22}^{(\epsilon)}$	3.48(.29)	3.19(.27)	2.21(.32)	2.57(.40)
$\theta_{33}^{(\epsilon)}$	3.34(.40)	3.70(.37)	4.81(.40)	4.40(.52)
$\theta_{44}^{(\epsilon)}$	3.88(.30)	3.62(.29)	2.68(.33)	3.07(.43)
$\theta_{31}^{(\epsilon)}$			1.89(.24)	1.62(.31)
$\theta_{42}^{(\epsilon)}$				.34(.26)
$\theta_{11}^{(\delta)}$		2.94(.50)	2.73(.52)	2.81(.51)
$\theta_{22}^{(\delta)}$		2.61(.18)	2.67(.18)	2.65(.18)
χ^2	61.11	71.47	6.33	4.73
df	1	6	5	4

$$\begin{pmatrix} x_1 \\ x_2 \end{pmatrix} = \begin{pmatrix} 1 \\ \lambda_3 \end{pmatrix} \begin{pmatrix} \delta_1 \\ \delta_2 \end{pmatrix} \tag{6.15}$$

$$\begin{pmatrix} \eta_1 \\ \eta_2 \end{pmatrix} = \begin{pmatrix} 0 & 0 \\ \beta & 0 \end{pmatrix} \begin{pmatrix} \eta_1 \\ \eta_2 \end{pmatrix} + \begin{pmatrix} \gamma_1 \\ \gamma_2 \end{pmatrix} \xi + \begin{pmatrix} \zeta_1 \\ \zeta_2 \end{pmatrix} \tag{6.16}$$

It is assumed that ζ_1 and ζ_2 are uncorrelated. The scales for η_1, η_2 and ξ have been chosen to be the same as for y_1, y_3, and x_1, respectively. In

Model B all four ϵ-terms are uncorrelated, whereas in Model C ϵ_1 and ϵ_3 are correlated, and in Model D ϵ_2 and ϵ_4 are correlated also.

Consider first the identification of Model B. Let $\phi = \text{Var}(\xi)$. We have six observed variables with 21 variances and covariances. Model B has 15 parameters (3 λ's, 1 β, 2 γ's, 1 ϕ, 2 ψ's, and 6 θ's), so that, *if* all these are identified, the model will have 6 degrees of freedom. The structural equations are

$$\begin{aligned} \eta_1 &= \gamma_1\xi + \zeta_1 \\ \eta_2 &= \beta\eta_1 + \gamma_2\xi + \zeta_2 \end{aligned}$$

with reduced form

$$\begin{aligned} \eta_1 &= \gamma_1\xi + \zeta_1 \\ \eta_2 &= (\gamma_2 + \beta\gamma_1)\xi + (\zeta_2 + \beta\zeta_1) = \pi\xi + \nu \ . \end{aligned}$$

Hence:

$$\begin{aligned} \text{Cov}(y_1, x_1) &= \text{Cov}(\eta_1, x_1) = \gamma_1\phi & (6.17) \\ \text{Cov}(y_2, x_1) &= \lambda_1\text{Cov}(\eta_1, x_1) = \lambda_1\gamma_1\phi & (6.18) \\ \text{Cov}(y_3, x_1) &= \text{Cov}(\eta_2, x_1) = \pi\phi & (6.19) \\ \text{Cov}(y_4, x_1) &= \lambda_2\text{Cov}(\eta_2, x_1) = \lambda_2\pi\phi & (6.20) \end{aligned}$$

If we use x_2 instead of x_1 in these equations, all four right sides will be multiplied by λ_3. Thus, λ_3 is overdetermined, since

$$\lambda_3 = \text{Cov}(y_i, x_2)/\text{Cov}(y_i, x_1) \qquad i = 1, 2, 3, 4 \ .$$

With λ_3 determined, ϕ is determined by

$$\text{Cov}(x_1, x_2) = \lambda_3\phi \ .$$

With ϕ determined, equations (6.17)–(6.20) determine γ_1, λ_1, π and λ_2, respectively. Furthermore,

$$\text{Cov}(y_1, y_2) = \lambda_1\text{Var}(\eta_1) = \lambda_1(\gamma_1^2\phi + \psi_{11}) \ ,$$

which determines ψ_{11}, and

$$\text{Cov}(y_3, y_4) = \lambda_2\text{Var}(\eta_2) = \lambda_2[\pi^2\phi + \text{Var}(\nu)] \ ,$$

which determines

$$\mathsf{Var}(\nu) = \psi_{22} + \beta^2 \psi_{11} \ .$$

For given λ_1, λ_2, γ_1, π, ϕ, and ψ_{11} the four equations

$$
\begin{align}
\mathsf{Cov}(y_1, y_3) &= \gamma_1 \pi \phi + \beta \psi_{11} & (6.21) \\
\mathsf{Cov}(y_1, y_4) &= \lambda_2(\gamma_1 \pi \phi + \beta \psi_{11}) & (6.22) \\
\mathsf{Cov}(y_2, y_3) &= \lambda_1(\gamma_1 \pi \phi + \beta \psi_{11}) & (6.23) \\
\mathsf{Cov}(y_2, y_4) &= \lambda_1 \lambda_2(\gamma_1 \pi \phi + \beta \psi_{11}) & (6.24)
\end{align}
$$

show that β is overdetermined. Then, with β determined, $\gamma_2 = \pi - \beta\gamma_1$ and ψ_{22} are obtained. The error variances $\theta_{ii}^{(\epsilon)}$ are determined from $\mathsf{Var}(y_i)$, $i = 1, 2, 3, 4$ and $\theta_{ii}^{(\delta)}$ from $\mathsf{Var}(x_i)$, $i = 1, 2$. Hence it is clear that Model B is identified and has six independent restrictions on Σ.

In Model D there are two more parameters, namely $\theta_{31}^{(\epsilon)}$ and $\theta_{42}^{(\epsilon)}$. These are added to the right sides of (6.21) and (6.24). However, since (6.22) or (6.23) can be used to determine β, it is clear that $\theta_{31}^{(\epsilon)}$ is determined by (6.21) and $\theta_{42}^{(\epsilon)}$ is determined by (6.24). Hence Model D is also identified and has four degrees of freedom.

The command file for Model B is:

```
Stability of Alienation, Model B (Uncorrelated Errors)
DA NI=6 NO=932
LA
ANOMIA67 POWERL67 ANOMIA71 POWERL71 EDUCATIN SOCIOIND
CM FI=EX64.COV
MO NY=4 NX=2 NE=2 NK=1 BE=SD PS=DI TE=SY
LE
ALIEN67 ALIEN71
LK
SES
FR LY(2,1) LY(4,2) LX(2,1)
VA 1 LY(1,1) LY(3,2) LX(1,1)
OU SE TV MI ND=2
```

The model includes all eight parameter matrices but only two need to be declared on the MO command: $\mathbf{B}$ is subdiagonal and $\boldsymbol{\Psi}$ is diagonal. As before, in order to see the modification indices for the off-diagonal elements of Θ_ϵ we also include the specification TE=SY. The free parameters λ_1, λ_2 and λ_3 in Λ_y and Λ_x must be declared free by a FR command. One element in each column of Λ_y and Λ_x is assigned the value one to fix the scales for η_1, η_2, and ξ. Note that neither ξ nor η_1 or η_2 are standardized in this example.

The value of χ^2 for this model is 71.47 with six degrees of freedom. This is not considered an acceptable fit. As in Model A, the modification indices for $\theta_{31}^{(\epsilon)}$ and $\theta_{42}^{(\epsilon)}$ are large: 63.71 and 37.26, respectively.

As in many other longitudinal studies, where the same measures are repeated over time, there is a tendency for the measurement errors in these measures to correlate over time due to memory or other retest effects. This suggests that the most likely improvement of the model is obtained by freeing the elements $\theta_{31}^{(\epsilon)}$ and $\theta_{42}^{(\epsilon)}$ of Θ_ϵ. The largest modification index is 63.71 for element $\theta_{31}^{(\epsilon)}$ of Θ_ϵ, predicting a drop in χ^2 of about 63.71 if $\theta_{31}^{(\epsilon)}$ is relaxed. This can be verified by running the model again adding TE(3,1) on the FR command. This is Model C. The χ^2 for this modified model is 6.33 with five degrees of freedom. The drop in χ^2 from Model B to Model C is 65.14 with one degree of freedom, which is about what the modification index predicted. Model C fits quite well. For Model C, the largest modification index, 1.59, now occurs for the element $\theta_{42}^{(\epsilon)}$ but this is not significant. By running Model D as well, one can verify that the estimate of $\theta_{42}^{(\epsilon)}$ is not significant. Thus, in this example, it seems that there is strong autocorrelation in the measurement error of ANOMIA only. The memory or retest effect in POWERLESSNESS seems to be much weaker. The results for Models B, C, and D are given in Table 6.6.

For this example (Model C), it may be instructive to examine the sections of the output called COVARIANCES and TOTAL AND INDIRECT EFFECTS.

The total effect of SES on Alienation 71 is almost equal to the direct effect of SES on Alienation 67, although the direct effect of SES on Alienation 71 is much smaller. The effects of SES on Alienation are negative, indicating that Alienation decreases when SES increases. Also shown in the section of TOTAL EFFECTS are the total effects of SES on the observed y-measures and also the total effects of η_1 and η_2 on these observed measures. Although, according to the model, SES does not have a direct effect on any observed

y, there are negative indirect effects via η_1 and η_2. Similarly, although η_1 does not have a direct effect on y_3 and y_4, η_1 affects y_3 and y_4 indirectly via η_2.

Example 6.5: Change in verbal and quantitative ability between grades 7 and 9

Source: Anderson & Maier (1963); Hilton (1969).

Educational Testing Service tested a nationwide sample of fifth graders in 1961, and then again in 1963, 1965, and 1967 as seventh, ninth, and eleventh graders, respectively. The test scores include the verbal (SCATV) and quantitative (SCATQ) parts of the Scholastic Aptitude Test (SCAT), and achievement tests in mathematics (MATH), science (SCI), social studies (SS), reading (READ), listening (LIST), and writing (WRIT). The examinees were divided into four groups according to sex and whether or not they participated in an academic curriculum in Grade 12. The four groups and their sample sizes are as follows:

Boys academic (BA):	$N = 373$
Boys nonacademic (BNA):	$N = 249$
Girls academic (GA):	$N = 383$
Girls nonacademic (GNA)	$N = 387$

Scores on each test have been scaled so that the unit of measurement is approximately the same at all occasions.

In this example we use the six tests MATH, SCI, SS, READ, SCATV, and SCATQ in Grades 7 and 9 only, and only for the group GA. Earlier studies (Jöreskog, 1970b) suggest that these tests measure two oblique factors that may reasonably be interpreted as a verbal (V) and a quantitative (Q) factor. We set up the model in Figure 6.4, which represents a model for the measurement of change in verbal and quantitative ability between Grades 7 and 9. Since there are no background variables in this model, we may for estimation purposes treat the pretests as the independent variables. Hence we use the notation x for these. Note that the model includes the following features:

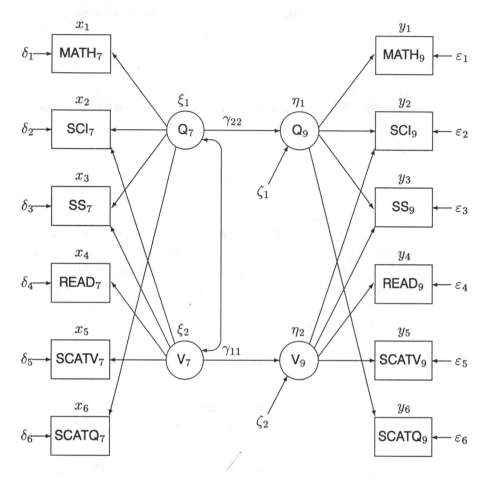

Figure 6.4   Verbal and Quantitative Ability in Grades 7–9

1. On each occasion the factor pattern is postulated to be restricted in the following way: MATH and SCATQ are pure measures of Q. READ and SCATV are pure measures of V. SCI and SS are composite measures of V and Q. This implies that there are four zero loadings in both Λ_x and Λ_y. To fix the scales for V and Q, we assume that they are measured in the same units as SCATV and SCATQ, respectively. This means that there is a fixed 1 in each column of Λ_x and Λ_y and SCATV and SCATQ are reference variables.

2. It is postulated that Q_7 affects Q_9 only and not V_9, and similarly for

V_7. This means that there are two zero coefficients in Γ. Furthermore, we postulate that the residuals ζ_1 and ζ_2 are uncorrelated, which means that, whatever remains in Q_9 and V_9 after Q_7 and V_7 are accounted for is uncorrelated with everything else.

3. The errors or unique factors in δ and ϵ are assumed to be uncorrelated both within and between occasions.

The command file for this model is:

```
Verbal and Quantitative Ability In Grades 7 and 9.
Model: GA = DI and PS = DI
DA   NI=12 NO=383
LA; MATH7 SCI7 SS7 READ7 SCATV7 SCATQ7 MATH9 SCI9 SS9 READ9 SCATV9 SCATQ9
KM   FI=EX65.DAT;            SD FI=EX65.DAT
SE;  7 8 9 10 11 12 1 2 3 4 5 6
MO   NX=6 NY=6 NK=2 NE=2 PS=DI
LE; Q9 V9;                LK; Q7 V7
FI   GA 1 2 GA 2 1
FR   LY 1 1 LY 2 1 LY 2 2 LY 3 1 LY 3 2 LY 4 2
FR   LX 1 1 LX 2 1 LX 2 2 LX 3 1 LX 3 2 LX 4 2
VA   1 LX 5 2 LX 6 1;      VA 1 LY 5 2 LY 6 1
OU   ND=2 SE TV MI RS
```

The maximum likelihood estimates are given in Table 6.7. The rather low loadings of SCI and SS on Q at both occasions may seem a little surprising. However, an inspection of the items in tests SCI and SS reveals that these are mostly verbal problems concerned with logical reasoning, in contrast to the items in SCATQ, which are mostly numerical items measuring the ability to work with numbers. The small residual variance 1.85 of ζ_2 means that V_9 can be predicted almost perfectly from V_7. This is not quite so for Q_7 since here we have a residual variance of 18.50. However, this may be due to the more rapid increase in variance of Q from Grade 7 to 9, which is manifested in the increase in variances, which is $143.55 - 103.87 = 39.68$ for Q and $117.15 - 115.40 = 1.75$ for V.

There is a reason not to look at each number in Table 6.7 too seriously, and this is the poor overall fit of the model as evidenced by the χ^2-value of 217.68 with 47 *df*. We shall therefore investigate the reason for this poor fit and demonstrate that LISREL may be used not only to assess or measure the goodness-of-fit of a model, but also to detect the parts of the

Table 6.7   Maximum Likelihood Estimates for the Model in Figure 6.4

$$\hat{\Lambda}_x = \begin{pmatrix} .97 & 0 \\ .20 & .52 \\ .25 & .84 \\ 0 & 1.21 \\ 0 & 1 \\ 1 & 0 \end{pmatrix} \qquad \hat{\Theta}_\delta = \begin{pmatrix} 32.25 \\ 30.14 \\ 43.63 \\ 46.19 \\ 19.69 \\ 50.40 \end{pmatrix}$$

$$\hat{\Lambda}_y = \begin{pmatrix} .89 & 0 \\ .24 & .64 \\ .36 & .69 \\ 0 & .95 \\ 0 & 1 \\ 1 & 0 \end{pmatrix} \qquad \hat{\Theta}_\epsilon = \begin{pmatrix} 23.07 \\ 43.20 \\ 52.46 \\ 42.15 \\ 19.95 \\ 67.71 \end{pmatrix}$$

$$\hat{\Gamma} = \begin{pmatrix} 1.10 & 0 \\ 0 & 1.00 \end{pmatrix} \qquad \hat{\Phi} = \begin{pmatrix} 103.87 & 92.58 \\ 92.58 & 115.40 \end{pmatrix}$$

$$\hat{\Psi} = \begin{pmatrix} 18.50 & 0 \\ 0 & 1.85 \end{pmatrix} \qquad \hat{\Omega} = \begin{pmatrix} 143.55 & 101.54 \\ 101.54 & 117.15 \end{pmatrix}$$

$\chi^2 = 217.68$ with $df = 47$

model where the fit is poor. Taking the more fundamental assumptions of linearity and multinormality for granted, lack of fit of the model in Figure 6.4 may be due to the fact that one or more of the postulates 1, 2, or 3 is not reasonable. We shall therefore investigate each of these separately.

To investigate postulate 1, we set up a factor analysis model of the pre- and post-tests separately, assuming the postulated two-factor structure. This gives $\chi^2 = 17.64$ for the pretests and $\chi^2 = 2.62$ for the post-tests, both with 10 degrees of freedom. Although the fit is not quite acceptable in Grade 7, we take the postulated factor structure to hold for both the pre- and post-tests. So we must continue to look for lack of fit due to postulate 2 or 3.

Table 6.8   Test of Postulate 2 for the Model in Figure 6.4

	Ψ diagonal	Ψ free	
Γ diagonal	$\chi^2_{47} = 217.7$	$\chi^2_{46} = 196.2$	$\chi^2_1 = 21.5$
Γ free	$\chi^2_{45} = 216.7$	$\chi^2_{44} = 193.6$	$\chi^2_1 = 23.1$
	$\chi^2_2 = 1.0$	$\chi^2_2 = 2.6$	

The subscripts on χ^2 denote degrees of freedom

Postulate 2 is concerned with the interrelationships between the four factors Q_7, V_7, Q_9, and V_9. The most general assumption is that these four factors are freely intercorrelated, and this is equivalent to a LISREL model with all four coefficients in Γ free and with Ψ free as a full symmetric matrix. Hence, it is clear that the assumption made in (2) is the intersection of the two hypotheses "Γ is diagonal" and "Ψ is diagonal." It is therefore useful to test each of the four possible hypotheses. The results of these analyses may be presented in a 2×2 table as in Table 6.8. The row marginals of the table represent χ^2-values with one degree of freedom for testing the hypothesis that Ψ is diagonal. It is seen that this hypothesis should be rejected. The column marginals represent χ^2-values with df = 2 for testing the hypothesis that Γ is diagonal. This hypothesis seems quite reasonable. From these analyses it is clear that "Γ diagonal and Ψ free" is the most reasonable assumption to retain. The overall fit of this model is $\chi^2 = 196.2$ with 46 df. Since this is still too large, we must continue to investigate postulate 3.

The assumption in postulate 3 is that the unique factors in δ and ϵ are uncorrelated both within and between sets. That they are uncorrelated within sets should not be questioned, since we have already found that the postulated factor-analysis model holds for both pre- and post-test. That they are uncorrelated between sets, however, is more questionable because of specific factors in each test. This means that the unique factors for corresponding tests should be allowed to correlate. To account for such correlations, Jöreskog (1970b) introduced so-called *test-specific factors*; that is, factors that do not contribute to correlations between tests within occasions but between the *same* tests at different occasions. In this case, when there are only two occasions, it is not possible to define (identify) test-specific factors; we can merely introduce correlations between unique factors for corresponding pre- and post-tests.

All these analyses are in fact unnecessary as the output file from the initial model (Figure 6.4) suggests immediately that the largest source of misspecification in the model is likely to be the autocorrelation, si i.e., the correlation between error terms for the same variables over time. This can be seen in the section of the output called STANDARDIZED RESIDUALS.

The model in Figure 6.4 is therefore modified as in Figure 6.5. This revised model can also be estimated with LISREL. In order to accommodate the correlated error terms we must write the model as a Submodel 3B with parameter matrices Λ_y, $\mathbf{B}$, $\mathbf{\Psi}$, and $\mathbf{\Theta}_\epsilon$.

The command file is:

```
Verbal and Quantitative Ability In Grades 7 and 9.
Model: BE Diagonal and Autocorrelated Errors
DA NI=12 NO=383
LA
MATH7 SCI7 SS7 READ7 SCATV7 SCATQ7 MATH9 SCI9 SS9 READ9 SCATV9 SCATQ9
KM FI=EX65.DAT
SD FI=EX65.DAT
MO NY=12 NE=4 BE=FU TE=SY
LE
Q7 V7 Q9 V9
FR LY 1 1 LY 2 1 LY 2 2 LY 3 1 LY 3 2 LY 4 2
FR LY 7 3 LY 8 3 LY 8 4 LY 9 3 LY 9 4 LY 10 4
VA 1 LY 5 2 LY 6 1
VA 1 LY 11 4 LY 12 3
FR BE 3 1 BE 4 2
FI PS 3 1 PS 3 2 PS 4 1 PS 4 2
FR TE 7 1 TE 8 2 TE 9 3 TE 10 4 TE 11 5 TE 12 6
OU SE TV RS
```

The analysis of the revised model gives results shown in Tables 6.9 and 6.10. All estimated parameters are significantly different from zero.

The test of overall goodness of fit gives $\chi^2 = 65.61$ with 40 df. This represents a reasonably good fit of the model to the data. An approximate test of the hypothesis that the unique factors are uncorrelated between

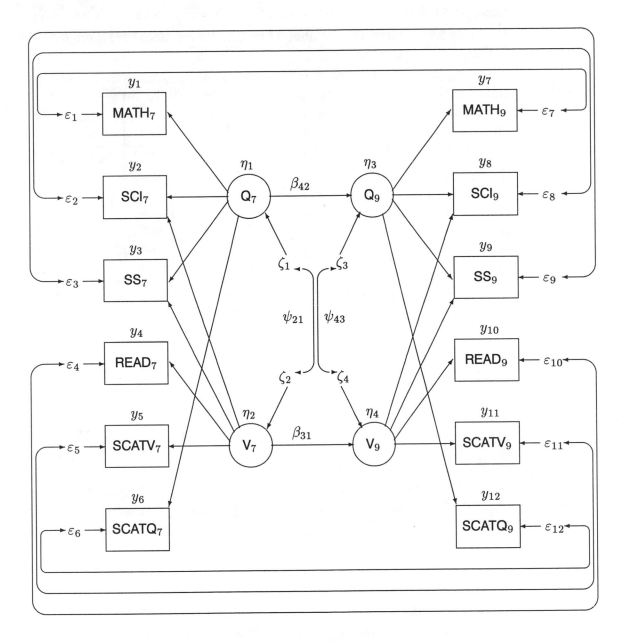

Figure 6.5
Verbal and Quantitative Ability. Model with Autocorrelated Errors.

Table 6.9 Maximum Likelihood Estimate for the Model in Figure 6.5

$$\hat{\Lambda}_y = \begin{pmatrix} 1.01 & 0 & 0 & 0 \\ .13 & .60 & 0 & 0 \\ .12 & .98 & 0 & 0 \\ 0 & 1.24 & 0 & 0 \\ 0 & 1 & 0 & 0 \\ 1 & 0 & 0 & 0 \\ 0 & 0 & .93 & 0 \\ 0 & 0 & .13 & .77 \\ 0 & 0 & .25 & .82 \\ 0 & 0 & 0 & .98 \\ 0 & 0 & 0 & 1 \\ 0 & 0 & 1 & 0 \end{pmatrix} \qquad \hat{\Theta}_\epsilon = \begin{pmatrix} 27.75 \\ 29.59 \\ 40.28 \\ 44.21 \\ 24.37 \\ 54.24 \\ 17.66 \\ 41.14 \\ 50.90 \\ 40.34 \\ 24.84 \\ 74.52 \end{pmatrix}$$

$$\hat{B} = \begin{pmatrix} 0 & 0 & 0 & 0 \\ 0 & 0 & 0 & 0 \\ 1.06 & 0 & 0 & 0 \\ 0 & 0.98 & 0 & 0 \end{pmatrix} \qquad \hat{\Psi} = \begin{pmatrix} 100.57 & & & \\ 90.53 & 110.45 & & \\ 0 & 0 & 22.63 & \\ 0 & 0 & 8.42 & 6.94 \end{pmatrix}$$

$\chi^2 = 65.61$ with $df = 40$

occasions is obtained as $\chi^2 = 196.2 - 65.6 = 130.6$ with 6 df, thus this hypothesis is quite unreasonable. The variances, covariances, and correlations of the unique factors are given in Table 6.10. A comparison of the covariances with their standard errors reveals that all covariances, except possibly the one between ϵ_1 and ϵ_7, are significantly non-zero.

6.5 Simplex models

A simplex model is a type of covariance structure which often occurs in longitudinal studies when the same variable is measured repeatedly on the same people over several occasions. The simplex model is equivalent to the covariance structure generated by a first-order non-stationary autoregressive process. Guttman (1954) used the term simplex also for vari-

Table 6.10   Variances, Covariances, and Correlations for the Unique Factors in Table 6.9

i	$\text{Var}(\epsilon_i)$	$\text{Var}(\epsilon_{i+6})$	$\text{Cov}(\epsilon_i\epsilon_{i+6})$	$\text{Corr}(\epsilon_i\epsilon_{i+6})$
1	27.75(3.78)	17.66(3.88)	-3.47(2.78)	$-.157$
2	29.59(2.37)	41.14(3.38)	9.60(2.10)	.275
3	40.28(3.60)	50.90(4.21)	6.16(2.82)	.136
4	44.21(4.25)	40.34(3.59)	7.52(2.89)	.178
5	24.37(2.47)	24.84(2.60)	12.04(2.05)	.489
6	54.24(4.87)	74.52(6.73)	22.83(4.40)	.359

ables which are not ordered through time but by other criteria. One of his examples concerns tests of verbal ability ordered according to increasing complexity. The typical feature of a simplex correlation structure is that the entries in the correlation matrix decrease as one moves away from the main diagonal.

Jöreskog (1970a) formulated various simplex models in terms of the well-known Wiener and Markov stochastic processes. A distinction was made between a perfect simplex and a quasi-simplex. A *perfect simplex* is reasonable only if the measurement errors in the variables are negligible. A *quasi-simplex*, on the other hand, allows for sizable errors of measurement.

Consider p fallible variables $y_1, y_2, \ldots, y_p$. The unit of measurement in the true variables η_i may be chosen to be the same as in the observed variables y_i. The equations defining the model are then

$$y_i = \eta_i + \epsilon_i, \qquad \eta_i = \beta_i\eta_{i-1} + \zeta_i, \qquad i = 2, 3, \ldots, p,$$

where the ϵ_i are uncorrelated among themselves and uncorrelated with all the η_i and where ζ_i is uncorrelated with η_{i-1} (where $i = 2, 3, \ldots, p$). A path diagram of the simplex model with $p = 4$ is given in Figure 6.6. The parameters of the model are $\omega_1 = \text{Var}(\eta_1)$, $\psi_i = \text{Var}(\zeta_i)$ $(i = 2, 3, \ldots, p)$, $\theta_i = \text{Var}(\epsilon_i)$ $(i = 1, 2, \ldots, p)$ and $\beta_2, \beta_3, \ldots, \beta_p$. Let $\omega_i = \text{Var}(\eta_i) = \beta_i^2\omega_{i-1} + \psi_i$ $(i = 2, 3, \ldots, p)$. Then there is a one-to-one correspondence between the parameters $\beta_2, \beta_3, \ldots, \beta_p, \omega_1, \psi_2, \psi_3, \ldots, \psi_p$ and the parameters

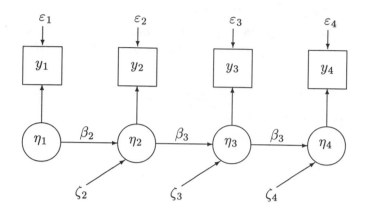

Figure 6.6   A Simplex Model

$\beta_2, \beta_3, \ldots, \beta_p, \omega_1, \omega_2, \ldots, \omega_p$. The ω's are not parameters in the LISREL model, so in LISREL the first set of parameters must be used. However, for identification purposes it is more convenient to use the second set of parameters. In terms of the ω's, for $p = 4$ measurement occasions, the covariance matrix of $y_1, y_2, \ldots, y_p$ has the form

$$\Sigma = \begin{pmatrix} \omega_1 + \theta_1 & & & \\ \beta_2\omega_1 & \omega_2 + \theta_2 & & \\ \beta_2\beta_3\omega_1 & \beta_3\omega_2 & \omega_3 + \theta_3 & \\ \beta_2\beta_3\beta_4\omega_1 & \beta_3\beta_4\omega_2 & \beta_4\omega_3 & \omega_4 + \theta_4 \end{pmatrix} . \tag{6.25}$$

It is seen from (6.25) that, although the product $\beta_2\omega_1 = \sigma_{21}$ is identified, β_2 and ω_1 are not separately identified. The product $\beta_2\omega_1$ is involved in the off-diagonal elements in the first column (and row) only. One can multiply β_2 by a non-zero constant and divide ω_1 by the same constant without changing the product. The change induced by ω_1 in σ_{11} can be absorbed in θ_1 in such a way that σ_{11} remains unchanged. Hence $\theta_1 = \text{Var}(\epsilon_1)$ is not identified. For η_2 and η_3 we have

$$\omega_2 = \frac{\sigma_{32}\sigma_{21}}{\sigma_{31}}, \qquad \omega_3 = \frac{\sigma_{43}\sigma_{32}}{\sigma_{42}},$$

so that ω_2 and ω_3, and hence also θ_2 and θ_3, are identified. With ω_2 and ω_3 identified, β_3 and β_4 are identified by σ_{32} and σ_{43}. The middle coefficient

β_3 is overidentified since

$$\beta_3 \omega_2 = \frac{\sigma_{31}\sigma_{42}}{\sigma_{41}} = \sigma_{32} \ .$$

Since both ω_4 and θ_4 are involved in σ_{44} only, these are not identified. Only their sum, σ_{44}, is identified.

This analysis of the identification problem shows that for the "inner" variables y_2 and y_3, the parameters ω_2, ω_3, θ_2, θ_3, and β_3 are identified, whereas there is an indeterminacy associated with each of the "outer" variables y_1 and y_4. To eliminate these indeterminacies one condition must be imposed on the parameters ω_1, θ_1, and β_2, and another on the parameters ω_4 and θ_4. In terms of the original LISREL parameters, β_2, $\psi_1 = \omega_1$, ψ_2, ψ_4, θ_1, and θ_4 are not identified whereas β_3, β_4, ψ_3, θ_2, and θ_3 are identified. One indeterminacy is associated with β_2, ψ_1, ψ_2 and θ_1 and another indeterminacy is associated with ψ_4 and θ_4. The parameters β_2, ψ_1, ψ_2, and θ_1 are only determined by the three equations

$$\sigma_{11} = \psi_1 + \theta_1 \ , \qquad \sigma_{21} = \beta_2 \psi_1 \ , \qquad \omega_2 = \beta_2^2 \psi_1 + \psi_2 \ ,$$

where ω_2 is identified. The parameters ψ_4 and θ_4 are only determined by the single equation

$$\sigma_{44} = \beta_4^2 \omega_3 + \psi_4 + \theta_4 \ ,$$

where ω_3 is identified. The most natural way of eliminating the indeterminacies is to set $\theta_1 = \theta_2$ and $\theta_4 = \theta_3$, which makes sense if the y-variables are on the same scale. It is not necessary to assume that all error variances are equal, only that the error variances for the first and last variable are each equal to one other error variance. The assumption of equal error variances across all variables is in fact testable with $p - 3$ degrees of freedom.

In the general simplex model with p variables, there are $3p - 3$ independent parameters and the degrees of freedom are $\frac{1}{2}p(p + 1) - 3p + 3$. If $p = 3$, this is zero and the model is a tautology. For testing a simplex model, p must be at least 4.

The *quasi-simplex* model is a LISREL submodel 3B with $\Lambda_y = \mathbf{I}$, Θ_ϵ diagonal, Ψ diagonal, and

$$\mathbf{B} = \begin{pmatrix} 0 & 0 & 0 & 0 \\ \beta_2 & 0 & 0 & 0 \\ 0 & \beta_3 & 0 & 0 \\ 0 & 0 & \beta_4 & 0 \end{pmatrix}.$$

This specification automatically defines ζ_1 as η_1 so that $\psi_1 = \omega_1$.

The *perfect simplex* is obtained by setting $\Theta_\epsilon = \mathbf{0}$ (TE=ZE). This can be tested when $p \geq 3$. The perfect simplex implies that the *partial correlation* $\rho_{ik \cdot j}$ is zero whenever $i < j < k$. Higher-order partial correlations, with two or more intermediate variables held constant, also vanish.

Example 6.6: A simplex model for academic performance

Source: Humphreys (1968).

The data, a correlation[1] matrix, is shown in Table 6.11. The variables include eight semesters of grade-point averages, $y_1, y_2, \ldots, y_8$, high school rank y_0 and a composite score on the American College Testing test y_0' for approximately 1600 undergraduate students at the University of Illinois.

We shall first use the variables $y_1, y_2, \ldots, y_8$ and illustrate what happens when one runs a model which is not identified. We have made three runs with the same data and model. In Run 1 we specified the model *as if* all the parameters were identified. The command file for this run is as follows:

```
Simplex Model for Academic Performance - Run 1
DA NI=10 NO=1600
LA
(10A3)
 YOYO' Y1 Y2 Y3 Y4 Y5 Y6 Y7 Y8
KM FI=EX66.COR
SE
3 4 5 6 7 8 9 10/
MO NY=8 NE=8 LY=ID BE=FU PS=DI
FR BE(2,1) BE(3,2) BE(4,3) BE(5,4) BE(6,5) BE(7,6) BE(8,7)
OU SS SE AD=OFF
```

---

[1]For standard errors and chi-squares to be correct, the covariance matrix should be analyzed.

Table 6.11   Correlations between Grade Point Averages, High School Rank, and an Aptitude Test

	y_0	y_0'	y_1	y_2	y_3	y_4	y_5	y_6	y_7	y_8
y_0	1.000									
y_0'	.393	1.000								
y_1	.387	.375	1.000							
y_2	.341	.298	.556	1.000						
y_3	.278	.237	.456	.490	1.000					
y_4	.270	.255	.439	.445	.562	1.000				
y_5	.240	.238	.415	.418	.496	.512	1.000			
y_6	.256	.252	.399	.383	.456	.469	.551	1.000		
y_7	.240	.219	.387	.364	.445	.442	.500	.544	1.000	
y_8	.222	.173	.342	.339	.354	.416	.453	.482	.541	1.000

In Run 2 we imposed the condition that $\theta_1 = \theta_2$ to eliminate the first indeterminacy and in Run 3 we imposed the condition $\theta_8 = \theta_7$, in addition, to eliminate the second indeterminacy also. The results are shown in Table 6.12. Run 1 gave the message that the parameter TE(1) may not be identified. TE(1) is θ_1, the last of the four parameters involved in the first indeterminacy. In Run 2 the corresponding message was that the parameter TE(8) may not be identified. TE(8) is θ_8, the last parameter involved in the second indeterminacy. In Run 3 no such message was given indicating that the model is identified. All three solutions in Table 6.12 have the same $\chi^2 = 23.91$ and it is seen that all parameters that are identified come out with the same parameter estimate in all three runs. Only the non-identified parameters vary over the three solutions. The values given for the non-identified parameters are of course arbitrary to some extent. However, these values are such that the following three quantities are invariant over all solutions:

$$\hat{\psi}_1 + \hat{\theta}_1 \qquad \hat{\beta}_2 \hat{\psi}_1 \qquad \hat{\psi}_8 + \hat{\theta}_8$$

These computer runs illustrate that LISREL behaves reasonably for models which are non-identified and that the program correctly identifies the last parameter involved in an indeterminacy as a non-identified parameter.

Table 6.12   Results for Simplex Model

Parameter number	Parameter	Parameter "Estimates"		
		Run 1	Run 2	Run 3
1	β_2	0.53	0.98	0.98
2	β_3	0.84	0.84	0.84
3	β_4	0.96	0.96	0.96
4	β_5	0.91	0.91	0.91
5	β_6	0.93	0.93	0.93
6	β_7	0.94	0.94	0.94
7	β_8	0.89	0.89	0.89
8	ψ_1	1.05	0.57	0.57
9	ψ_2	0.28	0.03	0.03
10	ψ_3	0.17	0.17	0.17
11	ψ_4	0.03	0.03	0.03
12	ψ_5	0.12	0.12	0.12
13	ψ_6	0.07	0.07	0.07
14	ψ_7	0.10	0.10	0.10
15	ψ_8	0.61	0.61	0.13
16	θ_1	−0.05	0.43	0.43
17	θ_2	0.43	0.43	0.43
18	θ_3	0.43	0.43	0.43
19	θ_4	0.44	0.44	0.44
20	θ_5	0.42	0.42	0.42
21	θ_6	0.42	0.42	0.42
22	θ_7	0.39	0.39	0.39
23	θ_8	−0.09	−0.09	0.39
	$\psi_1 + \theta_1$	1.00	1.00	1.00
	$\beta_2\psi_1$	0.56	0.56	0.56
	$\psi_8 + \theta_8$	0.52	0.52	0.52

Table 6.13   Intercorrelations of a Perfect Simplex

	η_2	η_3	η_4	η_5	η_6	η_7
η_2	1.000					
η_3	0.838	1.000				
η_4	0.812	0.969	1.000			
η_5	0.724	0.865	0.892	1.000		
η_6	0.677	0.809	0.834	0.935	1.000	
η_7	0.619	0.739	0.763	0.855	0.914	1.000

The option SS on the OU command gives the standardized solution, si i.e., the correlation matrix of $\boldsymbol{\eta}$. The intercorrelations among η_2, η_3, $\cdots$, η_7 are the same for all three solutions in Table 6.12. These are given in Table 6.13. Here every correlation ρ_{ij} with $\mid i - j \mid > 1$ is the product of the correlations just below the diagonal. For example, $\rho(\eta_5, \eta_2) = 0.838 \times 0.969 \times 0.892 = 0.724$. These correlations form a perfect simplex. The reliabilities of the semester grades $y_2, y_3, \ldots, y_7$ can be obtained directly from the solution in which the η's are standardized. The reliabilities are:

$$
\begin{array}{cccccc}
y_2 & y_3 & y_4 & y_5 & y_6 & y_7 \\
0.569 & 0.575 & 0.563 & 0.584 & 0.581 & 0.608
\end{array}
$$

A test of the hypothesis that all reliabilities are equal gives $\chi^2 = 2.17$ with five degrees of freedom, so that this hypothesis is not rejected by the data despite the large sample size.

Without identification conditions imposed, as in Run 1, the correlations $\rho(\eta_1, \eta_j), j \neq 1$, and $\rho(\eta_i, \eta_8), i \neq 8$, and the reliabilities of y_1 and y_8 are not identified. However, in view of the above test of equality of reliabilities it seems reasonable to assume that all reliabilities or equivalently all error variances in the standardized solution are equal for y_1 through y_8. This assumption makes it possible to estimate the intercorrelations among all the η's.

Assuming that y_0 and y_0' are indicators of pre-college academic achievement η_0 which is assumed to influence the true academic achievement in the first semester η_1, one can estimate again the quasi-Markov simplex and show how this use of y_0 and y_0' helps identify the parameters of the model. The only parameters which are now not identified are ψ_8 and θ_8. This gives a $\chi^2 = 36.92$ with 28 degrees of freedom. If we assume that the reliabilities of all the semester grades are equal, all parameters are identified and the goodness of fit becomes 45.22 with 34 degrees of freedom. The difference 8.30 with 6 degrees of freedom provides another test of equality of the reliabilities. Given that all error variances are equal, a test of the hypothesis that

$$\beta_1 = \beta_2 = \beta_3 = \cdots = \beta_8$$

gives $\chi^2 = 6.48$ with seven degrees of freedom so that this hypothesis cannot be rejected. The command file for the last run is:

```
Simplex Model for Academic Performance - Last Model
DA NI=10 NO=1600
LA
(10A3)
 YOYO' Y1 Y2 Y3 Y4 Y5 Y6 Y7 Y8
KM FI=EX66.COR SY
MO NY=10 NE=9 BE=FU PS=DI
FR LY 2 1 BE 2 1 BE 3 2 BE 4 3 BE 5 4 BE 6 5 BE 7 6 BE 8 7 BE 9 8
VA 1 LY 1 1 LY 3 2 LY 4 3 LY 5 4 LY 6 5 LY 7 6 LY 8 7 LY 9 8 LY 10 9
EQ TE 3 - TE 10
EQ BE 2 1 BE 3 2 BE 4 3 BE 5 4 BE 6 5 BE 7 6 BE 8 7 BE 9 8
ST .5 ALL
OU SE SS NS
```

Further analysis shows that the variances $\psi_1, \psi_2, \ldots, \psi_8$ of the random disturbance terms are not equal, so the whole autoregressive process is not completely stationary.

7 Analysis of ordinal and other non-normal variables

In previous chapters the observed variables were assumed to be quantitative, *i.e.*, representing measurements on an interval scale, at least approximately. If some or all of the observed variables are ordinal or discrete, the matrix of polychoric correlations should be analyzed with the WLS method, using the correct weight matrix, as explained in section 7.1. Section 7.2 discusses the special case when all variables are dichotomous.

The LISREL methodology is misused when arbitrary scale scores $(1, 2, 3, \ldots)$ for categories are treated as scores with interval scale properties. In particular, it is wrong to compute a covariance matrix or product-moment (Pearson) correlation matrix for such scores, or mixtures of ordinal and interval scale scores, and analyze these with the ML or GLS method. This may lead to greatly distorted parameter estimates and incorrect χ^2 goodness-of-fit measures and standard errors.

When the observed variables are quantitative, but *highly* non-normal, the χ^2 goodness-of-fit measure and standard errors are also unreliable when produced with the ML or GLS methods. In these instances, it may be best to use an ordinary sample covariance matrix and analyze this with WLS, using a correct weight matrix. This requires a large sample so that the asymptotic covariance matrix of the sample variances and covariances can be estimated accurately. A poorly estimated asymptotic covariance matrix, such as estimated from a small sample, can do more harm than good, when used with WLS. If the sample size is not sufficiently large to produce an accurate estimate of the asymptotic covariance matrix, it is probably better to use ML or GLS. The use of WLS with sample covariance matrices is discussed in Section 7.3. Section 7.4 shows how to analyze a matrix of product moment (Pearson) correlations with WLS to estimate a *correlation structure*.

7.1 Analysis of ordinal variables

In many cases, especially when data are collected through questionnaires, the variables are ordinal, *i.e.*, responses are classified into different ordered categories.

An ordinal variable z (z may be either a y- or an x-variable in LISREL sense) may be regarded as a crude measurement of an underlying unobserved or unobservable continuous variable z^*. For example, a four-point ordinal scale may be conceived as:

$$
\begin{aligned}
&\text{if} && z^* \leq \alpha_1, && z \text{ is scored 1,} \\
&\text{if} \quad \alpha_1 < z^* \leq \alpha_2, && z \text{ is scored 2,} \\
&\text{if} \quad \alpha_2 < z^* \leq \alpha_3, && z \text{ is scored 3,} \\
&\text{if} \quad \alpha_3 < z^*, && z \text{ is scored 4,}
\end{aligned}
$$

where $\alpha_1 < \alpha_2 < \alpha_3$ are threshold values for z^*. It is often assumed that z^* has a standard normal distribution, in which case the thresholds can be estimated from the inverse of the normal distribution function.

Suppose z_1 and z_2 are two ordinal variables with underlying continuous variables z_1^* and z_2^*, respectively. Assuming that z_1^* and z_2^* have a bivariate normal distribution, their correlation is called *the polychoric correlation coefficient*. A special case of this is *the tetrachoric correlation coefficient*, when both z_1 and z_2 are dichotomous. Now, suppose further that z_3 is a continuous variable measured on an interval scale. The correlation between z_1^* and z_3 is called *the polyserial correlation coefficient* assuming that z_1^* and z_3 have a bivariate normal distribution. A special case of this is the *biserial correlation* when z_1 is dichotomous.

An ordinal variable z does not have a metric scale. To use such a variable in a linear relationship we use the corresponding underlying variable z^* instead. The polychoric and polyserial correlations are not correlations computed from actual scores but are rather theoretical correlations of the underlying z^*-variables. These correlations are estimated from the observed pairwise contingency tables of the ordinal variables.

The weight matrix required for such an analysis is the inverse of the estimated asymptotic covariance matrix $\mathbf{W}$ of the polychoric and polyserial correlations. The asymptotic covariance matrix as well as the matrix of polychoric and polyserial correlations are obtained by PRELIS.

The steps involved in this analysis will be described in the following two examples. These examples involve only ordinal variables and only polychoric correlations. For other examples, involving also continuous and censored variables and other types of correlations, see the *PRELIS 2 User's Reference Guide.*[1]

Example 7.1: Attitudes of morality and equality

Source: Hasselrot & Lernberg (1980).

Swedish school children in grade 9 were asked questions about their attitudes regarding social issues in family, school, and society. Among the questions asked were the following eight items.

> *For me, questions about . . .*
> 1. *human rights*
> 2. *equal conditions for all people*
> 3. *racial problems*
> 4. *equal value of all people*
> 5. *euthanasia*
> 6. *crime and punishment*
> 7. *conscientious objectors*
> 8. *guilt and bad conscience*   *are:*
>
> *unimportant   not important   important   very important*

For the present example we use a subsample of 200 cases. Responses to the eight questions were scored 1, 2, 3, and 4, where 4 denotes very important. The data matrix consists of 200 rows and 8 columns, and is stored in the file EX71.RAW.

The PRELIS command file is:

---

[1]Published by SSI, Inc.

```
ATTITUDES OF MORALITY AND EQUALITY
DA NI=8
LA
HUMRGHTS EQUALCON RACEPROB EQUALVAL EUTHANAS CRIMEPUN CONSCOBJ GUILT
RA FI=EX71.RAW
OR ALL
OU MA=PM SM=EX71.PML SA=EX71.ACP PA
```

The matrix of polychoric correlations as printed by PRELIS is:

ESTIMATED CORRELATION MATRIX

	HUMRGHTS	EQUALCON	RACEPROB	EQUALVAL	EUTHANAS	CRIMEPUN
HUMRGHTS	1.000					
EQUALCON	.423	1.000				
RACEPROB	.219	.202	1.000			
EQUALVAL	.367	.631	.283	1.000		
EUTHANAS	.439	.703	.312	.692	1.000	
CRIMEPUN	.210	.232	.275	.423	.218	1.000
CONSCOBJ	.185	.291	.304	.340	.224	.312
GUILT	.102	.311	.234	.314	.337	.204

ESTIMATED CORRELATION MATRIX

	CONSCOBJ	GUILT
CONSCOBJ	1.000	
GUILT	.202	1.000

The polychoric correlations are saved in the file EX71.PML, which will be read by LISREL.

The asymptotic covariance matrix, saved in the file EX71.ACP, is not equal to the matrix given in the PRELIS output file, but is equal to N times this matrix, as required by LISREL, where N is the sample size.

There are $(1/2)8 \times 7 = 28$ correlations in the polychoric correlation matrix. Hence, there should be $(1/2)28 \times 29 = 406$ elements in the asymptotic covariance matrix. These are stored as 67 lines with six elements each plus one line with four elements.

The LISREL model to be estimated is a two-factor confirmatory factor analysis model, in which the variables HUMRGHTS, EQUALCON, EQUALVAL, and EUTHANAS are assumed to measure Equality and RACEPROB, CRIMEPUN, CONSCOBJ, and GUILT are assumed to measure Morality.

The LISREL command file is:

```
ATTITUDES OF MORALITY AND EQUALITY
DA NI=8 NO=200 MA=PM
LA
HUMRGHTS EQUALCON RACEPROB EQUALVAL EUTHANAS CRIMEPUN CONSCOBJ GUILT
PM FI=EX71.PML
AC FI=EX71.ACP
MO NX=8 NK=2 PH=ST
FR LX 1 1 LX 2 1 LX 4 1 LX 5 1 LX 3 2 LX 6 2 LX 7 2 LX 8 2
OU SE TV
```

The MA=PM on the DA command is essential. Otherwise, the program will think that a covariance matrix will be analyzed and, as a consequence, the program will think that the file EX71.ACP contains 666 elements instead of 406, as there are 666 asymptotic variances and covariances of the 36 variances and covariances in a covariance matrix for 8 variables.

The PM command tells the program to read the matrix of polychoric correlations and the AC command tells the program to read the asymptotic covariance matrix.

The AC command implies that the WLS method will be used as default method instead of the ML method. So it is not necessary to put ME=WLS on the OU command.

The results are shown in the last column of Table 7.1. For comparison, the results obtained by normal theory GLS and the results from using the product-moment correlations based on normal scores, are also given in Table 7.1. In this table, MA=KM means "matrix analyzed = matrix of product-moment correlations based on normal score" and MA=PM means "matrix analyzed = matrix of polychoric correlations." Only the results of WLS with MA=PM are asymptotically correct. WLS with MA=KM is incorrect because the product-moment correlations based on normal scores are biased (inconsistent). The standard errors of the GLS estimates are wrong because they are based on the wrong formula.

Example 7.2: A panel model for political efficacy

Source: Aish & Jöreskog (1990).

A study on political attitudes included three ordinal variables measured on the same people at two occasions. The variables were considered to be

Table 7.1   Results Using Different Types of Correlations and Different Estimation Methods (Standard Errors in Parentheses)

Parameter	Normal Theory GLS		Non-Normal Theory WLS	
	MA=KM	MA=PM	MA=KM	MA=PM
LX(1,1)	.430(.074)	.506(.070)	.431(.049)	.498(.053)
LX(2,1)	.733(.066)	.790(.062)	.763(.029)	.795(.046)
LX(3,2)	.470(.087)	.534(.082)	.429(.056)	.499(.065)
LX(4,1)	.769(.066)	.814(.061)	.804(.029)	.816(.047)
LX(5,1)	.801(.065)	.878(.059)	.876(.030)	.853(.048)
LX(6,2)	.450(.086)	.479(.081)	.456(.059)	.530(.066)
LX(7,2)	.469(.086)	.494(.081)	.485(.057)	.514(.064)
LX(8,2)	.439(.087)	.488(.082)	.496(.062)	.481(.064)
PH(2,1)	.690(.083)	.703(.070)	.708(.060)	.708(.070)
χ^2	20.06	37.15	37.27	11.11
GFI	.975	.953	.983	.992
AGFI	.952	.912	.969	.985
RMR	.042	.057	.050	.044

indicators of *Political Efficacy (see Figure 7.1). The attitude questions corresponding to these variables are:*

☐ *People like me have no say in what the government does (NOSAYPO)*

☐ *Voting is the only way that people like me can have any say about how the government runs things (VOTONLW)*

☐ *Sometimes politics and government seem so complicated that a person like me cannot really understand what is going on (POLCOMP)*

Responses to these questions were scored:

1	=	*agree strongly*	*4*	=	*disagree strongly*
2	=	*agree*	*8*	=	*don't know*
3	=	*disagree*	*9*	=	*no answer*

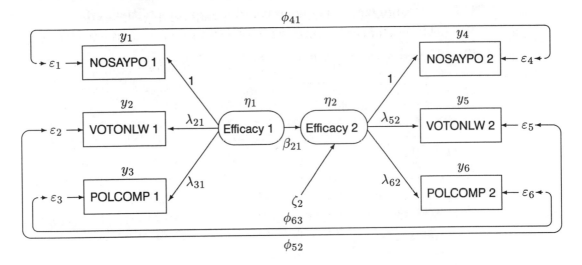

Figure 7.1   Panel Model for Political Efficacy

Table 7.2   Estimated Correlation Matrix for Political Efficacy Data

	y_1	y_2	y_3	y_4	y_5	y_6
NOSAYPO1	1					
VOTONLW1	0.542	1				
POLCOMP1	0.392	0.362	1			
NOSAYPO2	0.477	0.309	0.210	1		
VOTONLW2	0.341	0.511	0.308	0.482	1	
POLCOMP2	0.224	0.227	0.525	0.345	0.312	1

As in Example 7.1, PRELIS was used to compute the matrix of polychoric correlations and the corresponding asymptotic covariance matrix. Score 8 (*don't know*) and score 9 (*no answer*) were treated as missing values. Under listwise deletion (necessary to obtain the asymptotic covariance matrix) 410 cases remained in the sample. The correlation matrix for the variables of interest is given in Table 7.2.

The two files produced by PRELIS will now be used as external files for LISREL to analyze a two-wave panel model for political efficacy (see Figure 7.1).

The first command file is as follows.

```
LISREL 7: RUN 1
TWO-WAVE PANEL MODEL FOR POLITICAL EFFICACY
USING DATA: PANEL USA (6 VARIABLES X 2 OCCASIONS)
USING WLS WITH POLYCHORIC CORRELATIONS AND ASYMPTOTIC COVARIANCE MATRIX
OBTAINED IN PRELIS RUN 2
DA NI=12 NO=410 MA=PM
LA FI=PANEL.LAB
PM FI=PANELUSA.PML
AC FI=PANELUSA.ACP
SE
1 2 3 7 8 9 /
MO NY=6 NE=2 BE=SD PS=DI TE=SY
LE
Efficac1 Efficac2
FR LY 2 1 LY 3 1 LY 5 2 LY 6 2
VA 1 LY 1 1 LY 4 2
OU SE TV MI SS RS
```

This command file is similar to that of Example 7.1 but differs from it in the following ways.

- ❑ We select 6 variables out of 12 to be analyzed. The selection takes place in the ACP matrix as well as in the PML matrix.
- ❑ The model is a LISREL Submodel 3B, see Chapter 6 (In Example 7.1, the model was a Submodel 1).
- ❑ We specify TE=SY rather than TE=DI to obtain modification indices for off-diagonal elements of Θ_ϵ. As argued in Chapter 6, these may be interesting in a longitudinal model.

This first model assumes that the ϵ's are uncorrelated. The χ^2 goodness-of-fit measure is 58.44 with 8 degrees of freedom, indicating rather poor fit. The standardized residuals are:

STANDARDIZED RESIDUALS

	NOSAYPO1	VOTONLW1	POLCOMP1	NOSAYPO2	VOTONLW2	POLCOMP2
NOSAYPO1	.000					
VOTONLW1	2.555	.000				
POLCOMP1	-.905	-1.504	.000			
NOSAYPO2	2.386	-2.443	-2.742	.000		
VOTONLW2	-1.828	2.174	-1.670	1.377	.000	
POLCOMP2	-3.236	-2.361	4.889	.002	-1.587	.000

Note that the standardized residuals for cells (4,1), (5,2), and (6,3) are all positive and significant. This indicates that the error terms might be correlated over time for the same variable. This can also be seen in the modification indices for elements of Θ_ϵ and their estimated changes. Note that the estimated change is positive for these three elements.

MODIFICATION INDICES FOR THETA EPS

	NOSAYPO1	VOTONLW1	POLCOMP1	NOSAYPO2	VOTONLW2	POLCOMP2
NOSAYPO1	.000					
VOTONLW1	5.133	.000				
POLCOMP1	.588	2.698	.000			
NOSAYPO2	6.777	4.072	6.719	.000		
VOTONLW2	4.596	9.142	1.727	3.015	.000	
POLCOMP2	6.114	6.257	44.431	.020	2.931	.000

ESTIMATED CHANGE FOR THETA EPS

	NOSAYPO1	VOTONLW1	POLCOMP1	NOSAYPO2	VOTONLW2	POLCOMP2
NOSAYPO1	.000					
VOTONLW1	.180	.000				
POLCOMP1	-.055	-.119	.000			
NOSAYPO2	.178	-.145	-.180	.000		
VOTONLW2	-.156	.207	-.089	.141	.000	
POLCOMP2	-.174	-.174	.384	-.010	-.129	.000

To run the model with autocorrelated error terms, insert the following command between the MO and OU commands in the command file.

```
FR TE 4 1 TE 5 2 TE 6 3
```

The resulting solution is entirely satisfactory. It has a χ^2 goodness-of-fit measure of 2.05 with 5 degrees of freedom and no significant standardized residuals or modification indices. The standardized regression coefficient β_{21} is estimated as 0.66. The squared multiple correlation for Efficac2 on Efficac1 is 0.44.

7.2 Factor analysis of dichotomous variables

To factor analyze a set of dichotomous items to determine whether they can be used to represent an underlying unidimensional scale is a common problem in test theory. There are many methods and programs available for doing this. The following example demonstrates that it can also be done conveniently and efficiently with LISREL.

Example 7.3: Factor analysis of dichotomous variables

Source: Bock & Lieberman (1970); Christoffersson (1975).

Table 4.2 in the PRELIS User's Reference Guide gives the observed frequencies for the 32 response patterns arising from five dichotomous items (11 through 15) of Section 6 of the Law School Admissions Test (LSAT). The sample is a subsample of 1000 from a larger sample of those who took the test.

First we use the following PRELIS command file to produce the tetrachoric correlations and their asymptotic variances and covariances.

```
LSAT SECTION 6
DA NI=6 NO=1000; RA FI=LSAT6.DAT
WE 6; OR ALL
OU MA=PM SM=EX73.PML SA=EX73.ACP
```

This produces the asymptotic covariance matrix in the file EX73.ACP and the following matrix of tetrachoric correlations:

```
        ESTIMATED CORRELATION MATRIX

                VAR 1       VAR 2       VAR 3       VAR 4       VAR 5
        VAR 1   1.000
        VAR 2    .170       1.000
        VAR 3    .228        .189       1.000
        VAR 4    .107        .111        .187       1.000
        VAR 5    .067        .172        .105        .201       1.000
```

We can now analyze the data with LISREL using the following command file.

```
FACTOR ANALYSIS OF DICHOTOMOUS VARIABLES: LSAT6 DATA
DA NI=5 NO=1000 MA=PM
PM FI=EX73.PML; AC FI=EX73.ACP
MO NX=5 NK=1 LX=FR PH=ST
OU SE TV RS
```

The resulting output file shows the following solution, standard errors, and standardized residuals, indicating that the five items may well fit a unidimensional scale. The only item which is a little bit odd is item 5.

```
LISREL ESTIMATES (WEIGHTED LEAST SQUARES)

        LAMBDA X

              KSI 1
VAR 1         .389
VAR 2         .397
VAR 3         .471
VAR 4         .377
VAR 5         .342

        PHI

              KSI 1
KSI 1         1.000

        THETA DELTA

            VAR 1      VAR 2      VAR 3      VAR 4      VAR 5
             .848       .842       .778       .858       .883

        SQUARED MULTIPLE CORRELATIONS FOR X - VARIABLES

            VAR 1      VAR 2      VAR 3      VAR 4      VAR 5
             .152       .158       .222       .142       .117


        CHI-SQUARE WITH   5 DEGREES OF FREEDOM =    4.05 (P = .542)
                       GOODNESS OF FIT INDEX = .999
              ADJUSTED GOODNESS OF FIT INDEX = .998
                    ROOT MEAN SQUARE RESIDUAL =     .036


STANDARDIZED RESIDUALS

            VAR 1      VAR 2      VAR 3      VAR 4      VAR 5
VAR 1        .000
VAR 2       2.644       .000
VAR 3        .859       .035       .000
VAR 4      -2.053      -.583       .255       .000
VAR 5      -2.623       .456     -1.289      1.518       .000
```

```
STANDARD ERRORS

    LAMBDA X

              KSI 1
    VAR 1     .100
    VAR 2     .082
    VAR 3     .090
    VAR 4     .081
    VAR 5     .086

    THETA DELTA

         VAR 1     VAR 2     VAR 3     VAR 4     VAR 5
         .090      .079      .096      .076      .074
```

7.3 Analysis of continuous non-normal variables

When some or all observed variables are continuous, *i.e.*, measured on interval scales, it is best to analyze the covariance matrix S rather than the correlation matrix R. If the variables are highly non-normal, it is still an open question whether to use ML (or GLS) or WLS with a general weight matrix. The latter approach has been termed *Best Asymptotically Distribution Free Method* (ADF) by Browne (1984). Previous Monte Carlo studies have not given a clear-cut answer as to when it is necessary to use WLS rather than ML.

Rather than trying to give a general answer as to which method should be used in which situations, we shall provide a simple tool by which this methodological question can be studied. We shall also demonstrate how WLS is used to analyze a sample covariance matrix S.

There are very many non-normal distributions. Any robustness study will have to consider what type of non-normal distribution one would like to be robust against. Consider the following eight distributions.

1. Normal with mean 0 and variance 1
2. Chi-square with 5 degrees of freedom
3. Chi-square with 1 degree of freedom
4. Continuous Uniform Distribution

7 ANALYSIS OF ORDINAL AND OTHER NON-NORMAL VARIABLES

5. Binomial with $p = 0.5$ and $n = 6$
6. Binomial with $p = 0.25$ and $n = 10$
7. A three-point distribution with probabilities $\frac{1}{2}$, $\frac{1}{3}$, $\frac{1}{6}$ at 0, 1, and 2, respectively
8. A uniform discrete distribution with probability $\frac{1}{6}$ at $1, 2, \ldots, 6$

Only one of these is normal. The others vary with respect to skewness and kurtosis. Distributions 1, 4, 5, and 8 are symmetrical, 2, 3, 6, and 7 are skewed. The mean, variance, skewness, and kurtosis are shown in Table 7.3.

Table 7.3   Population Moments for Eight Distributions

Distribution	1	2	3	4	5	6	7	8
Mean	0.00	5.00	1.00	0.50	3.00	2.50	0.67	3.50
Variance	1.00	10.00	2.00	0.08	1.50	1.87	0.55	2.92
Skewness	0.00	1.26	2.82	0.00	0.00	0.36	0.63	0.00
Kurtosis	0.00	2.40	12.00	−1.20	−0.33	−0.07	−0.95	−1.27

Now consider the congeneric measurement model with 4 x-variables (see Section 3.1). We write this model as

$$x_i = \lambda_i \xi + \sqrt{\theta_i} \cdot \delta_i, \qquad i = 1, 2, 3, 4 \tag{7.1}$$

where ξ and δ_i are independently distributed, each having one of these eight distributions.

We can generate a random sample of x-vectors as follows.

1. Choose parameter values λ_i and θ_i.
2. Choose a distribution for ξ (1 through 8) and a distribution for each δ_i (1 through 8).
3. Generate random numbers for ξ and δ_1, δ_2, δ_3 and δ_4 and adjust these to zero mean and unit variance, using the population means and variances given in Table 7.3.

4. Compute $x_1, x_2, x_3,$ and x_4 from (7.1).

5. Repeat steps 3 and 4 N times, where N is the required sample size.

The program GENRAW2[2] generates raw data according to specifications provided in this way. Each x_i is a mixture of two distributions. For a fixed set of parameter values with four x-variables, there are $8^5 = 32768$ possible combinations of distributions that one can study in this way. The generated data matrix comes from a multivariate population with covariance matrix Σ in (3.5). However, the distribution is not multivariate normal, except in the case when all five distributions are specified to be normal.

To see how this works, we generated a random sample in the following way:

1. Parameter values: $\lambda = (0.9, 0.7, 0.5, 0.5)$, $\theta = (0.19, 0.51, 0.75, 0.75)$

2. Distribution for ξ: 3, distribution for δ_i: 2, for all i

3. Sample size: $N = 200$

The resulting raw data matrix is stored in the file EX74.RAW.

Example 7.4: Analysis of covariance matrices with WLS

To analyze the raw data in file EX74.RAW with WLS, we first run PRELIS to compute the sample variances and covariances and their asymptotic covariance matrix. This run will also give information about the skewness and kurtosis of each of the four variables. These measures are useful in evaluation of the robustness.

The PRELIS command file is:

```
ANALYSIS OF RAW DATA GENERATED BY GENRAW2
DA NI=4
RA FI=EX74.RAW
OU MA=CM SM=EX74.CML SA=EX74.ACC PA
```

The PRELIS output file gives the following summary statistics.

---

[2]With LISREL 8, this utility has become obsolete. See the section *Monte Carlo experiments* in Appendix C of the *PRELIS 2 User's Reference Guide*.

```
UNIVARIATE SUMMARY STATISTICS FOR CONTINUOUS VARIABLES
VARIABLE     MEAN  ST. DEV.  SKEWNESS  KURTOSIS  MINIMUM FREQ.  MAXIMUM FREQ.
   VAR 1     .071     .941     1.587     3.433   -1.213    1     4.788    1
   VAR 2     .092     .981      .845      .768   -1.517    1     3.929    1
   VAR 3     .079     .932     1.033     1.182   -1.537    1     3.313    1
   VAR 4    -.001    1.008     1.265     2.639   -1.536    1     4.908    1
```

These numbers suggest that the variables are consistent with the assumption of population mean zero and variance one, but they are far from being normally distributed. All variables are positively skewed and VAR 1 has an excessive kurtosis.

The sample covariance matrix is saved in the file EX74.CML and 200 times the asymptotic covariance matrix is saved in the file EX74.ACC.

The LISREL command file for WLS is:

```
ANALYSIS OF COVARIANCE MATRIX WITH WLS
DA NI=4 NO=200
CM FI=EX74.CML
AC FI=EX74.ACC
MO NX=4 NK=1 LX=FR PH=ST
OU SE
```

Parameter estimates and standard errors are shown in the last column of Table 7.4. For comparison, results are also given for all the other estimation methods.

We started out with the intention of generating variables which are highly non-normal in the hope of demonstrating the superiority of WLS over ML. The results of Table 7.4 do not lead to a clear conclusion. The model fits very well for all methods and, as far as parameter estimates are concerned, there are very small differences between methods. However, χ^2 and standard errors are larger for WLS than for the other methods. This suggests that χ^2 and standard errors produced by ULS, DWLS, GLS, and ML may be underestimated when the observed variables deviate far from normality.

This example represents only a single observation from which no safe conclusion can be drawn concerning possible bias in χ^2 and standard errors. A comprehensive Monte Carlo study is needed for this purpose.

Table 7.4 **Parameter Estimates for Hypothetical Model**
(Standard Errors in Parentheses)

Parameter	True	IV	TSLS	ULS	DWLS	GLS	ML	WLS
LX(1)	0.90	0.85	0.85	0.84	0.83	0.84(0.07)	0.84(0.07)	0.84(0.09)
LX(2)	0.70	0.63	0.63	0.64	0.65	0.65(0.07)	0.64(0.07)	0.66(0.07)
LX(3)	0.50	0.50	0.51	0.48	0.48	0.46(0.07)	0.46(0.07)	0.45(0.08)
LX(4)	0.50	0.49	0.49	0.51	0.51	0.52(0.07)	0.52(0.07)	0.52(0.10)
TD(1)	0.19	0.17	0.17	0.17	0.19	0.17(0.08)	0.17(0.08)	0.18(0.09)
TD(2)	0.51	0.57	0.56	0.56	0.54	0.53(0.07)	0.55(0.07)	0.52(0.10)
TD(3)	0.75	0.62	0.61	0.64	0.63	0.65(0.07)	0.66(0.07)	0.67(0.09)
TD(4)	0.75	0.77	0.78	0.76	0.76	0.73(0.08)	0.74(0.08)	0.71(0.09)
χ^2	0.00	n.a.	n.a.	2.10	2.12	2.29	2.19	2.52
GFI	1.00	n.a.	n.a.	1.00	1.00	0.99	1.00	0.99
AGFI	1.00	n.a.	n.a.	0.99	1.00	0.97	0.97	0.94
RMR	0.00	n.a.	n.a.	0.02	0.02	0.02	0.02	0.03

n.a. = not available

7.4 Estimating a correlation structure with WLS

Example 7.5: Estimating and testing a correlation structure

Psychologist A consults Statistician K about her data analysis problem.
She does not want to reveal her raw data but says that she has used PRELIS
to compute the product-moment (Pearson) correlations for her five variables
and that the PRELIS output suggests that the variables are non-normal.
Fortunately, she has also computed the asymptotic covariance matrix of
the product-moment correlations.

Psychologist A claims that her theory is that the correlations should be of the form

$$\mathbf{P}(\theta) = \begin{pmatrix} 1 & & & & \\ \rho_1 & 1 & & & \\ \rho_2 & \rho_2 & 1 & & \\ \rho_2 & \rho_2 & \rho_3 & 1 & \\ \rho_2 & \rho_2 & \rho_3 & \rho_3 & 1 \end{pmatrix},$$

where $\theta' = (\rho_1, \rho_2, \rho_3)$.

How should the data be analyzed to estimate and test this correlation structure?

The observed correlation matrix is

$$\mathbf{R} = \begin{pmatrix} 1.000 & & & & \\ .526 & 1.000 & & & \\ .402 & .482 & 1.000 & & \\ .391 & .424 & .400 & 1.000 & \\ .417 & .489 & .274 & .442 & 1.000 \end{pmatrix}$$

The asymptotic covariance matrix of product-moment correlations is not of the form (1.16). Hence, ML or GLS should not be used in this case. The only way to get correct χ^2, standard errors, standardized residuals, and modification indices is to use WLS with a weight matrix to the inverse of the asymptotic covariance matrix of the estimated correlations.

We assume that the correlation matrix is stored in the file EX75.KML and that the asymptotic covariance matrix is stored in the file EX75.ACK.

The LISREL command file is:

```
ESTIMATING AND TESTING OF A CORRELATION STRUCTURE
DA NI=5 NO=200 MA=KM
KM FI=EX75.KML
AC FI=EX75.ACK
MO NX=5 NK=5 LX=ID PH=ST TD=ZE
EQ PH 3 1 PH 3 2 PH 4 1 PH 4 2 PH 5 1 PH 5 2
EQ PH 4 3 PH 5 3 PH 5 4
OU SE TV RS MI
```

The MO command specifies $\Lambda_x = \mathbf{I}$ and $\Theta_\delta = \mathbf{0}$. By default, Φ is unconstrained. The VA command specifies Φ to be a correlation matrix. The EQ commands specify the equality constraints in the correlation structure.

The output file gives the following solution, standardized residuals, and modification indices.

```
LISREL ESTIMATES (WEIGHTED LEAST SQUARES)

     PHI

            VAR 1     VAR 2     VAR 3     VAR 4     VAR 5
  VAR 1     1.000
  VAR 2      .603     1.000
  VAR 3      .513      .513     1.000
  VAR 4      .513      .513      .429     1.000
  VAR 5      .513      .513      .429      .429     1.000


          CHI-SQUARE WITH  12 DEGREES OF FREEDOM =     16.31 (P = .177)
                    GOODNESS OF FIT INDEX = .986
              ADJUSTED GOODNESS OF FIT INDEX = .983
                  ROOT MEAN SQUARE RESIDUAL =        .072


     STANDARDIZED RESIDUALS

            VAR 1     VAR 2     VAR 3     VAR 4     VAR 5
  VAR 1      .000
  VAR 2     -.824      .000
  VAR 3    -2.254     -.649      .000
  VAR 4    -2.758    -1.109     -.430      .000
  VAR 5    -1.603     -.494   -10.111      .270      .000


     MODIFICATION INDICES FOR PHI

            VAR 1     VAR 2     VAR 3     VAR 4     VAR 5
  VAR 1      .000
  VAR 2      .000      .000
  VAR 3     2.816     4.759      .000
  VAR 4     1.033     1.302     1.838      .000
  VAR 5      .577     3.236    11.915     4.666      .000


     ESTIMATED CHANGE FOR PHI

            VAR 1     VAR 2     VAR 3     VAR 4     VAR 5
  VAR 1      .000
  VAR 2      .000      .000
  VAR 3     -.072      .060      .000
  VAR 4     -.066     -.069      .052      .000
  VAR 5     -.035      .041     -.161      .055      .000
```

The program gives correct results but *incorrect* degrees of freedom. The correct degrees of freedom is 7, the number of correlations (10) minus the number of parameters (3). By putting TD=FR (or TD default) instead of TD=ZE on the MO command, one will obtain identically the same results but with *correct* degrees of freedom. Incorrect degrees of freedom when TD=ZE are obtained because the program always assumes that a covariance structure is estimated, so that the diagonal elements of S are always counted in the degrees of freedom. The reason why TD=FR and TD=ZE give the same result, apart from the degrees of freedom, is that in both cases the same fit function of the parameters is minimized.

Both the standardized residuals and the modification indices show that $\hat{\rho}_{53}$ violates the equality constraint. The negative sign of the standardized residual and of the estimated change of ρ_{53} suggests that ρ_{53} should be smaller than the estimated value 0.43. In fact, the estimated change is -0.16.

When the model is reestimated with ρ_{53} free, the goodness-of-fit χ^2 is 4.40 with six degrees of freedom. This represents a very good fit. The estimate of ρ_{53} is 0.27, which is in fact just 0.16 smaller than the previous value.

The analysis suggests that A's "theory" is in agreement with the data, except that ρ_{53} is not equal to ρ_{43} and ρ_{54}.

8 Miscellaneous topics

8.1 Constraints

LISREL does not directly impose constraints on the covariance matrices Φ, Ψ, Θ_ϵ, and Θ_δ so as to make these positive definite. If an estimate of any one of these matrices is not positive definite, *when they are supposed to be so,* this is an indication that the model is wrong.

LISREL checks the positive definiteness of Φ, Ψ, Θ_ϵ, and Θ_δ as part of the admissibility test (see AD keyword on the OU command and the section *Admissibility of the estimates* on page 25). If after AD iterations (default value = 10) one of these matrices is not positive definite, the iterations will stop and the current "solution" will be printed. If one believes strongly that there is an admissible solution for the model and the data analyzed, one should increase the value of AD and rerun the problem with different and better starting values. Our experience suggests, however, that when the "solution" is non-admissible after 10 iterations, and the program is allowed to continue to iterate, it will either converge to a non-admissible solution or not converge at all. As already stated, this is usually the fault of the model rather than the program. However, this problem has also occurred in Monte Carlo studies for occasional odd samples, where it cannot be blamed on the model; Example 8.1 below illustrates this case.

Constraining error variances to be non-negative

Suppose we believe in the model and cannot accept a negative estimate of an error variance. If the LISREL estimates are admissible, there is no problem. However, if one or more of the estimates of error variances is negative one must reparameterize the model in a way to prevent this.

Suppose, for example, we are estimating a LISREL Submodel 1 with Θ_δ diagonal. This model can be reparameterized as

$$\Lambda_x^* = \left(\begin{array}{cc} \Lambda_x & \mathbf{D}_\delta \end{array} \right) \quad \Phi^* = \left(\begin{array}{cc} \Phi & \\ \mathbf{0} & \mathbf{I} \end{array} \right) \quad \Theta_\delta^* = \mathbf{0} , \qquad (8.1)$$

where $\mathbf{D}_\delta$ is a diagonal matrix such that $\Theta_\delta = \mathbf{D}_\delta^2$. It is easily verified that

$$\Lambda_x^* \Phi^* \Lambda_x^{*\prime} + \Theta_\delta^* = \Lambda_x \Phi \Lambda_x^\prime + \mathbf{D}_\delta^2 = \Lambda_x \Phi \Lambda_x^\prime + \Theta_\delta .$$

Estimates of error variances are obtained as $\hat{\mathbf{D}}_\delta^2$. The elements d_i of $\mathbf{D}_\delta$ may come out positive or negative (or zero), but the error variances are estimated as d_i^2, which cannot be negative.

It should be noted that the reparameterized model has NK > NX so that the IV and TSLS procedures for generating starting values will not work; see the section *Instrumental variables (IV) and two-stage least squares (TSLS)* on page 17. Starting values must be provided by the user.

Example 8.1: Gösta's bad sample

Source: Hägglund (1982).

In a Monte Carlo study random samples were generated from the following population parameters:

$$\Lambda_x = \begin{pmatrix} 1 & 0 \\ 0 & 1 \\ 0.889 & 0 \\ 0 & 0.857 \\ 0 & 0.714 \\ 0.333 & 0 \end{pmatrix} \quad \Phi = \begin{pmatrix} 0.810 & \\ 0.378 & 0.490 \end{pmatrix} \quad \Theta_\delta = \text{diag} \begin{pmatrix} 0.19 \\ 0.51 \\ 0.36 \\ 0.64 \\ 0.75 \\ 0.91 \end{pmatrix}$$

The population covariance matrix

$$\Sigma = \Lambda_x \Phi \Lambda_x^\prime + \Theta_\delta$$

formed from these parameter matrices is

$$\Sigma = \begin{pmatrix} 1.000 & & & & & \\ 0.378 & 1.000 & & & & \\ 0.720 & 0.336 & 1.000 & & & \\ 0.324 & 0.420 & 0.288 & 1.000 & & \\ 0.270 & 0.350 & 0.240 & 0.300 & 1.000 & \\ 0.270 & 0.126 & 0.240 & 0.108 & 0.090 & 1.000 \end{pmatrix}.$$

LISREL can be used to compute Σ from Λ_x, Φ, and Θ_δ. The following command file will do the job.

```
Ex8.1a: Computing Population Sigma
DA NI=6 NO=10
CM
1 0 1 2*0 1 3*0 1 4*0 1 5*0 1
MO NX=6 NK=2  PH=FI TD=FI
MA LX
1 0 0 1 .889 0 0 .857 0 .714 .333 0
MA PH
.810 .378 .490
MA TD
.19 .51 .36 .64 .75 .91
OU SI=EX81.SIG
```

The trick is to specify all parameter matrices to be fixed and enter the parameter matrices by MA commands. There are no parameters to estimate, so LISREL will just compute Σ and save it in the file EX81.SIG as requested in the OU command. However, LISREL always need some data to analyze. The matrix to be "analyzed" may be *any* positive-definite matrix. Here we use an identity matrix as this is particularly easy to enter.

Hägglund (1982) was concerned with unrestricted factor analysis. In this context, this corresponds to the model where all elements in rows 3–6 in Λ_x are unknown parameters. To see that LISREL works correctly, when the population Σ is analyzed, we run the following command file.

```
Ex8.1b: Analyzing Population Sigma
DA NI=6 NO=200
CM FI=EX81.SIG
MO NX=6 NK=2
FR LX(5)-LX(12)
VA 1 LX(1) LX(4)
OU SE
```

The output file reveals that LISREL correctly recovers all the parameters, including the zeros in Λ_x. (A program that does not do this for an identified model is not worth keeping as it means that it does not produce consistent estimates.) The output file also shows that all residuals are zero.

The sample size specified on the DA command is of course arbitrary and irrelevant. For reasons which will be obvious in a moment, we chose NO=200. The output file suggests that the *true* standard error of $\theta_{11}^{(\delta)}$ is 0.166. This suggests that if we were to take repeated random samples of size 200 from the population, the estimated $\hat{\theta}_{11}^{(\delta)}$ in these samples should fall in the interval $0.19 \pm (1.96 \times 0.166) = 0.19 \pm 0.33$ in 95 percent of cases. This interval is from -0.14 to 0.52. Thus, some of the estimates are likely to be negative. In fact, if the normality approximation holds, we should expect 13 percent negative estimates. It should therefore not come as a surprise that negative estimates of error variances (Heywood cases) occur in a Monte Carlo study designed like this.

Gösta Hägglund generated many random sample covariance matrices based on Σ. One of these is given in the file EX81.COV.

Although this matrix does not "look strange," it is an extremely odd sample. No matter what one does, one almost always ends up with a non-admissible solution. We shall illustrate how LISREL behaves in a case like this.

Suppose we proceed in the usual way to estimate the model with free λ's in rows 3–6. The command file is:

```
Ex8.1c: Analyzing Gosta's Bad Sample
DA NI=6 NO=200
CM FI=EX81.COV
MO NX=6 NK=2
FR LX(5)-LX(12)
VA 1 LX(1) LX(4)
OU
```

Since AD is default on the OU command, LISREL stops after 10 iterations (see Section 2.15) with a large negative estimate of TD(1). There is no admissible solution for this data and model. This can be verified by starting at different initial values and allowing the program to iterate further. For example, if one sets AD=OFF and IT=250, say, LISREL iterates "forever" producing larger and larger negative estimates of TD(1). This can also be verified by fixing TD(1) at zero and plotting the fit function against TD(1). This plot is given in Figure 8.1.

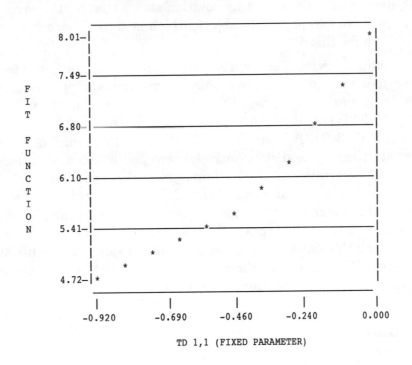

Figure 8.1   Plot of Fit Function against TD(1,1)

Next let us constrain the error variances to be non-negative using the reparameterized model (8.1). This can be done as follows.

```
Ex8.1d: Analyzing Gosta's Bad Sample by Reparameterized Model
DA NI=6 NO=200
CM FI=EX81.COV
MO NX=6 NK=8 LX=FI PH=FI TD=ZE
FR LX 1 3 LX 2 4 LX 3 5 LX 4 6 LX 5 7 LX 6 8
FR LX 3 1 LX 3 2 LX 4 1 LX 4 2 LX 5 1 LX 5 2 LX 6 1 LX 6 2
FR PH 1 1 PH 2 1 PH 2 2
VA 1 LX 1 1 LX 2 2 PH 3 3 PH 4 4 PH 5 5 PH 6 6 PH 7 7 PH 8 8
ST .5 ALL; ST 0 PH 2 1
OU NS AD=OFF
```

Note that starting values for $\mathbf{D}_\delta$ must be given. Otherwise, the matrix $\boldsymbol{\Sigma}$ computed at initial values is singular which means that the ML fit function cannot be computed. Also, as this is a very problematic case, we have to allow for more iterations than does the default value of IT (in this case 51 iterations). The resulting solution shows that all the error variances are positive except for variable 1, which is zero. There is no admissible solution for this data.

It should be emphasized that constraining error variances to be non-negative does not really solve the problem. Zero estimates of error variances are as unacceptable as are negative estimates. The root of the problem is that the model is empirically overparameterized. Instead of estimating *all* the λ's in rows 3–6 of $\boldsymbol{\Lambda}_x$, one should ask the question: which of these eight λ's are statistically (and substantively) zero and which are statistically (and substantively) non-zero? One can answer this question by starting with the model in which all eight λ's are fixed at zero and free one λ at a time using the information provided by the modification index and estimated change. If the non-zero λ's should be positive, one should not free a λ for which the estimated change is negative even if its modification index is large. When the four λ's which are zero in the population are fixed at zero, the following solution is obtained.

```
LISREL ESTIMATES (MAXIMUM LIKELIHOOD)

    LAMBDA X

          KSI 1      KSI 2
    VAR 1    1.000      .000
    VAR 2     .000     1.000
    VAR 3     .820      .000
    VAR 4     .000      .824
    VAR 5     .000      .788
    VAR 6     .142      .000

    PHI

          KSI 1      KSI 2
    KSI 1    1.143
    KSI 2     .569       .546

    THETA DELTA

        VAR 1      VAR 2      VAR 3      VAR 4      VAR 5      VAR 6
         .134       .579       .380       .581       .723       .989
```

This may be compared with the population parameters.

Constraining covariance matrices to be non-negative definite

Consider LISREL Submodel 1 with Φ free and suppose we want to constrain Φ to be non-negative definite. We can then specify Φ as

$$\Phi = \mathbf{T}_\phi \mathbf{T}'_\phi ,$$

where $\mathbf{T}_\phi$ is a lower-triangular matrix. This can be reparameterized as a Submodel 3A with

$$\Lambda_y = \Lambda_x, \ \mathbf{B} = 0, \ \Gamma = \mathbf{T}_\phi, \ \Phi = \mathbf{I}, \ \text{and} \Theta_\epsilon = \Theta_\delta .$$

The covariance matrix $\hat{\Phi} = \hat{\mathbf{T}}_\phi \hat{\mathbf{T}}'_\phi$ is obtained as the covariance matrix of η in the output.

To constrain Ψ to be non-negative definite in the full model, we can specify this as

$$
\begin{aligned}
\eta &= \mathbf{B}\Phi + \Gamma\xi + \zeta \\
&= \mathbf{B}\eta + \left(\begin{array}{cc} \Gamma & \mathbf{T}_\psi \end{array} \right) \left(\begin{array}{c} \xi \\ \zeta^* \end{array} \right) ,
\end{aligned}
$$

where $\mathbf{T}_\psi$ is a lower triangular matrix such that $\Psi = \mathbf{T}_\psi \mathbf{T}'_\psi$ and $\mathrm{Cov}(\zeta^*) = \mathbf{I}$.

8.2 Tests of hypotheses and power calculation

Once the validity of a model has been reasonably well established, various structural hypotheses about the parameters $\theta(t \times 1)$ in this model may be tested. One can test hypotheses stating that:

- ☐ Certain θ's have particular values.
- ☐ Certain θ's are equal.

Each of these two types of hypotheses leads to a model with fewer parameters ν, where $\nu(u \times 1)$ is a subset of the parameters in θ, $u < t$. In conventional statistical terminology, the model with parameters ν is called the *null hypothesis* H_0 and the model with parameters θ is called the *alternative hypothesis* H_1. Let χ_0^2 and χ_1^2 be the χ^2 goodness-of-fit measures for models H_0 and H_1, respectively. The test statistic for testing H_0 against H_1 is then

$$D^2 = \chi_0^2 - \chi_1^2 \,, \qquad (8.2)$$

which is used as χ^2 with $d = t - u$ degrees of freedom. The degrees of freedom can also be computed as the difference between the degrees of freedom associated with χ_0^2 and χ_1^2. To use the test statistic formally, one chooses a significance level α (probability of type 1 error) and rejects H_0 if D^2 exceeds the $(1 - \alpha)$ percentile of the χ^2 distribution with d degrees of freedom.

The test statistic D^2 can only be used with GLS, ML, and WLS and is valid under the following assumptions:

- With GLS and ML: the observed variables have a multivariate normal distribution and the sample covariance matrix is analyzed; with WLS if the correct weight matrix is used.
- The model H_0 is true.
- The sample size is large.

A common type of hypothesis H_0 postulates that a single parameter θ be restricted to a specified value θ_0. The corresponding alternative hypothesis H_1 specifies θ as a free parameter in the same model. In this case there are two alternative test statistics that can be used, both of which are easier to compute in that they require only one LISREL run rather than two as D^2 does. These alternatives are:

- Run LISREL under H_1 and use the t-value of $\hat{\theta}$ as a standard normal two-sided test statistic.
- Run LISREL under H_0 and use the modification index for $\theta = \theta_0$ as a χ^2 with one degree of freedom.

In very large samples, if H_0 is true, we have approximately:

$$t^2 = D^2 = \text{modification index}.$$

These three quantities will not be equal in small samples, however, and it can happen, although rarely, that only one or two are significant.

In the general context of (8.2), if H_0 cannot be rejected at a given level of significance α, it does not necessarily mean that H_0 is true, because the power of the test may be low. The *power* of a test is the probability of rejecting H_0 when H_1 is true (one minus the probability of type 2 error). The higher the power, the better the test.

The power of the D^2 test in (8.2) depends on:

- what the true model is
- the significance level α (power increases with α)
- the degrees of freedom (power decreases with degrees of freedom)
- the sample size (power increases with sample size)

The procedure for computing the power of the D^2 test is as follows:

Step 1: Specify the model completely under H_1. The power can only be computed for a completely specified model, *i.e.*, all parameters must be numerically specified and satisfy H_1.

Step 2: Compute the covariance matrix Σ for the model specified in Step 1. Σ is given by equation (1.4) but can be computed using LISREL. To do this, use any input covariance matrix and set IT=1 and SI= *filename* on the OU command. Σ will then be saved in the file specified by *filename*.

Step 3: Run LISREL under H_0 using the Σ matrix computed in Step 2 as input covariance matrix. The χ^2 measure obtained in this step is the noncentrality parameter λ.

Step 4: Using tables of the noncentral χ^2 distribution with noncentrality parameter λ and degrees of freedom $d = t - u$, determine the probability of obtaining a value larger than the $(1 - \alpha)$ percentile of the central χ^2 distribution with d degrees of freedom. Rather than using the tables of the non-central chi-square distribution, it may be more convenient to use our program LISPOWER (on the LISREL distribution diskette) to calculate the power. Just type LISPOWER and respond to the questions asked by specifying the significance level α, the degrees of freedom d, and the non-centrality parameter λ.

Example 8.2: Hypothesis testing and power calculation

To illustrate tests of hypotheses and power calculation, we use an artificial example. Suppose we have a random sample of 100 cases observed on x_1, x_2, y_1, y_2, y_3, and y_4 with the following sample covariance matrix:

$$S = \begin{pmatrix} 1.531 & & & & & \\ .579 & .991 & & & & \\ .644 & .502 & 1.449 & & & \\ .262 & .276 & .445 & .718 & & \\ .418 & .286 & .492 & .249 & 1.111 & \\ .464 & .279 & .523 & .276 & .657 & 1.144 \end{pmatrix}.$$

We are interested in the model shown in Figure 8.2. In particular, we are interested in whether $\gamma_{21} = 0$, i.e., whether the effect of ξ on η_2 is only indirect via η_1.

To test the hypothesis H_0: $\gamma_{21} = 0$, we first run LISREL under H_1 using the following command file.

```
EXAMPLE 8.2 Run 1. Using sample covariance matrix and Model H1
DA NI=6 NO=100
CM FI=EX82.COV
MO NY=4 NX=2 NE=2 NK=1 BE=SD PS=DI
FR LY(2,1) LY(4,2) LX(2)
VA 1 LY(1,1) LY(3,2) LX(1)
OU SE TV
```

This run gives a $\chi^2 = 1.97$ with six degrees of freedom, indicating that model H_1 fits well. The estimate of γ_{21} is 0.391 with a t-value of 1.80. Using this as a test statistic, H_0 cannot be rejected at the 5 percent level since the t-value does not exceed 1.96, the 97.5 percentile of the standard normal distribution. Next we run LISREL under H_0 to obtain the other two test statistics. Except for the title lines we can use the same command file and just add the command FI GA(2,1) and add MI on the OU command.

This run gives $\chi^2 = 4.52$ with seven degrees of freedom; the modification index for γ_{21} is 2.695. The D^2 statistic is computed as: $D^2 = 4.52 - 1.97 = 2.55$. Thus both D^2 and the modification index are non-significant at the 5 percent level since they do not exceed 3.84, the 95th percentile of the χ^2 distribution with one degree of freedom.

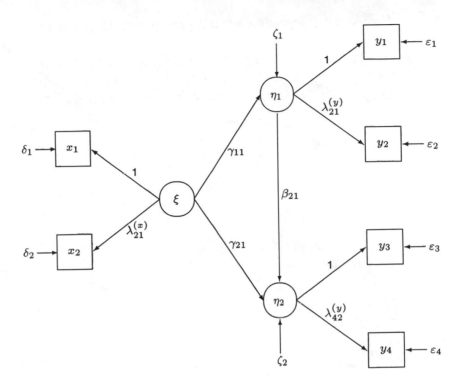

Figure 8.2   Hypothetical Model for Example 8.2

To calculate the power of the D^2 test we follow the steps outlined in the previous section.

Step 1: We are interested in testing $H_0 : \gamma_{21} = 0$ against the alternative $H_1 : \gamma_{21} = 0.3$, say. However, all the parameters of the H_1 model must be specified numerically. We choose these such that the parameter matrices in LISREL are:

$$\Lambda_y = \begin{pmatrix} 1 & 0 \\ .7 & 0 \\ 0 & 1 \\ 0 & .6 \end{pmatrix} \qquad \Theta_\epsilon = \text{diag}(.5, .5, .5, .5)$$

$$\Lambda_x = \begin{pmatrix} 1 \\ .8 \end{pmatrix} \qquad \Theta_\delta = \text{diag}(.5, .5)$$

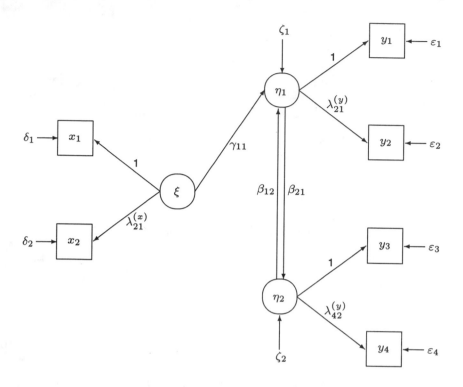

Figure 8.3   Equivalent Model

$$\mathbf{B} = \begin{pmatrix} 0 & 0 \\ .4 & 0 \end{pmatrix} \quad \mathbf{\Gamma} = \begin{pmatrix} .5 \\ .3 \end{pmatrix} \quad \mathbf{\Phi} = (1) \quad \mathbf{\Psi} = \mathrm{diag}(.5, .5)$$

Step 2: To illustrate how Σ can be computed, we use a command file with an identity matrix as input covariance matrix. The sample covariance matrix or any other positive definite matrix may also be used.

```
EXAMPLE 8.2 Run 3. Computing Sigma
DA NI=6 NO=100
CM
1 0 1  2*0 1  3*0 1  4*0 1  5*0 1
MO NY=4 NX=2 NE=2 NK=1 BE=FU,FI GA=FI PH=FI PS=DI,FI TE=FI TD=FI
MA LY
1 0 .7 0 0 1 0 .6
MA LX
1 .8
```

```
MA BE
0 0 .4 0
MA GE
.5 .3
MA PH
1
MA PS
.5 .5
MA TE
.5 .5 .5 .5
MA TD
.5 .5
OU SI=EX82.SIG
```

The resulting Σ in file EX82.SIG is

$$\Sigma = \begin{pmatrix} 1.250 & & & & & \\ .525 & .868 & & & & \\ .450 & .315 & 1.330 & & & \\ .270 & .189 & .498 & .799 & & \\ .500 & .350 & .500 & .300 & 1.500 & \\ .400 & .280 & .400 & .240 & .800 & 1.140 \end{pmatrix}.$$

Step 3: The command file for this step is the same as in run 1 except that the file EX82.SIG is used instead of EX82.COV, *i.e.*, Σ is "analyzed" instead of **S**. This results in $\chi^2 = 3.12$, which is the required non-centrality parameter λ. Note that this value is approximately the same as the modification index for γ_{21}.

Step 4: The power computed by our LISPOWER program for $d = 1$, $\alpha = 0.05$, and $\lambda = 3.12$ is 0.42.

8.3 Equivalent models

By merely observing y_1 and y_2, one cannot infer whether y_1 causes y_2 (Figure 8.4, Part A) or y_2 causes y_1 (Figure 8.4, Part B). In fact, all one can do is to determine whether or not y_1 and y_2 are correlated (Figure 8.4, Part C). For causal inference, one must know something more than just the observed values of y_1 and y_2. For example, such additional information may come from:

- An experiment in which values of y_1 are controlled or manipulated to produce effects on y_2; then models B and C can be excluded *a priori*.
- A longitudinal design in which y_1 is measured or observed before y_2; this excludes model B.
- A substantive theory for the mechanism that generate values of y_1 and y_2, such that model B, say, can be excluded.

These well-known facts can be extended to more complex situations. If there are three y-variables, y_1, y_2, and y_3, many models are possible depending on the causal ordering of the three variables. Figure 8.5, Parts A–C, shows three models in which y_1 is first. There will be three similar models with y_2 first and three more with y_3 first. We may also include the "model" in Figure 8.5, Part D. Hence there are at least ten possible models for three y-variables. With four y-variables there are 24 models just within the class of recursive models. If we allow correlated error terms or reciprocal causation or both, there will be many more.

Such models are *equivalent* in the sense that they all fit a given dataset equally well. To claim that only one particular model is valid, one must be able to exclude logically all the other equivalent models.

Equivalent models have the same number of independent parameters, the same fitted residuals and the same goodness-of-fit measures (χ^2, GFI, AGFI, and RMR). In the examples just considered all the models are "saturated" in the sense that they fit the data perfectly, *i.e.*, all residuals are zero. However, equivalent models also exist for overidentified models. For instance, in the examples just considered, if we replace all the y-variables with η-variables and add y-variables assumed to measure these η-variables, then all these models are still equivalent, regardless of the structure of the measurement model for the y-variables. These models are equivalent but they do not have a perfect fit. As a second example, consider the models in Figures 8.2 and 8.3. These are equivalent but they are not saturated.

How can equivalent models be recognized?

Suppose we have an overidentified model which does not fit the data well. We can then examine the modification indices for the fixed parameters. If

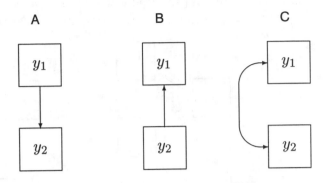

Figure 8.4   **Equivalent Models with Two y-Variables**

some of these are equal, this indicates that the corresponding models are equivalent. To illustrate this we use the data from Example 8.2 Run 2.

Two of the modification indices are equal to 2.695, namely for β_{12} and γ_{21}. This indicates that the two models of Figures 8.2 and 8.3 are equivalent. Note that the output also shows that if β_{12} is freed, $\hat{\beta}_{12}$ will be negative, whereas if γ_{21} is freed, $\hat{\gamma}_{21}$ will be positive. If negative values of β_{12} are unreasonable or undesirable, this result can be used to exclude the model in Figure 8.3 in favor of the model in Figure 8.3.

It should be noted that the modification indices for β_{12} and γ_{21} will be equal regardless of what covariance matrix is analyzed. For example, it can be verified that if the population covariance matrix is analyzed instead, the two modification indices will both be 3.262.

Model equivalence is a property of models independently of the data being analyzed. Equivalent models represent *different* (conceptual) parameterizations of the same covariance matrix. For two equivalent models there is usually a one-to-one transformation between the two sets of parameters.

The problem of model equivalence should not be confused with the problem of identification. In the identification problem we have a *given* parameterization of a model and ask whether there are two or more sets of parameter *values* that generate the same covariance matrix.

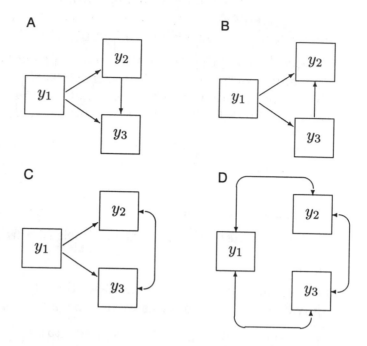

Figure 8.5   Equivalent Models with Three y-Variables

Specification searches

The LISREL methodology works best when it is applied to designed studies based on a definite theory and with a clear objective. The initial model of the investigator need not be correct or best for the data, but the number of alternative models should be fairly limited. However, LISREL has often been applied to more exploratory situations in which the initial model is set up more or less arbitrarily and then successively modified, perhaps numerous times, so as to improve the parsimony and fit of the model. This process has been termed *specification search*. Search procedures are supposed to detect and correct for *specification errors*. Specification errors represent a lack of correspondence between a model studied and the "true" model characterizing the population and variables under study. The goal of the search procedure is to find a model which fits the data well and in which all parameters have real significance and substantive meaning. After such an exploratory search it is important that the final model is cross-validated on a different data set.

A typical step in the specification search procedure involves the examination and assessment of fit of the current model, in particular, the t-values of estimated parameters and the modification indices for fixed parameters. The modification of the model may involve:

☐ elimination of parameters with small t-values

☐ adding parameters with a large modification index

Because there may be many equivalent models and many models that fit the data *about* the same, these steps must be used with very careful judgment. LISREL can only discriminate sharply between models that fit the data *very badly* and those that fit the data *fairly well*. One should only add a parameter if its estimated value can be interpreted and justified from a substantive point of view. The table of modification indices also contains values of estimated change, *i.e.*, in what direction and to what extent the parameter will change if it is set free. This can be used to exclude models for which a parameter changes in the wrong direction.

It is best to change only one parameter in each step but it does not have to be the one with the largest modification index. If it makes more sense from a substantive point of view to free a parameter with a smaller modification index this could (should) be done.

Eliminating a parameter on the basis of its t-value may also be dangerous, especially in a small sample. Even non-significant parameters may be of practical importance. If the substantive theory suggests that a particular parameter should be included in the model, it is probably better to retain it even though it is not significant, because the sample size may be too small to detect its real significance. This can be examined more closely by hypothesis testing and power calculation; see Section 8.2.

In exploratory situations with many variables and weak or non-existing substantive theory, LISREL is probably not a useful tool. For exploring measurement models (Submodel 1) one should use exploratory factor analysis, and for exploring structural relationships (Submodel 2) one can regress every variable on all other variables, an option that is included in PRELIS.

9   Multi-sample analysis

9.1   Analysis based on covariance matrices

In the previous chapters we have shown how LISREL models and LISREL methodology can be used to analyze data from a single sample. LISREL can also be used to analyze data from several samples simultaneously according to LISREL models for each group with some or all parameters constrained to be equal over groups.

Consider a set of G populations. These may be different nations, states, or regions, culturally or socioeconomically different groups, groups of individuals selected on the basis of some known or unknown selection variables, groups receiving different treatments, etc. In fact, they may be any set of mutually exclusive groups of individuals that are clearly defined. It is assumed that a number of variables have been measured on a number of individuals from each population. This approach is particularly useful in comparing a number of treatment and control groups, regardless of whether individuals have been assigned to the groups randomly or not.

It is assumed that a LISREL model of the form (1.1), (1.2), and (1.3) holds in each group. The model for group g is defined by the parameter matrices

$$\Lambda_y^{(g)}, \ \Lambda_x^{(g)}, \ \mathbf{B}^{(g)}, \ \Gamma^{(g)}, \ \Phi^{(g)}, \ \Psi^{(g)}, \ \Theta_\epsilon^{(g)}, \ \Theta_\delta^{(g)} \ ,$$

where the superscript (g) refers to the g-th group, $g = 1, 2, \ldots, G$. Each of these matrices may contain fixed, free, and constrained parameters as before. If there are no constraints across groups, each group can be analyzed separately. However, if there are constraints across groups, the data from all groups must be analyzed simultaneously to get fully efficient estimates of the parameters.

Multi-sample LISREL analysis can be used to test whether the covariance or correlation matrices of the observed variables are equal for different groups.

To test the equality of covariance matrices of $\mathbf{x}$, one specifies $\Lambda_x^{(g)} = \mathbf{I}$ and $\Theta_\delta^{(g)} = \mathbf{0}$ for all groups and tests the hypothesis that $\mathbf{\Phi}^{(1)} = \mathbf{\Phi}^{(2)} = \cdots = \mathbf{\Phi}^{(G)}$.

To test the equality of correlation matrices of $\mathbf{x}$, one specifies that $\Theta_\delta^{(g)} = \mathbf{0}$ for all groups and that $\Lambda_x^{(g)}$ is a diagonal matrix of standard deviations of $\mathbf{x}$ for the g-th group. The test of equality of correlation matrices is then equivalent to the specification that

$$\mathbf{\Phi}^{(1)} = \mathbf{\Phi}^{(2)} = \cdots = \mathbf{\Phi}^{(G)} \,,$$

all $\mathbf{\Phi}$-matrices having ones in the diagonal. The standard deviations in the diagonal of the Λ_x-matrices are estimated from the data and their estimates are not necessarily equal to the sample standard deviations in each group.

One can also test various forms of less strong equalities. For example, with measurement models of the forms (1.2) and (1.3), if the measurement properties of the observed variables are the same in all groups, one would postulate that

$$\Lambda_y^{(1)} = \Lambda_y^{(2)} = \cdots = \Lambda_y^{(G)} \,,$$
$$\Lambda_x^{(1)} = \Lambda_x^{(2)} = \cdots = \Lambda_x^{(G)} \,,$$

and perhaps also that

$$\Theta_\epsilon^{(1)} = \Theta_\epsilon^{(2)} = \cdots = \Theta_\epsilon^{(G)} \,,$$
$$\Theta_\delta^{(1)} = \Theta_\delta^{(2)} = \cdots = \Theta_\delta^{(G)} \,.$$

The possible differences between groups would then be represented by differences in the distributions of the latent variables, $i.e..$, by $\mathbf{\Phi}^{(g)}$ and $\mathbf{\Psi}^{(g)}$. By postulating

$$\mathbf{B}^{(1)} = \mathbf{B}^{(2)} = \cdots = \mathbf{B}^{(G)} \,,$$
$$\mathbf{\Gamma}^{(1)} = \mathbf{\Gamma}^{(2)} = \cdots = \mathbf{\Gamma}^{(G)} \,,$$

one can test the hypothesis that the structural relations are also invariant over groups.

In general, any degree of invariance can be tested, from the one extreme where all parameters are assumed to be invariant over groups to the other extreme when there are no constraints across groups. For example, if $\mathbf{\Phi}^{(g)}$, $g = 1, 2, \ldots, G$, are matrices of order 3×3, one can specify that $\phi_{31}^{(g)}$, $\phi_{32}^{(g)}$, and $\phi_{33}^{(g)}$ should be equal across groups whereas $\phi_{11}^{(g)}$, $\phi_{21}^{(g)}$, and $\phi_{22}^{(g)}$ are free parameters for each group.

To estimate all the models simultaneously, LISREL minimizes the fit function

$$F = \sum_{g=1}^{G} (N_g/N) F_g(\mathbf{S}^{(g)}, \mathbf{\Sigma}^{(g)}, \mathbf{W}^{(g)}) \,, \tag{9.1}$$

where F_g is any of the fit functions defined in the sections *Unweighted least squares (ULS)* on page 20 through *Diagonally weighted least-squares (DWLS)* on page 23, *i.e.*, ULS, GLS, ML, DWLS, and WLS. Here N_g is the sample size in group g and $N = N_1 + N_2 + \cdots + N_G$ is the total sample size; $\mathbf{S}_g$ and $\mathbf{\Sigma}_g$ are the sample and population covariance matrices in group g, and $\mathbf{W}^{(g)}$ is the weight matrix for group g. When $G = 1$, (9.1) reduces to the fit function (1.15) defined in the section *Generally weighted least-squares (WLS)* on page 21.

Initial estimates are first computed by IV and TSLS for each group separately, as before, ignoring all equality constraints among groups. Parameters which are specified to be equal across groups are then replaced by their mean value.

As before, the χ^2 goodness-of-fit measure is defined as N times the minimum of F. This is a measure of the fit of all LISREL models in all groups, including all constraints, to the data from all groups. The degrees of freedom are

$$d = \frac{1}{2}G(p+q)(p+q+1) - t \,, \tag{9.2}$$

where t is the total number of independent parameters estimated in all groups. Thus, in a multi-sample analysis, only one χ^2 goodness-of-fit measure is given, whereas the GFI, AGFI, and RMR measures are given for each group.

9.2 Command file for multi-sample analysis

The command files are stacked after each other. They are set up as described in Chapter 2, with the following additional rules:

◇ NG must be defined on the DA command for the first group.

◇ For each group g ($g = 2, 3, \ldots, G$), every option or keyword that has the same value as in the previous group may be omitted.

◇ Pattern matrices and non-zero fixed values as well as starting values are defined as before. A matrix element such as BE(4,3), with one or two indices, refers to the element in the current group. To refer to an element in another group one must use three indices where the first one refers to the group number. For example, BE(2,4,3) refers to β_{43} in $\mathbf{B}^{(2)}$.

◇ To define equality constraints between groups, one specifies the constrained elements as free for the first group, and equality constraints in each of the other groups. For example, if β_{43} is to be invariant over groups, one specifies

> in group 1: FR BE(4,3)
> in group 2: EQ BE(1,4,3) BE(4,3)
> in group 3: EQ BE(1,4,3) BE(4,3), etc.

◇ If a matrix is specified as ID or ZE in group 1, it must not be specified as DI, FU, or SY in subsequent groups. Similarly, if a matrix is specified as DI in group 1, it must not be specified as FU or SY in any subsequent group.

◇ In addition to the matrix specifications described for the MO command in Chapter 2, the following specifications are possible on the MO command for groups $2, 3, \ldots, G$:

> o SP means that the matrix has the *same pattern* of fixed and free elements as the corresponding matrix in the previous group.
> o SS means that the matrix will be given the *same starting values* as the corresponding matrix in the previous group.
> o PS means *same pattern and starting values* as the corresponding matrix in the previous group.
> o IN means that the matrix is *invariant* over groups, *i.e.*., all parameter matrices have the same pattern of fixed and free elements, and

all elements which are defined as free in group 1 are supposed to be equal across groups.

In principle, NY, NX, NE, and NK must all be the same in all groups. However, if the numbers of variables are different in different groups, it is possible to introduce pseudo-variables (observed or latent) so as to make the number of variables equal in all groups. These pseudo-variables are artificial variables that, if chosen properly, have no effects on anything (see Example 10.3).

Important Note: *The number of variables and the form (ZE, ID, DI, SY, FU) of each parameter matrix is specified on the MO command for the first group. These specifications must not be contradicted by a different specification on the MO command for subsequent groups. This does not refer to the specification of a fixed or free matrix, the matrix mode.*

Example 9.1: Testing equality of factor structures

Source: Sörbom (1976).

The covariance matrices in Table 9.1 are based on scores on the ETS Sequential Test of Educational Progress (STEP) for two groups of boys who took the test in both Grade 5 and Grade 7. The two groups were defined according to whether or not they were in the academic curriculum in Grade 12.

A *Test the hypothesis $H_\Sigma : \Sigma^{(1)} = \Sigma^{(2)}$*

B *Assuming that a measurement (factor analysis) model of the form $x = \Lambda_x \xi + \delta$ holds in both groups, test the hypothesis that there are two correlated common factors in both groups with a factor pattern of the form*

$$\Lambda_x = \begin{pmatrix} * & 0 \\ * & 0 \\ 0 & * \\ 0 & * \end{pmatrix}$$

C *Assuming* **B***, test the hypothesis $H_\Lambda : \Lambda_x^{(1)} = \Lambda_x^{(2)}$*

D *Assuming* **C***, test the hypothesis $H_{\Lambda\Theta} : \Theta_\delta^{(1)} = \Theta_\delta^{(2)}$*

E *Assuming* **D***, test the hypothesis $H_{\Lambda\Phi\Theta} : \Phi^{(1)} = \Phi^{(2)}$*

Table 9.1　Covariance Matrices for STEP Reading and Writing for Academic and Non-Academic Boys

Boys Academic ($N = 373$)				
STEP Reading, Grade 5	281.349			
STEP Writing, Grade 5	184.219	182.821		
STEP Reading, Grade 7	216.739	171.699	283.289	
STEP Writing, Grade 7	198.376	153.201	208.837	246.069

Boys Non-Academic ($N = 249$)				
STEP Reading, Grade 5	174.485			
STEP Writing, Grade 5	134.468	161.869		
STEP Reading, Grade 7	129.840	118.836	228.449	
STEP Writing, Grade 7	102.194	97.767	136.058	180.460

All five problems may be solved by using a LISREL Submodel 1, *i.e.*,

$$\mathbf{x} = \mathbf{\Lambda}_x \mathbf{\xi} + \mathbf{\delta} \ .$$

In problem **A**, we set $\mathbf{\Lambda}_x^{(1)} = \mathbf{\Lambda}_x^{(2)} = \mathbf{I}$ and $\mathbf{\Theta}_\delta^{(1)} = \mathbf{\Theta}_\delta^{(2} = \mathbf{0}$. This means that $\mathbf{x} \equiv \mathbf{\xi}$ so that $\mathbf{\Sigma}^{(g)} = \mathbf{\Phi}^{(g)}$ for $g = 1, 2$. The hypothesis $\mathbf{\Sigma}^{(1)} = \mathbf{\Sigma}^{(2)}$ is therefore the same as $\mathbf{\Phi}^{(1)} = \mathbf{\Phi}^{(2)}$. The command file is extremely simple, as follows (the data file EX91.DAT contains both labels and covariance matrices).

```
TESTING EQUALITY OF FACTOR STRUCTURES. HYPOTHESIS A.    GROUP BA
GROUP: BOYS ACADEMIC
DA NG=2 NI=4 NO=373
LA FI=EX91.DAT; CM FI=EX91.DAT
MO NX=4 NK=4 LX=ID TD=ZE
OU
TESTING EQUALITY OF FACTOR STRUCTURES. HYPOTHESIS A.    GROUP BNA
GROUP: BOYS NON-ACADEMIC
DA NO=249
LA FI=EX91.DAT; CM FI=EX91.DAT
MO PH=IN
OU
```

In group 1, Φ is free by default. In group 2, Φ is declared invariant (PH=IN). Note that on the MO command for the second group, the parameters NX, NK, LX, and TD need not be given since they are the same as for the first group.

In problem **B**, we assume a common factor model with two common factors and leave $\Phi(2 \times 2)$ to be a free covariance matrix in both groups. To fix the scale for the two factors ξ_1 and ξ_2, we fix the elements λ_{11} and λ_{32} of Λ_x equal to one for both groups. The other elements λ_{21} and λ_{42} and the diagonal elements of Θ_δ are free in both groups. The hypothesis in problem **B** does not impose any equality constraints on parameters; it only states that the *number* of factors is the same for both groups. The command file for problem **B** is:

```
TESTING EQUALITY OF FACTOR STRUCTURES.   HYPOTHESIS B. GROUP BA
GROUP: BOYS ACADEMIC
DA NG=2 NI=4 NO=373
LA FI=EX91.DAT; CM FI=EX91.DAT
MO NX=4 NK=2
FR LX 2 1 LX 4 2
VA 1 LX 1 1 LX 3 2
OU
TESTING EQUALITY OF FACTOR STRUCTURES.   HYPOTHESIS B. GROUP BNA
GROUP: BOYS NON-ACADEMIC
DA NO=249
LA FI=EX91.DAT; CM FI=EX91.DAT
MO LX=PS
OU
```

The matrices $\Phi^{(1)}$ and $\Phi^{(2)}$ are both free by default. The matrices $\Theta_\delta^{(1)}$ and $\Theta_\delta^{(2)}$ are diagonal and free, also by default. The elements λ_{21} and λ_{42} are declared free in group one. Starting values for these are estimated by the program using two-stage least-squares. In group 2, Λ_x is specified to have the same pattern and the same starting values as for group 1 (LX=PS).

As no equality constraints across groups are imposed, the overall χ^2-value obtained in problem **B** is the sum of the two χ^2's that would be obtained if the two groups were analyzed separately.

In problems **C**, **D**, and **E**, the input for group 1 is the same as in problem **B**. In problem **C**, the input for group 2 differs from that of problem **B**

Table 9.2   Summary of Results for Example 9.1

Problem	Hypothesis	χ^2	df	p-value	Decision
A	H_Σ	38.08	10	0.000	Rejected
B	$H_{n=2}$	1.52	2	0.468	Accepted
C	H_Λ	8.77	4	0.067	Accepted
D	$H_{\Lambda\Theta}$	21.55	8	0.006	Rejected
E	$H_{\Lambda\Phi\Theta}$	38.22	11	0.000	Rejected

only in that Λ_x is declared invariant, *i.e..*, LX=IN instead of only LX=PS. In problem **D**, TD=IN in addition and in problem **E**, PH=IN in addition. The command files for the three problems may be stacked together to let LIS-REL analyze hypotheses **C**, **D**, and **E** in one run.

In the output file from a multi-sample analysis, all requested parts of the output are given for each group. Note that the GFI and the root mean squared residual are given for each group, but the χ^2 measure is only given for the last group. This χ^2 is a measure of the overall fit of *all* models in *all* groups.

The results of the tests are given in Table 9.2. The most reasonable hypothesis to retain is H_Λ. The two groups have an invariant factor pattern, but there is some evidence that they differ in error variances and in factor covariance matrices.

Example 9.2: Testing equality of factor correlation matrices

Source: Werts, *et al.* (1976).

Table 9.3 gives observed covariance matrices for two random samples ($N_1 = 865$, $N_2 = 900$, *respectively*) *of candidates who took the Scholastic Aptitude Test in January 1971. The four measures are, in order:*

$x_1 =$ *a 40-item verbal aptitude section*
$x_2 =$ *a separately timed 50-item verbal aptitude section*
$x_3 =$ *a 35-item math aptitude section*
$x_4 =$ *a separately timed 25-item math aptitude section*

Table 9.3   Covariance Matrices for SAT Verbal and Math Sections

Tests	Group 1	Group 2
x_1	63.382	67.898
x_2	70.984 110.237	72.301 107.330
x_3	41.710 52.747 60.584	40.549 55.347 63.203
x_4	30.218 37.489 36.392 32.295	28.976 38.896 39.261 35.403

We use the data to illustrate how one can test equality of factor correlations in a confirmatory factor analysis model. In problem **D** of the previous example, it was postulated that factor patterns in Λ_x and error variances in Θ_δ are invariant over groups. This means that differences between groups, if any, must manifest themselves in different factor covariance matrices Φ. By contrast, in this example, we allow Λ_x and Θ_δ to vary over groups and test the hypothesis that the correlation between the two factors is the same in both groups.

The model is a LISREL Submodel 1 with

$$\Lambda_x = \begin{pmatrix} * & 0 \\ * & 0 \\ 0 & * \\ 0 & * \end{pmatrix} \qquad \Phi = \begin{pmatrix} 1 & \\ * & 1 \end{pmatrix} \qquad \Theta_\delta = \mathrm{diag} \begin{pmatrix} * \\ * \\ * \\ * \end{pmatrix}$$

and the test is $\phi_{21}^{(1)} = \phi_{21}^{(2)}$.

The command file is:

```
TESTING EQUALITY OF FACTOR CORRELATIONS    GROUP 1
DATA      NG=2 NI=4 NO=865;     CMATRIX FI=EX92.COV
MODEL     NX=4 NK=2 PH=FI
VALUE 1   PH 1 1 PH 2 2
FREE      LX 1 1 LX 2 1 LX 3 2 LX 4 2 PH 2 1
OUTPUT
TESTING EQUALITY OF FACTOR CORRELATIONS    GROUP 2
DATA      NI=4 NO=900;          CMATRIX FI=EX92.COV
MODEL     PH=IN
FREE      LX 1 1 LX 2 1 LX 3 2 LX 4 2
OUTPUT
```

The overall goodness-of-fit measure for the model with the equality constraint imposed is $\chi^2 = 4.03$ with three degrees of freedom. When the equality constraint is relaxed, χ^2 drops to 2.18, so obviously the model is good and the hypothesis of equal factor correlations is tenable. The common correlation is estimated at 0.765.

Example 9.3: Son's and parents' reports of parental socioeconomic characteristics

Source: Mare & Mason (1981).

Table 9.4 gives the covariance matrices for six variables and three populations. The variables are:

SOFED	*Son's report of father's education*
SOMED	*Son's report of mother's education*
SOFOC	*Son's report of father's occupation*
FAFED	*Father's report of his own education*
MOMED	*Mother's report of her own education*
FAFOC	*Father's report of his own occupation*

The three populations are:

Group 1:	*White Sixth Graders*
Group 2:	*White Ninth Graders*
Group 3:	*White Twelfth Graders*

The model is shown in Figure 9.1, where the latent variables represent the true father's education (Trfed), mother's education (Trmed), and father's occupation (Trfoc), respectively. This model can be specified as a LISREL Submodel 1 with:

$$\Lambda_x = \begin{pmatrix} * & 0 & 0 \\ 0 & * & 0 \\ 0 & 0 & * \\ 1 & 0 & 0 \\ 0 & 1 & 0 \\ 0 & 0 & 1 \end{pmatrix} \quad \Phi = \begin{pmatrix} * & & \\ * & * & \\ * & * & * \end{pmatrix} \quad \Theta_\delta = \begin{pmatrix} * & & & & & \\ * & * & & & & \\ 0 & 0 & * & & & \\ 0 & 0 & 0 & * & & \\ 0 & 0 & 0 & 0 & * & \\ 0 & 0 & 0 & 0 & 0 & * \end{pmatrix}$$

Table 9.4
Covariance Matrices for White Sixth, Ninth, and Twelfth Graders
Son's and Parent's Reports of Parental Socioeconomic Characteristics

	1.	2.	3.	4.	5.	6.
Sixth Grade						
1. SOFED	5.86					
2. SOMED	3.12	3.32				
3. SOFOC	35.28	23.85	622.09			
4. FAFED	4.02	2.14	29.42	5.33		
5. MOMED	2.99	2.55	19.20	3.17	4.64	
6. FAFOC	35.30	26.91	465.62	31.22	23.38	546.01
Ninth Grade						
1. SOFED	8.20					
2. SOMED	3.47	4.36				
3. SOFOC	45.65	22.58	611.63			
4. FAFED	6.39	3.16	44.62	7.32		
5. MOMED	3.22	3.77	23.47	3.33	4.02	
6. FAFOC	45.58	22.01	548.00	40.99	21.43	585.14
Twelfth Grade						
1. SOFED	5.74					
2. SOMED	1.35	2.49				
3. SOFOC	39.24	12.73	535.30			
4. FAFED	4.94	1.65	37.36	5.39		
5. MOMED	1.67	2.32	15.71	1.85	3.06	
6. FAFOC	40.11	12.94	496.86	38.09	14.91	538.76

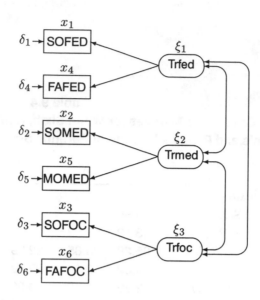

Figure 9.1
Path Diagram for Reports of Parental Socioeconomic Characteristics

Mare & Mason (1981) considered many models. One of them was that Φ and $\theta_{44}^{(\delta)}$, $\theta_{55}^{(\delta)}$, and $\theta_{66}^{(\delta)}$, are invariant over groups and that $\theta_{21}^{(\delta)}$ is zero in Group 3 (but not in the other groups).

A LISREL command file for this model is:

```
SON'S AND PARENTS' REPORTS OF PARENTAL SOCIOECONOMIC CHARACTERISTICS;
GRADE 6
DA   NI=6 NO=80 NG=3
CM
5.86 3.12 3.32 35.28 23.85 622.09 4.02 2.14 29.42 5.33 2.99 2.55 19.20 3.17
4.64 35.30 26.91 465.62 31.22 23.38 546.01
LA;  'SOFED' 'SOMED' 'SOFOC' 'FAFED' 'MOMED' 'FAFOC'
MO   NX=6 NK=3 TD=SY
LK;  'Trfed' 'Trmed' 'Trfoc'
FR   LX 1 1 LX 2 2 LX 3 3 TD 2 1
VA 1 LX 4 1 LX 5 2 LX 6 3
OU   SE TV MI ND=2
```

9 MULTI-SAMPLE ANALYSIS

```
SON'S AND PARENTS' REPORTS OF PARENTAL SOCIOECONOMIC CHARACTERISTICS;
GRADE 9
DA
CM
8.20 3.47 4.36 45.65 22.58 611.63 6.39 3.16 44.62 7.32 3.22 3.77 23.47 3.33
4.02 45.58 22.01 548.00 40.99 21.43 585.14
LA;  'SOFED' 'SOMED' 'SOFOC' 'FAFED' 'MOMED' 'FAFOC'
MO   LX=PS PH=IN TD=SY
LK;  'Trfed' 'Trmed' 'Trfoc'
FR   TD 2 1
EQ   TD 1 4 4 TD 4 4
EQ   TD 1 5 5 TD 5 5
EQ   TD 1 6 6 TD 6 6
OU
SON'S AND PARENTS' REPORTS OF PARENTAL SOCIOECONOMIC CHARACTERISTICS;
GRADE 12
DA
CM
5.74 1.35 2.49 39.24 12.73 535.30 4.94 1.65 37.36 5.39 1.67 2.32 15.71 1.85
3.06 40.11 12.94 496.86 38.09 14.91 538.76
LA;  'SOFED' 'SOMED' 'SOFOC' 'FAFED' 'MOMED' 'FAFOC'
MO   LX=PS PH=IN TD=SY
LK;  'Trfed' 'Trmed' 'Trfoc'
EQ   TD 1 4 4 TD 4 4
EQ   TD 1 5 5 TD 5 5
EQ   TD 1 6 6 TD 6 6
OU
```

The output file reveals the reliabilities (squared multiple correlations) shown in Table 9.5.

Table 9.5   Computed Reliabilities for Example 9.3

	SOFED	SOMED	SOFOC	FAFED	MOMED	FAFOC
Grade 6	.64	.45	.71	.85	.94	.90
Grade 9	.78	.86	.93	.89	.94	.91
Grade 12	.91	.77	.95	.85	.92	.90

This is a somewhat remarkable result because in grade 12, the sons' reports of their fathers' education and occupation are more reliable than the fathers' reports of their own education and occupation.

9.3 Standardized solutions in multi-sample analysis

It is important to understand that in a multi-sample analysis with constraints across groups, one must not standardize the variables within each group. Neither the observed nor the latent variables should be standardized. To compare parameters across groups, the variables must be measured in a common metric for all groups. For example, if $\mathbf{\Lambda}_x$ is invariant over groups when x and ξ are in a common metric, the $\mathbf{\Lambda}_x$-matrices will not be equal when x and/or ξ is standardized within each group if the variances of x and/or ξ are different over groups. This means that sample covariance matrices must be analyzed and the scales of the latent variables must be set by fixing non-zero elements in $\mathbf{\Lambda}_y$ and $\mathbf{\Lambda}_x$ in such a way that the latent variables are on a common scale.

For reasons just stated, the meaning of *standardized solution* (SS) in multi-sample analysis is not what one might think. If SS is requested on the OU command, the program scales the latent variables so that a *weighted average* of their covariance matrix is a correlation matrix, thereby *retaining a scale common to all groups*.

The computation of these standardized solutions is as follows. Let $\hat{\mathbf{\Phi}}^{(g)}$ and $\hat{\mathbf{\Omega}}^{(g)}$ be the covariance matrices of ξ and η in group g, where

$$\hat{\mathbf{\Omega}}^{(g)} = (\mathbf{I} - \hat{\mathbf{B}}^{(g)})^{-1}\hat{\mathbf{\Gamma}}^{(g)}\hat{\mathbf{\Phi}}^{(g)}\hat{\mathbf{\Gamma}}'^{(g)} + \hat{\mathbf{\Phi}}^{(g)})(\mathbf{I} - \hat{\mathbf{B}}'^{(g)})^{-1} \ . \qquad (9.3)$$

Compute

$$\hat{\mathbf{\Phi}} = (1/n)\sum_{g=1}^{G} n_g \hat{\mathbf{\Phi}}^{(g)} \ , \qquad (9.4)$$

$$\hat{\mathbf{\Omega}} = (1/n)\sum_{g=1}^{G} n_g \hat{\mathbf{\Omega}}^{(g)} \ , \qquad (9.5)$$

where $n_g = N_g - 1$, $n = n_1 + n_2 + \cdots + n_G = N - G$. The scale factors for the common metric are then defined as

$$\mathbf{D}_\xi = (\text{diag}[\hat{\mathbf{\Phi}}])^{\frac{1}{2}} \ , \qquad (9.6)$$

$$\mathbf{D}_\eta = (\text{diag}[\hat{\mathbf{\Omega}}])^{\frac{1}{2}} \ . \qquad (9.7)$$

This standardized solution *is not* such that the covariance matrix of the latent variables is a correlation matrix in *each* group. Instead, a weighted average of these covariance matrices is a correlation matrix. By computing the standardized solution in this way, we achieve the property that if $\hat{\Lambda}_y$ and/or $\hat{\Lambda}_x$ are invariant in the unstandardized solution, they will also be so in the standardized solution.

In LISREL output, the standardized solution defined in this way is called SOLUTION STANDARDIZED TO A COMMON METRIC.

To illustrate this, consider the output from Example 9.1, Problem **C** (with the option SS on the OU command).

The $\hat{\Lambda}_x$-matrices in these solutions are the same for both groups and the corresponding $\hat{\Phi}$-matrices are such that

$$\frac{372\hat{\Phi}_1 + 248\hat{\Phi}_2}{620}$$

is a correlation matrix.

LISREL 7 also introduces a solution standardized *within* groups. This standardizes the latent variables to unit variance *for each group*. As before, it does *not* standardize the observed variables. In LISREL output, the relevant section is called: WITHIN GROUP STANDARDIZED SOLUTION.

Again, consider the output from Example 9.1, Problem **C** (with the option SS on the OU command). Now each $\hat{\Phi}$ matrix is a correlation matrix, but the $\hat{\Lambda}_x$ matrices are no longer the same.

As in the case of a single sample, *neither* the solution standardized to a common metric *nor* the within group standardized solution standardizes the observed variables; *they are still retained in their original metric*.

To standardize the observed variables, one must put SC on the OU command. Even in this case, there are two standardized solutions: the WITHIN GROUP COMPLETELY STANDARDIZED SOLUTION and the COMMON METRIC COMPLETELY STANDARDIZED SOLUTION. The first simply standardizes the observed and latent variables within each group as is done for a single group. Equality constraints within and between groups are usually lost. The second SC solution standardizes the observed variables to a common correlately metric, by computing

$$\hat{\Sigma} = (1/n) \sum_{g=1}^{G} n_g \hat{\Sigma}^{(g)} ,$$ (9.8)

where $\hat{\Sigma}^{(g)}$ is the fitted covariance matrix in each group. Let

$$\mathbf{D}_z = (\mathrm{diag}[\hat{\Sigma}])^{\frac{1}{2}} ,$$ (9.9)

and let $\mathbf{D}_y$ and $\mathbf{D}_x$ be the diagonal matrices formed by the first p and the last q elements of $\mathbf{D}_z$, respectively.

For Example 9.1C, the within group completely standardized solution is:

```
TESTING EQUALITY OF FACTOR STRUCTURES.   HYPOTHESIS C. GROUP: BA
WITHIN GROUP COMPLETELY STANDARDIZED SOLUTION

  LAMBDA X

             KSI 1      KSI 2
READ-GR5      .906       .000
WRIT-GR5      .897       .000
READ-GR7      .000       .907
WRIT-GR7      .000       .871

  THETA DELTA

          READ-GR5   WRIT-GR5   READ-GR7   WRIT-GR7
            .180       .195       .178       .242

  PHI

             KSI 1      KSI 2
  KSI 1     1.000
  KSI 2      .935      1.000


TESTING EQUALITY OF FACTOR STRUCTURES.   HYPOTHESIS C. GROUP: BNA
WITHIN GROUP COMPLETELY STANDARDIZED SOLUTION

  LAMBDA X

             KSI 1      KSI 2
READ-GR5      .937       .000
WRIT-GR5      .843       .000
READ-GR7      .000       .841
WRIT-GR7      .000       .800
```

THETA DELTA

READ-GR5	WRIT-GR5	READ-GR7	WRIT-GR7
.122	.290	.293	.360

PHI

	KSI 1	KSI 2
KSI 1	1.000	
KSI 2	.816	1.000

And the common metric completely standardized solution is:

TESTING EQUALITY OF FACTOR STRUCTURES.   HYPOTHESIS C. GROUP: BA
COMMON METRIC COMPLETELY STANDARDIZED SOLUTION

LAMBDA X

	KSI 1	KSI 2
READ-GR5	.915	.000
WRIT-GR5	.879	.000
READ-GR7	.000	.885
WRIT-GR7	.000	.847

PHI

	KSI 1	KSI 2
KSI 1	1.134	
KSI 2	1.071	1.157

TESTING EQUALITY OF FACTOR STRUCTURES.   HYPOTHESIS C. GROUP: BNA
COMMON METRIC COMPLETELY STANDARDIZED SOLUTION

LAMBDA X

	KSI 1	KSI 2
READ-GR5	.915	.000
WRIT-GR5	.879	.000
READ-GR7	.000	.885
WRIT-GR7	.000	.847

PHI

	KSI 1	KSI 2
KSI 1	.799	
KSI 2	.638	.764

In this solution both observed and latent variables are standardized to a common metric and Λ_x is still invariant. Such a common metric facilitates comparison of factor variances and covariances. Note that the factor variances and covariances are larger in group 1 than in group 2.

Example 9.4: Subjective and objective social class

Source: Sörbom & Jöreskog (1981).

Table 9.6 presents data on subjective and objective social class. There are three variables measuring objective status and four variables measuring subjective status. The objective status measures are:

- *Education – indicated by five categories ranging from less than ninth grade to college graduate.*
- *Occupation – indicated by the two-digit Duncan SEI score.*
- *Income – indicated by the total yearly family income before taxes in 1967, coded in units of $2,000 and ranging from under $2,000 to $16,000 or more.*

All subjective class indicators were structured questions asking respondents to place themselves in one of four class categories: lower, working, middle, or upper. The questions asked the respondents to indicate which social class they felt their occupation, income, way of life, and influence

Table 9.6   Correlations, Means and Standard Deviations for Indicators of Objective Class and Subjective Class

Variables	y_1	y_2	y_3	x_1	x_2	x_3	x_4	Mean	(s.d.)
EDUC	—	.404	.268	.216	.233	.211	.207	1.274	(1.106)
OCC	.495	—	.220	.277	.183	.270	.157	2.347	(1.622)
INC	.398	.292	—	.268	.424	.325	.282	4.041	(2.097)
SC-OCC	.218	.282	.184	—	.550	.574	.482	1.288	(0.747)
SC-INC	.299	.166	.383	.386	—	.647	.517	1.129	(0.814)
SC-LST	.272	.161	.321	.396	.553	—	.647	1.235	(0.786)
SC-INF	.269	.169	.191	.382	.456	.534	—	1.318	(0.859)
Mean	1.655	3.670	5.040	1.543	1.548	1.542	1.601		
(s.d.)	(1.203)	(2.128)	(2.198)	(0.640)	(0.670)	(0.623)	(0.624)		

Data for Whites Below Diagonal and for Blacks Above Diagonal
N(Whites) = 432 N(Blacks) = 368

9 MULTI-SAMPLE ANALYSIS

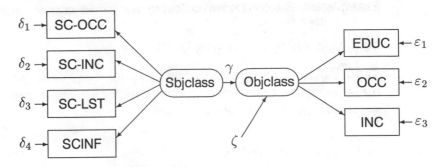

Figure 9.2   Path Diagram for Subjective and Objective Social Class

were most like. The criteria, in terms of which class self-placements were made, correspond directly to the Weberian dimensions of economic class (occupation and income), status (lifestyle), and power (influence).

For the present purpose we consider the model of Figure 9.2. We want to test whether the relationship between objective and subjective class is the same for whites and blacks. We do this by testing the equality of the structural parameter γ.

The analysis reveals that the model fits very badly; $\chi^2 = 121.76$ with 27 degrees of freedom. The modification index for $\theta_{21}^{(\epsilon)}$ is large for both groups. This indicates that the objective class measures are not congeneric. Education and occupation correlate more than can be accounted for by objective class. Allowing ϵ_1 and ϵ_2 to correlate freely in both groups gives $\chi^2 = 86.93$ with 25 degrees of freedom. Relaxing the equality constraint on γ gives $\chi^2 = 76.90$ with 24 degrees of freedom. The drop in χ^2 is 10.03 which is significant at the 0.5 percent level, so the hypothesis of equal γ must be rejected. The estimates of γ, with standard errors in parentheses, are:

Whites: $\hat{\gamma} = 1.345(0.210)$
Blacks: $\hat{\gamma} = 0.631(0.119)$

The command file for the last model is:

```
LISREL MODEL FOR SUBJECTIVE AND OBJECTIVE SOCIAL CLASS   WHITES
DA NG=2 NI=7 NO=432
LA FI=EX94.DAT
KM FI=EX94.DAT
SD FI=EX94.DAT
MO NY=3 NX=4 NE=1 NK=1 LY=FR LX=FR TE=SY
LE
Objclass
LK
Sbjclass
FR TE 2 1
FI LY 1 LX 1
VA 1 LY 1 LX 1
OU MI SE
LISREL MODEL FOR SUBJECTIVE AND OBJECTIVE SOCIAL CLASS   BLACKS
DA NI=7 NO=368
LA FI=EX94.DAT
KM FI=EX94.DAT
SD FI=EX94.DAT
MO
LE
Objclass
LK
Sbjclass
FR TE 2 1
FI LY 1 LX 1
VA 1 LY 1 LX 1
OU
```

Note that the file EX94.DAT contains labels, correlations, and standard deviations.

10 LISREL with mean structures

10.1 The extended LISREL model

In Chapter 1 the LISREL model was defined by (1.1), (1.2), and (1.3), in which all random variables were assumed to have zero means. This assumption will now be relaxed and the model will be extended to include four new parameter matrices in addition to the previous eight. These new parameter matrices contain intercept term in the relationships and mean values of the latent variables.

The LISREL model is now defined by the following three equations corresponding to (1.1), (1.2), and (1.3), respectively:

$$\boldsymbol{\eta} = \boldsymbol{\alpha} + \mathbf{B}\boldsymbol{\eta} + \boldsymbol{\Gamma}\boldsymbol{\xi} + \boldsymbol{\zeta} \ , \tag{10.1}$$

$$\mathbf{y} = \boldsymbol{\tau}_y + \boldsymbol{\Lambda}_y\boldsymbol{\eta} + \boldsymbol{\epsilon} \ , \tag{10.2}$$

$$\mathbf{x} = \boldsymbol{\tau}_x + \boldsymbol{\Lambda}_x\boldsymbol{\xi} + \boldsymbol{\delta} \ , \tag{10.3}$$

where $\boldsymbol{\alpha}$, $\boldsymbol{\tau}_y$, and $\boldsymbol{\tau}_x$ are vectors of constant intercept terms. As before, we assume that $\boldsymbol{\zeta}$ is uncorrelated with $\boldsymbol{\xi}$, $\boldsymbol{\epsilon}$ is uncorrelated with $\boldsymbol{\eta}$ and that $\boldsymbol{\delta}$ is uncorrelated with $\boldsymbol{\xi}$. We also assume, as before, that $E(\boldsymbol{\zeta}) = \mathbf{0}$, $E(\boldsymbol{\epsilon}) = \mathbf{0}$, and $E(\boldsymbol{\delta}) = \mathbf{0}$, but it is not assumed that $E(\boldsymbol{\xi})$ and $E(\boldsymbol{\eta})$ are zero (E is the expected value operator). The mean of $\boldsymbol{\xi}$, $E(\boldsymbol{\xi})$, will be a parameter denoted by $\boldsymbol{\kappa}$. The mean of $\boldsymbol{\eta}$, $E(\boldsymbol{\eta})$, is obtained by taking the expectation of (10.1):

$$E(\boldsymbol{\eta}) = (\mathbf{I} - \mathbf{B})^{-1}(\boldsymbol{\alpha} + \boldsymbol{\Gamma}\boldsymbol{\kappa}) \ . \tag{10.4}$$

By taking the expectations of (10.2) and (10.3), we find the mean vectors of the observed variables to be

$$\boldsymbol{\mu}_y = \boldsymbol{\tau}_y + \boldsymbol{\Lambda}_y(\mathbf{I} - \mathbf{B})^{-1}(\boldsymbol{\alpha} + \boldsymbol{\Gamma}\boldsymbol{\kappa}) \ , \tag{10.5}$$

$$\mu_x = \tau_x + \Lambda_x \kappa \ . \qquad (10.6)$$

In general, in a single population, all the mean parameters τ_y, τ_x, α, and κ will not be identified without further conditions imposed. However, in simultaneous analysis of data from several groups, simple conditions (see Jöreskog & Sörbom, 1985) can be imposed to make all the mean parameters identified.

The LISREL model with mean structures introduces four new parameter matrices (actually vectors): τ_y, τ_x, α, and κ. These parameter matrices can be referred to in the same way as the other parameter matrices in LISREL. The LISREL notation and default forms for these are shown in Table 10.1. Each of these parameter matrices is fixed at zero by default. *They will be included in the model as soon as they are explicitly mentioned on the* MO *command.* They can be declared either fixed (FI), free (FR), or invariant (IN); or with the same pattern (SP), same starting values (SS), or both (PS) as in the previous group; see Section 9.2.

The fit function for the extended LISREL model with mean parameters is defined as

$$F = \sum_{g=1}^{G} \frac{N_g}{N} F_g \ , \qquad (10.7)$$

where

$$F_g = (\mathbf{s}^{(g)} - \boldsymbol{\sigma}^{(g)})' \mathbf{W}_{(g)}^{-1} (\mathbf{s}^{(g)} - \boldsymbol{\sigma}^{(g)}) + (\bar{\mathbf{z}}^{(g)} - \boldsymbol{\mu}^{(g)})' \mathbf{V}_{(g)}^{-1} (\bar{\mathbf{z}}^{(g)} - \boldsymbol{\mu}^{(g)}) \quad (10.8)$$

Table 10.1   Additional Parameter Matrices in LISREL

Name	Math Symbol	Order	LISREL Name	Possible Modes†
TAU-Y	τ_y	NY × 1	TY	FI,FR,IN,PS,SP,SS
TAU-X	τ_x	NX × 1	TX	FI,FR,IN,PS,SP,SS
ALPHA	α	NE × 1	AL	FI,FR,IN,PS,SP,SS
KAPPA	κ	NK × 1	KA	FI,FR,IN,PS,SP,SS

† *Since these are vectors, Form is not relevant, only Mode is*

and $\boldsymbol{\mu}^{(g)} = (\boldsymbol{\mu}_y^{(g)}, \boldsymbol{\mu}_x^{(g)})'$.

The first term in (10.8) is the same as (1.15). The second term involves the sample mean vector $\bar{\mathbf{z}}^{(g)}$, the population mean vector $\boldsymbol{\mu}^{(g)}$, a function of parameters by (10.5) and (10.6), and the weight matrix $\mathbf{V}_{(g)}$ defined as:

$$\mathbf{V}_{(g)} = \mathbf{S}^{(g)} \qquad \text{for ULS, GLS, WLS, DWLS}$$

$$\mathbf{V}_{(g)} = \hat{\boldsymbol{\Sigma}}^{(g)} \qquad \text{for ML}$$

It should be noted that if τ_y, τ_x, $\boldsymbol{\alpha}$, and $\boldsymbol{\kappa}$ are all default, the second term in (10.8) is a constant, independent of parameters, in which case the problem reduces to the one described in Chapter 9 and no mean structures are needed.

If the observed variables have a multivariate normal distribution the ML case defined above yields maximum likelihood estimates in the sense of maximizing the multinormal likelihood function. Under the same assumption, ML and GLS give asymptotically efficient estimators. The fit function (10.7) may be justified under the more general assumption that $\bar{\mathbf{z}}^{(g)}$ and $\mathbf{S}^{(g)}$ are asymptotically uncorrelated. This holds, in particular, if the observed variables have no skewness. The case of completely non-normal distributions is dealt with in Section 7.4.

10.2 Estimation of factor means

Although the mean of a latent variable is undefined (not identified) in a single group, group differences in the means of latent variables can be estimated if the latent variables are on the same scale in all groups. Sörbom (1974) extended the classical model of factorial invariance, so that factor means could also be estimated. Sörbom's model is a LISREL Submodel 1 with mean structures defined as

$$\mathbf{x}^{(g)} = \boldsymbol{\tau}_x + \boldsymbol{\Lambda}_x \boldsymbol{\xi}^{(g)} + \boldsymbol{\delta}^{(g)}, \qquad g = 1, 2, \dots, G,$$

with the mean of $\boldsymbol{\xi}^{(g)} = \boldsymbol{\kappa}^{(g)}$. To define the origins and the units of measurement of the ξ-factors, one can set $\boldsymbol{\kappa}^{(G)} = \mathbf{0}$ and fix one non-zero value in each column of $\boldsymbol{\Lambda}_x$. The parameters to be estimated are:

$$\boldsymbol{\tau}_x, \boldsymbol{\Lambda}_x,$$ assumed to be invariant over groups

$$\boldsymbol{\kappa}^{(1)}, \boldsymbol{\kappa}^{(2)}, \ldots, \boldsymbol{\kappa}^{(G-1)},$$ mean vectors of $\boldsymbol{\xi}$

$$\boldsymbol{\Phi}^{(1)}, \boldsymbol{\Phi}^{(2)}, \ldots, \boldsymbol{\Phi}^{(G)},$$ covariance matrices of $\boldsymbol{\xi}$

$$\boldsymbol{\Theta}_\delta^{(1)}, \boldsymbol{\Theta}_\delta^{(2)}, \ldots, \boldsymbol{\Theta}_\delta^{(G)},$$ error covariance matrices

The error covariance matrices $\boldsymbol{\Theta}_\delta$ may be postulated to be invariant over groups, if desired. In most cases these matrices are diagonal.

Example 10.1: Nine psychological variables with factor means

Source: Holzinger & Swineford (1939).

Nine variables were selected to measure three latent factors: Space, Verbal, and Memory. The groups consist of eighth-grade children from two schools in Chicago: the Pasteur and the Grant-White schools. The children from each school were divided into two groups according to whether they scored above or below the median on a speeded addition test. Thus the groups are:

1. *Pasteur Low ($N_1 = 77$)*   3. *Grant-White Low ($N_3 = 74$)*
2. *Pasteur High ($N_2 = 79$)*   4. *Grant-White High ($N_4 = 71$)*

The variables, correlations, standard deviations, and means are given in Tables 10.2 and 10.3. The standard deviations and means have been scaled so that the weighted estimate (see Section 9.3) of the within groups covariance matrix is a correlation matrix.

The nine labels are stored in the file EX101.LAB. All the remaining data are stored in the file EX101.DAT in the order: correlations for group 1, standard deviations for group 1, means for group 1, correlations for group 2, standard deviations for group 2, etc. In both files we use FORTRAN formats to record the data. Each group of data begins with a format line. After the last right parenthesis in the format, one can write any text. This can be used to identify the particular part of the data for which the format is intended. After the format follows the data.

The model used here is that outlined previously, with $\boldsymbol{\Lambda}_x$ and $\boldsymbol{\Theta}_\delta$ invariant over groups. The command file is shown below. The first line for each group is a title line. The DA command for the first group specifies

Table 10.2 Nine Psychological Variables: Correlations

Pasteur	\multicolumn{9}{c}{Group 1 above diagonal; Group 2 below diagonal}								
Test	1	2	3	4	5	6	7	8	9
Visual Perception	—	.32	.48	.28	.26	.40	.42	.12	.23
Cubes	.24	—	.33	.01	.01	.26	.32	.05	−.04
Paper Form Board	.23	.22	—	.06	.01	.10	.22	.03	.01
General Information	.32	.05	.23	—	.75	.60	.15	−.08	−.05
Sentence Completion	.35	.23	.18	.68	—	.63	.07	.06	.10
Word Classification	.36	.10	.11	.59	.66	—	.36	.19	.24
Figure Recognition	.22	.01	−.07	.09	.11	.12	—	.29	.19
Object-Number	−.02	−.01	−.13	.05	.08	.03	.19	—	.38
Number-Figure	.09	−.14	−.06	.16	.02	.12	.15	.29	—

Grant-White	\multicolumn{9}{c}{Group 3 above diagonal; Group 4 below diagonal}								
Test	1	2	3	4	5	6	7	8	9
Visual Perception	—	.34	.41	.38	.40	.42	.35	.16	.35
Cubes	.32	—	.21	.32	.16	.13	.27	.01	.27
Paper Form Board	.34	.18	—	.31	.24	.35	.30	.09	.09
General Information	.31	.24	.31	—	.69	.55	.17	.31	.34
Sentence Completion	.22	.16	.29	.62	—	.65	.20	.30	.27
Word Classification	.27	.20	.32	.57	.61	—	.31	.34	.27
Figure Recognition	.48	.31	.32	.18	.20	.29	—	.31	.38
Object-Number	.20	.01	.15	.06	.19	.15	.36	—	.38
Number-Figure	.42	.28	.40	.11	.07	.18	.35	.44	—

the number of groups: NG=4. The next line actually contains three commands, separated by semicolons. These commands tell the program to read the correlations (KM), the standard deviations (SD), and the means (ME), in that order. As the correlation matrix in the data file has been recorded with one row per line, the option SY on the KM command is essential; otherwise, the program would expect the correlations as one long line. The file EX101.LAB will be rewound after it has been read, so that the same labels may be read again for the next group. Note that the rewind (RE) option only applies to the file EX101.LAB, not to the file EX101.DAT.

The next five commands specify the model for the first group. The model includes the parameter matrices τ_x, κ, Λ_x, Φ, and Θ_δ. LX, PH, and TD are

Table 10.3
Nine Psychological Variables: Means and Standard Deviations

Group	Standard Deviations				Means			
	1	2	3	4	1	2	3	4
Visual Perception	1.06	0.96	0.95	1.03	4.20	4.30	4.29	4.21
Cubes	1.20	0.86	1.03	0.86	5.25	5.03	5.32	5.33
Paper Form Board	1.02	0.99	0.92	1.06	4.96	5.06	5.02	5.09
General Information	1.03	0.96	0.99	1.01	2.98	3.41	3.72	4.15
Sentence Completion	1.08	1.06	0.96	0.91	3.20	3.38	3.78	3.88
Word Classification	0.99	1.01	0.95	1.05	4.45	4.76	5.17	5.59
Figure Recognition	1.17	1.01	0.81	0.98	13.42	13.62	13.70	13.72
Object-Number	1.00	1.10	0.83	1.04	1.74	2.14	1.30	1.78
Number-Figure	1.04	1.00	0.88	1.07	2.10	2.16	1.87	2.44

default, TX is declared free for the first group and is declared invariant for the other groups, and KA is specified as fixed for the first group and free for the others. The OU command for the first group requests t-values (TV), standardized solution (SS), and 2 decimals (ND=2). Note that this information is automatically carried onto the OU command for groups 2–4. Similarly, the information on the MO command for the second group is automatically carried onto the MO commands for groups 3 and 4. For the same reason, only the NO keyword needs to be specified on the DA command for groups 2, 3, and 4. The general rule is that options and keywords that are the same as in the previous group need not be specified.

```
Holzinger-Swineford Data : LX and TD invariant : PASTEUR Low
DA NI=9 NG=4 NO=77
KM SY FI=EX101.DAT;SD FI=EX101.DAT;ME FI=EX101.DAT
LA FI=EX101.LAB Rewind
MO NX=9 NK=3 TX=FR KA=FI
LK
Space Verbal Memory
PA LX
3(1 0 0) 3(0 1 0) 3(0 0 1)
FI LX 1 1 LX 4 2 LX 7 3
VA 1 LX 1 1 LX 4 2 LX 7 3
OU TV SS ND=2
```

```
Holzinger-Swineford Data : LX and TD invariant : PASTEUR High
DA NO=79
KM SY FI=EX101.DAT;SD FI=EX101.DAT;ME FI=EX101.DAT
LA FI=EX101.LAB Rewind
MO LX=IN TX=IN KA=FR TD=IN
LK
Space Verbal Memory
OU
Holzinger-Swineford Data : LX and TD invariant : GRANT-WHITE Low
DA NO=74
KM SY FI=EX101.DAT;SD FI=EX101.DAT;ME FI=EX101.DAT
LA FI=EX101.LAB Rewind
MO
LK
Space Verbal Memory
OU
Holzinger-Swineford Data : LX and TD invariant : GRANT-WHITE High
DA NO=71
KM SY FI=EX101.DAT;SD FI=EX101.DAT;ME FI=EX101.DAT
LA FI=EX101.LAB Rewind
MO
LK
Space Verbal Memory
OU
```

The maximum likelihood solution is shown in Table 10.4.

Example 10.2: Head start summer program

Source: Magidson (1977), Sörbom (1981).

Sörbom used data on 303 white children from the Head Start summer program, consisting of a Head Start sample (N = 148) and a matched Control sample (N = 155). The correlations, standard deviations, and means are given in Table 10.5. The children were matched on sex and kindergarten attendance but no attempt had been made to match on social status variables. The variables used in Sörbom's reanalysis were:

$$
\begin{aligned}
x_1 &= \textit{Mother's education} \quad x_2 = \textit{Father's education} \\
x_3 &= \textit{Father's occupation} \quad x_4 = \textit{Family income} \\
y_1 &= \textit{Score on the Metropolitan Readiness Test} \\
y_2 &= \textit{Score on the Illinois Test of Psycholinguistic Abilities}
\end{aligned}
$$

Table 10.4
Maximum Likelihood Estimates for Nine Psychological Variables with Factor Means (Solution Standardized to Common Metric)

Factor Loadings

Test	Space	Verbal	Memory	Error Variance	Intercept
Visual Perception	0.72	0	0	0.48	4.20
Cubes	0.43	0	0	0.82	5.20
Paper Form Board	0.52	0	0	0.73	5.00
General Information	0	0.83	0	0.34	3.06
Sentence Completion	0	0.79	0	0.32	3.08
Word Classification	0	0.79	0	0.43	4.51
Figure Recognition	0	0	0.47	0.75	13.56
Object-Number	0	0	0.57	0.70	1.68
Number- Figure	0	0	0.61	0.63	2.07

Factor Covariance Matrices

School	Factor	Low Level			High Level		
Pasteur	Space	1.37			0.72		
	Verbal	0.44	1.12		0.51	1.03	
	Memory	0.58	0.24	1.16	0.04	0.20	0.93
Grant-White	Space	0.90			1.02		
	Verbal	0.63	0.92		0.54	0.92	
	Memory	0.54	0.52	0.59	0.96	0.33	1.33

Factor Means

Group	Space	Verbal	Memory
Pasteur Low	0.00	0.00	0.00
Pasteur High	0.05	0.32	0.18
Grant-White Low	0.09	0.70	−0.14
Grant-White High	0.06	1.01	0.19

We want to do the following:

A Test whether x_1, x_2, x_3 and x_4 can be regarded as indicators of a single construct ξ = "Socio-economic status," for both groups. Is the measurement model the same for both groups? Is there a difference in the mean of ξ between groups?

B Assuming that y_1 and y_2 can be used as indicators of another construct η = "cognitive ability," test whether the same measurement model applies to both groups. Test the hypothesis of no difference in the mean of η between groups.

C Estimate the structural equation

$$\eta = \alpha + \gamma\xi + \zeta \ .$$

Is γ the same for the two groups? Test the hypothesis $\alpha = 0$. Interpret the results.

Consider the measurement model for the four socio-economic status indicators x_1, x_2, x_3, and x_4. The model assumes that the x-variables can be accounted for by a single common factor ξ:

$$x_i^{(g)} = \tau_i + \lambda_i\xi^{(g)} + \delta_i^{(g)}, \qquad i = 1, 2, 3, 4 \ .$$

The superscript, g, is running over the two groups, $g = 1$ for Head Start children and $g = 2$ for control children. There is no superscript for τ and λ, since we are using the same observed variables in the two groups. Our main interest is in the mean κ of ξ. Assuming $E(\delta_i^{(g)}) = 0$, we find

$$E(x_i^{(g)}) = \tau_i + \lambda_i\kappa \ .$$

If we add a constant c to κ, this can be compensated for by subtracting $\lambda_i c$ from τ_i. This means that κ and τ_i cannot be identified simultaneously, or phrased in other words: there is no definite origin for the construct ξ. All we can do is estimate differences among groups, i.e., we can specify the mean of ξ to be zero in the control group, and then κ is the mean difference in socio-economic status between the experimental group and the control group.

The command file for problem **A** can be patterned after the previous example. We leave it as an exercise.

Table 10.5
Correlations, Standard Deviations and Means for the Head Start Data

Head Start Group

Variable	Correlations						Stand. Dev.	Means
x_1	1						1.332	3.520
x_2	.441	1					1.281	3.081
x_3	.220	.203	1				1.075	2.088
x_4	.304	.182	.377	1			2.648	5.358
y_1	.274	.265	.208	.084	1		3.764	19.672
y_2	.270	.122	.251	.198	.664	1	2.677	9.562

Control Group

Variable	Correlations						Stand. Dev.	Means
x_1	1						1.360	3.839
x_2	.484	1					1.195	3.290
x_3	.224	.342	1				1.193	2.600
x_4	.268	.215	.387	1			3.239	6.435
y_1	.230	.215	.196	.115	1		3.900	20.415
y_2	.265	.297	.234	.162	.635	1	2.719	10.070

For problem **A** we get an overall χ^2 measure of goodness-of-fit of the model equal to 35.9 with 10 degrees of freedom, indicating that the fit of the model is not very good. An examination of the modification indices reveals that there might be a correlation between the errors δ_1 and δ_2, i.e., when the correlation among the observed variables caused by the construct ξ has been accounted for, there seems to be a correlation left between x_1 and x_2. This correlation can be interpreted as an indication that parents' education levels correlate more than can be explained by socio-economic status. By adding the covariance θ_{21} we get a model with an acceptable fit: $\chi^2 = 6.5$ with $df = 8$. The difference in degrees of freedom from the previous model is two, since we have added two parameters, namely the covariances $\theta_{21}^{(1)}$ and $\theta_{21}^{(2)}$ in the two groups. The estimates and their estimated standard errors are given in Table 10.6. It is seen that the groups differ significantly in socio-economic status, the difference being 0.340 with a

Table 10.6

**Head Start: Estimates for the Measurement Model for Social Status
(Standard Error Estimates within Parentheses)**

	Head Start Group	Control Group	Common Parameters	
$\theta_{11}^{(\delta)}$	1.494 (0.190)	1.554 (0.200)	$\tau_1^{(x)}$	3.848 (0.092)
$\theta_{22}^{(\delta)}$	1.473 (0.183)	1.154 (0.149)	$\tau_2^{(x)}$	3.326 (0.082)
$\theta_{33}^{(\delta)}$	0.715 (0.137)	0.789 (0.164)	$\tau_3^{(x)}$	2.579 (0.091)
$\theta_{44}^{(\delta)}$	4.305 (0.799)	6.942 (1.127)	$\tau_4^{(x)}$	6.463 (0.236)
$\theta_{21}^{(\delta)}$	0.534 (0.143)	0.500 (0.134)	$\lambda_{21}^{(x)}$	0.864 (0.163)
κ	−0.340 (0.096)	0.0	$\lambda_{31}^{(x)}$	1.384 (0.290)
ϕ	0.242 (0.092)	0.329 (0.121)	$\lambda_{41}^{(x)}$	3.305 (0.684)

standard error equal to 0.096. In order to specify the scale of ξ, λ_{11} has been fixed to 1.

Magidson (1977) used two cognitive ability tests as criteria: the Metropolitan Readiness Test (MRT) and the Illinois Test of Psycholinguistic Abilities (ITPA). Magidson made separate analyses for the two tests, but here we will use the two tests to define the construct cognitive ability. This model is the same as before, except that there are only two x-variables. As a matter of fact, the model has no degrees of freedom, so one can compute the estimates simply by equating the first and second order moments implied by the model to their observed counterparts. In cognitive ability the Head Start group is also inferior to the Control group in the sense that the estimated mean difference is negative (-0.743). However, the difference is not significant, having a standard error equal to 0.440.

For problem **C** we use the combined model as depicted in Figure 10.1, where the main focus is on the structural equation

$$\eta^{(g)} = \alpha^{(g)} + \gamma^{(g)}\xi^{(g)} + \zeta^{(g)}.$$

Here ξ is "socio-economic status (Ses)" and η is "cognitive ability (Ability)."

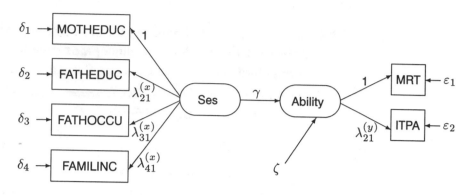

Figure 10.1   Head Start: Model for Problem C

Previously, we could not find an absolute origin for ξ, now there is no way to find an absolute origin for η. All we can do is compare groups and look at differences. For example, we could fix α in the Control group to be zero, and then α in the Head Start group could be interpreted as the effect of the Head Start program when socio-economic status has been controlled for.

The command file for problem **C** is:

```
HEAD START SUMMER PROGRAM: EXPERIMENTALS
DA    NI=6 NOBS=149 NG=2
KM    FI=EX102.DAT;    SD FI=EX102.DAT;    ME FI=EX102.DAT
LA    FI=EX102.DAT;    SE FI=EX102.DAT
MO    NX=4 NK=1 NY=2 NE=1 LX=FR LY=FR TY=FR TX=FR AL=FR KA=FR TD=SY
LE;   Ability
LK;   Ses
FR    TD 2 1
FI    LX 1 LY 1
VA 1 LX 1 LY 1
OU    SE TV MI
HEAD START SUMMER PROGRAM:   CONTROLS
DA    NOBS=156
KM    FI=EX102.DAT;    SD FI=EX102.DAT;    ME FI=EX102.DAT
LA    FI=EX102.DAT;    SE FI=EX102.DAT
MO    LX=IN TX=IN LY=IN TY=IN GA=IN TD=SP AL=FI KA=FI
LE;   Ability
LK;   Ses
OU
```

10 LISREL WITH MEAN STRUCTURES

Table 10.7   Head Start: Estimates for the Combined Model
(Standard Error Estimates within Parentheses)

	Head Start Group	Control Group	Common Parameters	
$\theta_{11}^{(\delta)}$	1.417 (0.186)	1.467 (0.194)	$\tau_1^{(x)}$	3.869 (0.094)
$\theta_{22}^{(\delta)}$	1.438 (0.182)	1.085 (0.144)	$\tau_2^{(x)}$	3.339 (0.083)
$\theta_{33}^{(\delta)}$	0.714 (0.125)	0.839 (0.147)	$\tau_3^{(x)}$	2.573 (0.090)
$\theta_{44}^{(\delta)}$	4.619 (0.736)	7.448 (1.059)	$\tau_4^{(x)}$	6.420 (0.228)
$\theta_{11}^{(\epsilon)}$	6.308 (1.527)	7.321 (1.593)	$\tau_1^{(y)}$	20.357 (0.286)
$\theta_{22}^{(\epsilon)}$	1.471 (0.983)	1.645 (0.999)	$\tau_2^{(y)}$	10.085 (0.216)
$\theta_{21}^{(\delta)}$	0.481 (0.140)	0.422 (0.129)	$\lambda_{21}^{(x)}$	0.853 (0.143)
α	0.183 (0.377)	0.0	$\lambda_{31}^{(x)}$	1.207 (0.221)
ϕ	0.315 (0.106)	0.405 (0.131)	$\lambda_{41}^{(x)}$	2.756 (0.515)
ψ	6.347 (1.474)	6.185 (1.465)	$\lambda_{21}^{(y)}$	0.850 (0.141)
κ	−0.382 (0.103)	0.0	γ	2.136 (0.549)

The χ^2 for the combined model equals 27.52 with 22 degrees of freedom, so the fit of the model is acceptable. An examination of the γ parameters in the two groups shows that they are probably equal, since $\hat{\gamma}^{(1)} = 2.296$ and $\hat{\gamma}^{(2)} = 2.027$ with estimated standard errors equal to 0.741 and 0.625, respectively. Thus, the final model is a model with the γ's constrained to be equal. The χ^2 for this model is 27.64 with 23 degrees of freedom. The difference in χ^2 for the last two models can be used as a test of the hypothesis that the γ's are equal. The χ^2 with one degree of freedom is 0.12, thus we can treat the γ's as equal. As the slopes are parallel, it is meaningful to talk about α as a measure of the effect of Head Start. The estimates of the model are given in Table 10.7. There seems to be no significant effect for the Head Start program when controlling for social status, although the inclusion of social class has changed the negative effect to be positive. The estimate of α is 0.183 with a standard error equal to 0.377.

In the more general case, when there are more than two groups, or more than one dependent variable, or both, one can test the hypothesis of no effect by re-estimation of the model with the restriction $\alpha^{(g)} = 0$ added, and then compare the χ^2's. In the above case we obtain χ^2 equal to 27.87 with 24 degrees of freedom. Thus, the test of no effect results in a χ^2 with one degree of freedom equal to 0.23, which in this case is the same as the estimate of α divided by its standard error, squared.

10.3   Incomplete data problems

Incomplete data is a common problem in social science investigations. In estimating models, researchers often need to combine data from two or more samples or subsamples, each with a somewhat different set of variables. LISREL's multisample option may be used to deal with incomplete data problems. The following interesting example was provided by Allison (1987).

Example 10.3: Estimating a correlation from incomplete data

Source: Bielby, *et al.* (1977), Allison (1987).

"Suppose the aim is to estimate the correlation between father's occupational status (FAOC) and father's educational attainment (FAED) for black men in the U.S. Using a sample of 2020, Bielby, et al. (1977) estimated that correlation to be 0.433. They recognized, however, that this correlation may be attenuated by random measurement error. To estimate and possibly correct for this error, they took a random subsample of 348 from the original sample of 2020 black males and reinterviewed them approximately three weeks later. Consequently, their original sample can be divided into two groups: a small subsample of 348 with complete data and a larger subsample 1672 with incomplete data" (Allison, 1987, p. 84). Therefore, the complete data sample has two indicators x_1 and x_2 of FAOC and two indicators x_3 and x_4 of FAED, whereas the incomplete data sample has only data on x_1 and x_3. The design of the study suggests that the missing data are missing at random.

Table 10.8 Means and Covariance Matrices for Measures of Father's Occupation and Education

| | Complete Data Subsample | | | | Incomplete Data Subsample | | | |
| | Father's Occupation | | Father's Education | | Father's Occupation | | Father's Education | |
	x_1	x_2	x_3	x_4	x_1	x_2	x_3	x_4
x_1	180.90				217.27			
x_2	126.77	217.56			0.00	1.00		
x_3	23.96	30.20	16.24		25.57	0.00	16.16	
x_4	22.86	30.47	14.36	15.13	0.00	0.00	0.00	1.00
Mean	16.52	17.39	6.65	6.75	16.98	0.00	6.83	0.00

Data on x_2 and x_4 are missing in the incomplete data sample

Table 10.8 gives sample variances, covariances, and means for the two groups. For the missing variables, pseudo values of 1 have been entered for the variances and pseudo-values of 0 for the covariances and the means. The use of such pseudo-values was suggested originally by Jöreskog (1971a). Allison (1987) showed that, when combined with pseudo-values for appropriate parameters, such pseudo-values still produce correct ML estimates in LISREL. Allison used LISREL 6 and analyzed moment matrices as described in the next section. Here we use the extended LISREL model, which makes it much easier.

The model is a Submodel 1 with parameters τ_x, Λ_x, Φ, and Θ_δ:

$$\tau_x = \begin{pmatrix} * \\ * \\ * \\ * \end{pmatrix} \quad \Lambda_x = \begin{pmatrix} 1 & 0 \\ * & 0 \\ 0 & 1 \\ 0 & * \end{pmatrix} \quad \Phi = \begin{pmatrix} * & \\ * & * \end{pmatrix} \quad \Theta_\delta = \text{diag} \begin{pmatrix} * \\ * \\ * \\ * \end{pmatrix}$$

The two latent variables ξ_1 and ξ_2 represent true FAOC and FAED, respectively. The two 1's in Λ_x define the scales for these. For the incomplete sample, we set $\tau_2^{(x)}$, $\tau_4^{(x)}$, $\lambda_{21}^{(x)}$, and $\lambda_{42}^{(x)}$ equal to 0 and $\theta_2^{(\delta)}$ and $\theta_4^{(\delta)}$ equal to 1. All free parameters (the ✶'s in the model above) are constrained to be equal across subsamples.

The command file is:

```
FATHERS SES                      COMPLETE DATA
DATA          NG=2 NI=4 NO=348;  CMATRIX FI=EX103.DAT;  MEANS FI=EX103.DAT
MODEL         NX=4 NK=2 TX=FR
VALUE 1       LX 1 1 LX 3 2
FREE          LX 2 1 LX 4 2
MATRIX PH; 100 25 10
MATRIX TX; 16 16 6 6
OUTPUT        SE SS
FATHERS SES                      INCOMPLETE DATA
DATA          NO=1672;           CMATRIX FI=EX103.DAT;  MEANS FI=EX103.DAT
MODEL         PH=IN
FIX           TX 2 TX 4 TD 2 TD 4
VALUE 1       LX 1 1 LX 3 2 TD 2 TD 4
EQUAL         TX 1 1 1 TX 1
EQUAL         TX 1 3 3 TX 3
EQUAL         TD 1 1 1 TD 1
EQUAL         TD 1 3 3 TD 3
MATRIX TX; 16 0 6 0
OUTPUT
```

As this is a somewhat unusual model, LISREL has problems generating good starting values. Starting values are therefore given for τ_x and Φ, using MA commands.

The results agree almost exactly with those reported by Allison (1987). The goodness-of-fit χ^2 is 7.74 with 15 degrees of freedom. However, the degrees of freedom are incorrect, because LISREL has counted the nine pseudo-values in the data as real data values. The correct degrees of freedom should be six. The value of χ^2 still represents a very good fit.

The estimated covariance between true FAOC and true FAED is 25.18 with a standard error of 1.41. This should be compared with the estimate 23.31 with a standard error of 3.13 obtained from the complete data sample alone. By using the incomplete data sample, the standard error is reduced to less than half. Thus, there is a major gain in precision by using all available data.

We may also compare estimated correlations between true FAOC and true FAED. Based on both samples, this is 0.62. This may be compared with the attenuated estimate of 0.43 reported by Bielby et al. (1977).

10.4 Growth Curves

A general form of *the multivariate linear model* may be formulated as follows. Rows of the data matrix $\mathbf{Y}$ of order $N \times p$ are independently distributed with the same covariance matrix $\boldsymbol{\Sigma}$ and with means of the form

$$E(\mathbf{Y}) = \mathbf{X}\boldsymbol{\Xi}\mathbf{P} , \tag{10.9}$$

where $\mathbf{X}(N \times q)$ and $\mathbf{P}(r \times p)$ are fixed design matrices of ranks q and r, respectively, and $\boldsymbol{\Xi}(q \times r)$ is a matrix of parameters. If $r = p$ and $\mathbf{P}$ is nonsingular, this is a multivariate regression model with regression matrix $\mathbf{P}'\boldsymbol{\Xi}'$, with elements which are linear functions of the parameters in $\boldsymbol{\Xi}$.

This model can be specified in LISREL as a submodel 3A in the form of (10.1) and (10.2) with Fixed-x. Put $\boldsymbol{\Lambda}_y = \mathbf{P}'$, $\boldsymbol{\Gamma} = \boldsymbol{\Xi}'$, $\boldsymbol{\Psi} = \boldsymbol{\Sigma}$ and leave $\boldsymbol{\tau}_y$, $\boldsymbol{\alpha}$, $\boldsymbol{\kappa}$, and $\mathbf{B}$ default.

This model is often used to estimate growth curves from panel data or longitudinal data in which the outcome variable is measured repeatedly on the same persons over several periods of time.

Consider a response variable y being measured on N individuals at T points in time $t_1, t_2, \ldots, t_T$. The raw data take the form of a data matrix $\mathbf{Y}$ of order $N \times T$, where y_{ij} is the observed measurement on individual i at time t_j. It is assumed that the rows of $\mathbf{Y}$ are independently distributed with the same covariance matrix $\boldsymbol{\Sigma}$. Also, the mean vectors of the rows are assumed to be the same, namely $\boldsymbol{\mu}' = (\mu_1, \mu_2, \ldots, \mu_T)$.

However, here we focus attention on the mean μ_t as a function of t. This gives a growth curve describing how the mean of y changes over time.

We consider polynomial growth curves of the form

$$\mu_t = \kappa_0 + \kappa_1 t + \kappa_2 t^2 + \cdots + \kappa_h t^h$$

or

$$\mu = \begin{pmatrix} 1 & t_1 & t_1^2 & \cdots & t_1^h \\ 1 & t_2 & t_2^2 & \cdots & t_2^h \\ \vdots & \vdots & \vdots & \ddots & \vdots \\ 1 & t_T & t_T^2 & \cdots & t_T^h \end{pmatrix} \begin{pmatrix} \kappa_0 \\ \kappa_1 \\ \vdots \\ \kappa_h \end{pmatrix} . \tag{10.10}$$

The degree of the polynomial h is assumed to be less than or equal to $T - 1$. When $h < T - 1$, the mean vector μ is constrained and there is not a one-to-one correspondence between $\mu_1, \mu_2, \ldots, \mu_T$ and the polynomial coefficients $\kappa_0, \kappa_1, \ldots, \kappa_h$. In this section we consider the estimation of these polynomial coefficients.

The above generalizes easily to the case of several groups of individuals with possibly different mean vectors. Suppose, for example, that there are two groups with n_1 and n_2 individuals in each group. Let the first n_1 rows of $\mathbf{Y}$ be the measurements on individuals in Group 1 and let the last n_2 rows be the measurements on individuals in Group 2. The growth curves for the two groups may differ, so we assume that there are two distinct growth curves to be estimated, that is,

$$E(y_{it}^{(g)}) = \kappa_0^{(g)} + \kappa_1^{(g)}t + \cdots + \kappa_h^{(g)}t^h, \qquad g = 1, 2 .$$

In multiple-group comparisons one may be interested in the following type of questions:

- ❑ Should the growth curves be represented by third-degree polynomials, or are quadratic or linear growth curves adequate?
- ❑ Should separate growth curves be used for different groups or do all groups have the same growth curve?

Often we conceive of the effect of treatment as represented by a parallel displacement of the whole growth curve for one group in relation to another. This cannot be taken for granted, however, but must be tested by means of data. In addition, growth curves can differ in terms of the degree of the polynomial but also in the shape for the same degree of polynomial. The covariance matrices Σ may be the same in different groups, or the correlation matrices may be the same and the standard deviations different, or the covariance matrices may be all different. The covariance matrices may also be structured in various ways.

Growth curves can be estimated more efficiently and tests about the growth curves will be more powerful if the covariance structure, which arises naturally in repeated measurements, is taken into account. This covariance structure very often has an autoregressive nature. Therefore, we focus attention to the deviation $e_t = y_t - \mu_t$ of y_t from its mean value

μ_t on the growth curve and consider various autoregressive models for this.

The first-order autoregressive model is

$$e_t = \beta_t e_{t-1} + z_t , \qquad t = 2, 3, \ldots, T ,$$

where the residual z_t is uncorrelated with e_{t-1}. It is also assumed that $z_2, z_3, \ldots, z_T$ are all uncorrelated.

It is readily verified that

$$\text{Cov}(y_t, y_{t-1}) = E(e_t e_{t-1}) = \beta_t \sigma_{t-1}^2 ,$$

where

$$\sigma_{t-1}^2 = \text{Var}(y_{t-1}) = E(e_{t-1}^2) ,$$

and that

$$\text{Cov}(y_t, y_{t-k}) = \beta_t \beta_{t-1} \cdots \beta_{t-k+1} \sigma_{t-k}^2, \qquad k = 1, 2, \ldots$$

Hence, the covariance matrix of $\mathbf{y}$ is (in the case of $T = 4$)

$$\Sigma = \begin{pmatrix} \sigma_1^2 & & & \\ \beta_2 \sigma_1^2 & \sigma_2^2 & & \\ \beta_3 \beta_2 \sigma_1^2 & \beta_3 \sigma_2^2 & \sigma_3^2 & \\ \beta_4 \beta_3 \beta_2 \sigma_1^2 & \beta_4 \beta_3 \sigma_2^2 & \beta_4 \sigma_3^2 & \sigma_4^2 \end{pmatrix}$$

It is seen that Σ is constrained; its 10 variances are functions of only seven parameters. Since the variances are free parameters, it is the six covariances that are functions of the three parameters β_2, β_3, and β_4.

This model is the perfect Markov simplex mentioned in Sec. 6.5. If all $\beta_i = 1$, we have the perfect Wiener simplex, see Jöreskog (1970a). Higher-order autoregressive models may also be considered. For example, a second-order model has

$$e_t = \beta_{t,t-1} e_{t-1} + \beta_{t,t-2} e_{t-2} + z_t , \qquad t = 3, 4, \ldots, T .$$

The model can be estimated directly with LISREL using the following specification corresponding to (10.1) and (10.2):

$$\begin{pmatrix} \mathbf{e} \\ \boldsymbol{\eta} \end{pmatrix} = \begin{pmatrix} \mathbf{0} \\ \boldsymbol{\kappa} \end{pmatrix} + \begin{pmatrix} \mathbf{T}_\beta & \mathbf{0} \\ \mathbf{0} & \mathbf{0} \end{pmatrix} \begin{pmatrix} \mathbf{e} \\ \boldsymbol{\eta} \end{pmatrix} + \begin{pmatrix} \mathbf{z} \\ \mathbf{0} \end{pmatrix} \qquad (10.11)$$

$$y = \left(\begin{array}{cc} \mathbf{I} & \mathbf{P} \end{array}\right) \left(\begin{array}{c} \mathbf{e} \\ \eta \end{array}\right) + \mathbf{0}, \qquad\qquad (10.12)$$

where $\mathbf{T}_\beta$, in the case of a second-order autoregressive model, is a square matrix whose subdiagonal non-zero elements are

$$\beta_{21}, \beta_{31}, \beta_{32}, \beta_{42}, \beta_{43}, \beta_{53}, \beta_{54}, \ldots, \beta_{T,T-2}, \beta_{T,T-1} \,.$$

The matrix $\mathbf{P}$ is the fixed matrix of order $T \times (h+1)$ given in (10.10). When $\mathbf{T}_\beta$ is present in (10.11), the covariance matrix of $\mathbf{z}$ should be diagonal. The case of an unstructured $\boldsymbol{\Sigma}$ is obtained by setting $\mathbf{T}_\beta$ to zero and letting the covariance matrix of $\mathbf{z}$ be free.

Example 10.4: Berkeley guidance study

Source: Tuddenham & Snyder (1954).

As an illustration of growth curve estimation, we use data on stature for boys and girls aged 3–7 ($T = 5$). The means, variances, and covariances of the stature measurements for the two groups are given in Table 10.9.

We begin by testing the hypothesis that the covariance matrix of the measured variables are equal for boys and girls. This is done as in Example 9.1A. The means are not involved. The likelihood ratio test statistics gives $\chi^2 = 21.59$ with 15 degrees of freedom. The p-value is 0.12, so the hypothesis is not rejected.

Next, we test the hypothesis of equal mean vectors for boys and girls without assuming equal covariance matrices. For this we use Submodel 1 in the form of (10.3). Take $\boldsymbol{\Lambda}_x = \mathbf{I}$ and $\boldsymbol{\Theta}_\delta = \mathbf{0}$. Then the mean vector is $\boldsymbol{\tau}_x$ and the covariance matrix is $\boldsymbol{\Phi}$. The command file for this is as follows:

```
Testing Equality of Mean Vectors.              Input for Girls
DATA    NG=2 NI=5 NO=70;  CMATRIX FI=GIRLS.COV;  MEANS FI=GIRLS.MEA
MODEL   NX=5 NK=5 TX=FR LX=ID TD=ZE
OUTPUT  SE TV MI
Testing Equality of Mean Vectors.              Input for Boys
DATA    NO=66;            CMATRIX FI=BOYS.COV;   MEANS FI=BOYS.MEA
MODEL   TX=IN
OUTPUT
```

Table 10.9   Berkeley Guidance Study

Age	Observed and Fitted Means				
	3	4	5	6	7
Girls					
Observed	95.45	102.99	110.26	117.25	123.41
Fitted	95.46	102.95	110.27	117.18	123.39
Boys					
Observed	96.71	104.27	111.13	117.47	124.01
Fitted	96.70	104.32	111.11	117.54	124.03

Observed (Above) and Fitted (Below) Covariance Matrices

Girls

3	12.110				
	12.628				
4	12.454	15.132			
	12.570	14.504			
5	13.491	16.074	18.148		
	13.270	14.963	16.423		
6	14.061	16.424	18.567	20.612	
	14.134	15.757	17.379	19.793	
7	14.822	17.133	19.587	21.534	23.426
	15.051	16.592	18.408	20.663	22.461

Boys

3	13.177				
	12.628				
4	12.693	13.838			
	12.570	14.504			
5	13.055	13.784	14.592		
	13.270	14.963	16.423		
6	14.211	15.049	16.118	18.923	
	14.134	15.757	17.379	19.793	
7	15.294	16.018	17.156	19.738	21.437
	15.051	16.592	18.408	20.663	22.461

The test gives $\chi^2 = 25.87$ with 5 degrees of freedom, so the hypothesis is rejected. Boys and girls have different mean vectors.

We proceed by estimating a growth curve for boys and girls under the assumption that the covariance matrices are equal. The model is the one defined in (10.11) and (10.12) with $\mathbf{T}_\beta = \mathbf{0}$ and $\text{Cov}(\mathbf{z})$ equal in the two groups but otherwise unconstrained. We assume that the growth curves are cubic, *i.e.*, $h = 3$. Measuring time as age -5, the matrix $\mathbf{P}$ is (one can of course use orthogonal polynomials instead):

$$\mathbf{P} = \begin{pmatrix} 1 & -2 & 4 & -8 \\ 1 & -1 & 1 & -1 \\ 1 & 0 & 0 & 0 \\ 1 & 1 & 1 & 1 \\ 1 & 2 & 4 & 8 \end{pmatrix}$$

In LISREL we take $p = 5$, $m = 9$, $\Lambda_y = \begin{pmatrix} \mathbf{I} & \mathbf{P} \end{pmatrix}$, $\Theta_\epsilon = \mathbf{0}$, $\alpha = \mathbf{a}$ (9×1) vector, where the last four elements are the coefficients of the growth curve polynomial, $\mathbf{B}$ $(9 \times 9) = \mathbf{0}$, and Ψ a 9×9 symmetric matrix where the last four rows are fixed zeros.

```
Estimating Third Degree Growth Curve for Girls
Assuming Sigma(Girls) = Sigma(Boys)
DATA      NG=2 NI=5 NO=70
CMATRIX  FI=GIRLS.COV
MEANS    FI=GIRLS.MEA
MODEL    NY=5 NE=9 AL=FR PS=FI TE=ZE
MATRIX   LY
1 0 0 0 0 1 -2 4 -8
0 1 0 0 0 1 -1 1 -1
0 0 1 0 0 1  0 0  0
0 0 0 1 0 1  1 1  1
0 0 0 0 1 1  2 4  8
FIX      AL 1 - AL 5
FREE     PS 1 1 - PS 5 5
MATRIX   PS
12.110
12.454     15.132
13.491     16.074     18.148
14.061     16.424     18.567     20.612
14.822     17.133     19.587     21.534     23.426 /
OUTPUT   NS SE TV RS AD=OFF
```

```
Estimating Third Degree Growth Curve for Boys
Assuming Sigma(Girls) = Sigma(Boys)
DATA       NO=66
CMATRIX    FI=BOYS.COV
MEANS      FI=BOYS.MEA
MODEL      AL=PS LY=PS PS=IN
OUTPUT
```

Since NE is larger than NY, starting values must be provided and NS must
be entered on the OU command. It is sufficient to provide starting values
for the first five rows of Ψ for the first group. These starting values are
taken to be the covariance matrix for girls. Note that the slash is necessary because Ψ is actually of order 9×9. Λ_y is the same fixed matrix in
both groups. Ψ is specified to be invariant. The joint covariance matrix of
boys and girls is in the upper left 5×5 submatrix of Ψ. All other elements
of Ψ are fixed zeros. The polynomial coefficients are the last 4 elements
of α. The first 5 elements of α are fixed zeros. AD is set OFF because Λ_y
does not have full column rank and Ψ is not positive definite.

This model gives an overall χ^2 of 23.13 with 17 degrees of freedom. The
p-value is 0.145. The polynomial growth curves are estimated as

$$
\text{Girls:} \quad \mu_t \;=\; \underset{(0.487)}{110.278} \;+\; \underset{(0.119)}{7.165t} \;-\; \underset{(0.030)}{0.214t^2} \;-\; \underset{(0.025)}{0.046t^3} \tag{10.13}
$$

$$
\text{Boys:} \quad \mu_t \;=\; \underset{(0.502)}{111.112} \;+\; \underset{(0.123)}{6.537t} \;-\; \underset{(0.031)}{0.186t^2} \;+\; \underset{(0.025)}{0.074t^3} \tag{10.14}
$$

The quantities in parentheses are the standard errors of the polynomial
coefficients. Table 10.9 presents the observed and fitted means and the
observed and fitted variances and covariances. It is seen that the differences between the observed and the fitted quantities are generally small
so the overall fit of the model can be regarded as good.

Do boys and girls have the same growth curves? We can test this hypothesis by re-estimating the model under the constraint that the polynomial
coefficients are the same and calculating the difference in χ^2-values. This
gives $\chi^2 = 24.46$ with 4 df, so the hypothesis is rejected. Inspection of the
polynomial coefficients in (10.13) and (10.14) in relation to their standard
errors suggest that each coefficient is different for boys and girls. Also,

the coefficient κ_3 for girls is not significant. So a quatratic curve would be sufficient for girls. It looks like the two growth curves are entirely different. However, in the range of t from -2 to $+2$ ($t = age - 5$), the two curves are in fact close to each other.

Further analysis can be done by including $\mathbf{T}_\beta$ in (10.11) and letting $\mathbf{\Psi}$ be diagonal. A test of the Wiener simplex structure gives an overall $\chi^2 = 59.63$ with 27 df. Although the Wiener simplex is fairly consistent with the observed covariance matrices, the fit is not sufficiently good. A test of the Markov simplex gives $\chi^2 = 46.93$ with 23 df. This model does not fit the data either. For this data it seems best to retain the model with a joint but unstructured covariance matrix.

11 Hints on resolving problem cases

LISREL works well when the model is right for the data. In such cases, the program produces good initial estimates and converges after a few iterations to an admissible solution. However, in practice many different deviations from this ideal situation may occur, because:

☐ The proposed model is wrong for the data or the data are inadequate for the model.

☐ Mistakes are made in the command file or the data, so that in fact a model or data different from the intended is analyzed.

This chapter explains how LISREL behaves in such cases and it gives some hints on how to resolve problem cases.

Our basic philosophy in writing the program is to try to detect most errors and inconsistencies as early as possible and stop the program. However, it is not possible to check everything and it is of course impossible to reject a bad but otherwise formally correct model without running it through. Such models are therefore not detected until after some computation.

LISREL will detect most syntax errors in the command file. For example, it will detect:

☐ Invalid command names, option names, and keyword names as well as invalid keyword values

☐ Missing DA, MO, and OU commands

☐ Logical errors on MO, FR, FI, VA, and ST commands, such as references to LY when NY and/or NE has not been defined

It is harder to detect errors in data (labels, raw data, covariance matrices, etc.). To help the program detect errors in the data, we recommend that all data be read from external files. *Do not put the data in the command file. Put different kinds of data in different files.* If these recommendations are followed, the program will detect if there are too few elements in the data and if there are illegal characters in the data. The program cannot detect if there are too many elements in the data file or if an element has an unreasonable (but legal) value. *Always check the matrix to be analyzed in the output file to see if it is correct.*

Erroneous values in covariance or correlation matrices often lead to matrices that are not positive definite. This will result in one of the following error messages:

```
W_A_R_N_I_N_G : Matrix to be analyzed is not positive definite,
                ridge option taken with ridge constant = 1.000

F_A_T_A_L  E_R_R_O_R : Matrix to be analyzed is not positive definite.
```

The value of the ridge constant reported in the error message may differ from the value 1.000 reported here.

Suppose the problem has passed the syntax and data checks without errors. Things can still go wrong because either the model defined in the command file is not the one intended or simply because the model is wrong or bad for the data. LISREL "protests violently.. against bad models in the following ways:

- Bad initial estimates are produced. In some cases these may be so bad that iterations cannot begin because the matrix Σ estimated at the initial estimates of parameters is not positive definite. This produces the following error message:

```
F_A_T_A_L  E_R_R_O_R : Unable to start iterations because matrix
        SIGMA is not positive definite. Provide better starting values.
```

- After iterations have started, a bad model may be detected at the admissibility check, which occurs after the tenth iteration, unless some other value of AD is specified on the OU command. *Do not set the admissibility check off unless the model has fixed zero diagonal elements in* Φ, Ψ, Θ_ϵ, *or* Θ_δ *by intention.* The admissibility check has been included as a result of critique from users of earlier versions of LISREL, which could run for many iterations without producing any useful results. Although there may be exceptions, our experience suggests that if a solution is not admissible after 10 iterations, it will remain non-admissible if the program is allowed to continue to iterate. The error message which stops the program when the model is not admissible is:

```
F_A_T_A_L  E_R_R_O_R : Admissibility test failed.
```

There will also be warning messages in the output file indicating for which parameter matrix the test fails.

If this message occurs, one should check the data and the model carefully to see if they are as intended. If they are and the admissibility test still fails after 10 iterations, one can set AD to some large value such as 20 or 30. *Do not set* AD=OFF.

The admissibility of the final solution will always be checked, so that bad models that need fewer iterations than 10 (or whatever is set by AD) are still detected.

- If a model passes the admissibility test, there could still be something wrong with the model specification. This will most likely result in non-convergence of iterations after IT iterations which produce the following message:

```
W_A_R_N_I_N_G : The number of iterations exceeded  51
```

or the following message:

```
F_A_T_A_L  E_R_R_O_R : Serious problems encountered during mini-
    mization. Unable to continue iterations. Check your model and data.
```

In both cases, the program stops iterating and writes the "solution" at that point to the output file. This solution usually indicates what is wrong in the model.

If the data and the model specification are correct and the "problem" still does not converge in IT iterations, one can set IT to a larger value to allow more iterations. It may also be a good idea to put FD (first derivatives) on the OU command in case the program will produce the second warning above. The first derivatives give an indication of how "close" the "solution" is (see below).

The most likely explanation for the occurrence of the second warning is that the model is empirically non-identified, in the sense that the information matrix is nearly singular. This can be checked by asking for PC (for print correlations of estimates) on the OU command, which produces a correlation matrix of order $t \times t$, where t is the number of parameters estimated. This correlation matrix is an estimate of the asymptotic covariance matrix of the parameter estimates scaled to a correlation matrix. Very large correlations in this matrix indicate that the fit function is nearly flat and that it is impossible to obtain sufficiently good parameter estimates.

This problem can usually be resolved by imposing more constraints on the model. For example, one could fix off-diagonal elements of $\mathbf{\Psi}$ or one could set more elements of $\mathbf{\Lambda}_y$ or $\mathbf{\Lambda}_x$ to zero.

The remainder of this chapter explains some technical keywords and options, most of them not mentioned in Chapter 2. Exceptionally, a problem case can only be solved by changing the default values of these keywords.

Technical keywords

In addition to the keywords TM and IT (see Chapter 2), which limit the *computer time* and the *number of iterations*, respectively, several technical keywords are available in LISREL 7 to control the *minimization algorithm* used to obtain the LISREL solution (ULS, GLS, ML, WLS, and DWLS). The default values for these keywords have been chosen after considerable experimentation so as to optimize the algorithm. *Most users of* LISREL *do not have a reason to change these keywords.* However, they *can* be changed and users may do so at their own risk. The technical keywords and their default values are given in Table 11.1.

To change any of these keywords, simply assign a new value on the OU command. For example, to change MT to 15, write:

```
OU  ....  MT=15 ....
```

In addition to these keywords, the technical options PT (print technical output) and FD (first derivatives) may be entered on the OU command.

Table 11.1 Technical Keywords and their Default Values

Function	Keyword	Default Value
Maximum iterations	IT	$3 \times$ number of parameters
Convergence criterion	EPS	0.000001
Iteration method	IM	2
Iteration line search	IS	2
Identification criterion	IC	5×10^{-11}
Maximum trials per iteration	MT	20

Iteration algorithm

To describe the function of each of these technical keywords we will briefly describe the minimization algorithm. Let $\theta(t \times 1)$ be the vector of independent model parameters to be estimated and let $F(\theta)$ be the general fit function (1.15). Let $\theta^{(0)}$ represent the initial estimates obtained by IV, TSLS, or specified by the user. The minimization algorithm generates successive points $\theta^{(1)}$, $\theta^{(2)}$, ..., in the parameter space such that

$$F[\theta^{(s+1)}] < F[\theta^{(s)}] .$$

The process ends when the convergence criterion (see below) is satisfied or when $s = $ IT, whichever occurs first. For $s = 0, 1, 2, \ldots$, let $\mathbf{g}^{(s)}$ be the gradient vector at $\theta = \theta^{(s)}$, let $\alpha^{(s)}$ be a sequence of positive scalars, and let $\mathbf{E}^{(s)}$ be a sequence of positive definite matrices. Then the minimization algorithm is

$$\theta^{(s+1)} = \theta^{(s)} - \alpha^{(s)}\mathbf{E}^{(s)}\mathbf{g}^{(s)} . \tag{11.1}$$

The keyword IS controls the choice of $\alpha^{(s)}$ and the keyword IM controls the choice of $\mathbf{E}^{(s)}$, as follows:

IS=1 $\alpha^{(s)} = 1$ if $F[\theta^{(s+1)}] < F[\theta^{(s)}]$, otherwise $\alpha^{(s)}$ is determined by *line search* (see below).

IS=2 $\alpha^{(s)}$ is determined by line search.

IM=1 $\mathbf{E}^{(s+1)} = \mathbf{E}^{(s)}$, *i.e.*, $\mathbf{E}^{(s)}$ is held constant.

IM=2 $\mathbf{E}^{(s+1)}$ is determined from $\mathbf{E}^{(s)}$ by the method of Davidon-Fletcher-Powell.

IM=3 $\mathbf{E}^{(s+1)} =$ The inverse of the information matrix (defined below) evaluated at $\theta = \theta^{(s+1)}$.

In all three cases of IM, $\mathbf{E}^{(0)}$ equals the inverse of the *information matrix* evaluated at $\theta = \theta^{(0)}$.

Combinations of IS and IM give rise to six alternative minimization algorithms that can be used. The combination IS=2 and IM=2 is the Davidon-Fletcher-Powell algorithm. This is used by default. The combination IS=1 and IM=3 is the Fisher's Scoring algorithm. This requires the fewest iterations but takes more time in each iteration due to the computation and inversion of the information matrix. The combination IM=1 with IS=1 takes the least time per iteration but usually requires more iterations. Our experience is that no combination is optimal for all problems. The behavior of the iterative procedure depends strongly on how good or bad the initial estimates are and on how well-behaved the data are.

Information matrix

The *information matrix* is defined as a probability limit:

$$\mathbf{E} = \text{plim } \partial^2 F / \partial\theta\partial\theta' \, . \tag{11.2}$$

For the ML fit function which is the negative of the logarithm of a likelihood function, this corresponds to Fisher's information matrix. We will use the term information matrix also for the other methods. If the model is identified, *i.e.*, if all its parameters are identified, the information matrix is positive definite. This is a mathematical statement. In practice, the information matrix must be evaluated at a point in the parameter space estimated from the data, and the positive definiteness of $\mathbf{E}$ can only be assessed within the numerical accuracy by which computations are performed. Successive pivotal quantities $\|\mathbf{E}_{11}\|$, $\|\mathbf{E}_{22}\|$, $\|\mathbf{E}_{33}\|$, $\ldots$, $\|\mathbf{E}_{tt}\|$ are computed, where $\mathbf{E}_{ii}$ is the submatrix of $\mathbf{E}$ formed by the first i rows and columns and $\|\mathbf{E}_{ii}\|$ is the determinant of $\mathbf{E}_{ii}$. If $\mathbf{E}$ is positive definite all the pivotal quantities are positive. In the program, the keyword IC, with default value 5×10^{-11}, has the following function. If $\|\mathbf{E}_{i-1,i-1}\| \geq$ IC and $\|\mathbf{E}_{ii}\| <$ IC, then the matrix $\mathbf{E}_{i-1,i-1}$ is considered positive definite, $\mathbf{E}_{ii}$ is considered singular, and the program prints a message suggesting that the parameter θ_i may not be identified. This is usually an indication that θ_i is involved in an indeterminacy with one or more of the parameters $\theta_1, \theta_2, \ldots, \theta_{i-1}$ and it may well be that some of the parameters involved in this indeterminacy are not identified. For an illustration of how the program behaves when the model is not identified see Example 6.6.

Convergence criterion

The convergence criterion is satisfied if for all $i = 1, 2, \ldots, t$

$$|\partial F / \partial \theta_i| < \text{EPS} \quad \textit{if} \quad |\theta_i| \leq 1 \tag{11.3}$$

and

$$|(\partial F / \partial \theta_i) / \theta_i| < \text{EPS} \quad \textit{if} \quad |\theta_i| > 1 , \tag{11.4}$$

where the bars indicate absolute values. The default value, 0.000001, of EPS has been chosen so that the solution is usually accurate to three significant digits. However, this cannot be guaranteed to hold for all problems. If a less accurate solution is sufficient, EPS may be increased and if a more accurate solution is required, EPS should be decreased. This does not necessarily mean, however, that EPS=0.00001 gives a solution with two correct digits, nor that EPS=0.0000001 gives a solution correct to four digits.

Line search

Let $\boldsymbol{\theta}$ be a given point in the parameter space and let $\mathbf{g}$ and $\mathbf{E}$ be the corresponding gradient vector and positive definite weight matrix, respectively. In this section we consider the problem of minimizing $F(\boldsymbol{\theta})$ along the line

$$\theta - \alpha \mathbf{Eg}, \ \alpha \geq 0 \,.$$

Along this line the function $F(\theta)$ may be regarded as a function $f(\alpha)$, of the distance α from the point θ, si i.e.,

$$f(\alpha) = F(\theta - \alpha \mathbf{Eg}), \ \alpha \geq 0 \,. \tag{11.5}$$

The slope of $f(\alpha)$ at any point α is given by

$$s(\alpha) = -\mathbf{g}'\mathbf{Eg}_\alpha \,, \tag{11.6}$$

where $\mathbf{g}_\alpha$ is the gradient vector of $F(\theta)$ at $\theta - \alpha \mathbf{Eg}$. In particular, the slope at $\alpha = 0$ is $s(0) = -\mathbf{g}'\mathbf{Eg}$, which is negative unless $\mathbf{g} = \mathbf{0}$. If $\mathbf{g} = \mathbf{0}$, the minimum of $F(\theta)$ is located at θ. If $s(0) < 0$, $f(\alpha)$ has a minimum for some $\alpha > 0$, since $F(\theta)$ is continuous and non-negative. In most cases the fit function $F(\theta)$ is convex at least in a region around the minimum. However, convexity may not hold for all data and models at all points in the parameter space. The procedure to be described is capable of handling such situations as well.

The minimizing α may be approximated by various interpolation and extrapolation procedures. For example, one takes a trial value α^* of α and determines $f(\alpha^*)$ and $s(\alpha^*)$. If $s(\alpha^*)$ is positive, one interpolates cubically for the minimum, using function values and slope values at $\alpha = 0$ and $\alpha = \alpha^*$. If $s(\alpha^*)$ is negative, one extrapolates linearly for the zero of $s(\alpha)$ using only slope values at $\alpha = 0$ and $\alpha = \alpha^*$. Although this procedure is satisfactory in most cases, a more complicated procedure is necessary if a very accurate determination of the minimum is required or if $f(\alpha)$ and $s(\alpha)$ have rather irregular forms. The following procedure is capable of locating the minimum to any desired degree of accuracy, within machine capacity, and it can also handle various irregular shapes of the curves $f(\alpha)$ and $s(\alpha)$.

The behavior of $f(\alpha)$ is investigated at a sequence of test points $P^* = [\alpha^*, s(\alpha^*), f(\alpha^*)]$. Three triples

$$P_1 = [\alpha_1, s(\alpha_1), f(\alpha_1)],$$
$$P_2 = [\alpha_2, s(\alpha_2), f(\alpha_2)], \quad \text{and}$$
$$P_3 = [\alpha_3, s(\alpha_3), f(\alpha_3)]$$

are used to save information about the function. The value α_3 is the smallest value for which $s(\alpha_3) > 0$, α_2 is the largest value with $s(\alpha_2) < 0$, and α_1 is the second largest value with $s(\alpha_1) < 0$. If only one point with negative slope is known, P_1 and P_2 are assumed to be the same point. By these definitions, $\alpha_1 \leq \alpha_2 < \alpha_3$ and α_1 and α_2 cannot decrease and α_3 cannot increase. At the beginning only one point is known namely $P_0 = [0, s(0), f(0)]$, where $s(0) < 0$, so that P_1 and P_2 are both equal to P_0 and no point P_3 is known.

Each test point $P^* = [\alpha^*, s(\alpha^*), f(\alpha^*)]$ is examined as follows. First the truth values of each of the following five logical statements are determined:

- ☐ B$_1$: $s(\alpha^*) < cs(0)$, where c is a small positive constant
- ☐ B$_2$: $f(\alpha^*) > f(0)$
- ☐ B$_3$: $s(\alpha^*) > 0$
- ☐ B$_4$: (B$_1$ *or not*-B$_3$) *and* B$_2$
- ☐ B$_5$: $[s(\alpha^*) > s(\alpha_2)]$ *and* $[s(\alpha_2) \geq s(\alpha_1)]$

Statements B$_1$, B$_2$, and B$_3$ involve relations between P^* and P_0 only, B$_4$ is a function of B$_1$, B$_2$, and B$_3$, and B$_5$ involves P^*, P_1, and P_2 only. The eight possible outcomes of B$_1$, B$_2$ and B$_3$ and the consequent outcome of B$_4$ are shown in Table 11.2.

Statement B$_4$ is examined first. If B$_4$ is true (lines 1, 2 and 6) it means that P^* is in a region "too far out". The trial step α^* is therefore decreased by multiplying by a constant scale factor $b < 1$ and starting anew with the decreased α^*, disregarding information from previous test points, if any. If B$_4$ is false, B$_1$ is examined. If B$_1$ is true (lines 3 and 4), the minimum is at P^*. If B$_1$ is false, B$_3$ is examined. If B$_3$ is true (lines 5 and 7), the test point P^* has positive slope, yielding a P_3, and a new test point

Table 11.2   All Possible Truth Values of B1, B2, B3, and B4

line	B1	B2	B3	B4	line	B1	B2	B3	B4
1	T	T	T	T	5	F	T	T	F
2	T	T	F	T	6	F	T	F	T
3	T	F	T	F	7	F	F	T	F
4	T	F	F	F	8	F	F	F	F

T = True   F = False

is determined by cubic interpolation using the information provided by P_2 and P_3. If B_3 is false (line 8), the test point P^* has negative slope, yielding a P_2. Then, if a previous P_3 is available, a new test point is interpolated between P_2 and P_3, as above; otherwise B_5 is examined. If B_5 is true, a new test point is obtained by extrapolation using P_1 and P_2. Otherwise, the step size α^* is increased by multiplying by a constant scale factor $a > 1$.

Successive test points are examined in this way until B_4 is false and B_1 is true. This usually occurs after two test points, but if the search is done in a region far away from the minimum of $F(\theta)$, more test points may be required. If a point where B_1 is true is found, this is the new point $\theta^{(s+1)}$. The information matrix is then updated to $\mathbf{E}^{(s+1)}$ as explained above.

During the line search, the point with the smallest function value is saved. At most MT (default value = 20) test points are permitted in each direction. After MT test points, the program examines the smallest function value obtained. If this is smaller than $f(0)$, the point with the smallest function value is taken as the new point $\theta^{(s+1)}$ and $\mathbf{E}^{s+1}$ is computed by inverting the information matrix at that point.

If no test point with function value smaller than $f(0)$ is found, the program changes the direction of search to the steepest descent direction represented by the line $\theta - \alpha\mathbf{g}$. If the line search along this direction is successful this yields a new point $\theta^{(s+1)}$. If no point with function value smaller than $f(0)$ is found along the steepest descent direction, the program gives up and prints the message:

```
F_A_T_A_L  E_R_R_O_R: Serious problems encountered during mini-
    mization. Unable to continue iterations. Check your data and model.
```

In most cases, the problem is in the data or the model. However, it can also occur in ill-conditioned problems (model being nearly non-identified, information matrix being nearly singular), where it is impossible to obtain the accuracy required by the convergence criterion due to insufficient arithmetic precision. The latter case is often characterized by a solution which is very close to the minimum — sufficiently close for most practical purposes. This can be evaluated by putting the option FD (for First Derivatives) on the OU command and inspecting these derivatives in the output file.

The constants a, b and c referred to in this section are fixed in the program at 2.0, 0.75, and 0.1, respectively.

Users of LISREL who are interested in studying the behavior of the iterative procedure should request the technical output (PT) where the values of α, $s(\alpha)$, and $f(\alpha)$ are given at each test point. The option PT is given on the OU command.

A New features in LISREL 8

A.1 New command language

LISREL 8 accepts two different command languages in the input file. To distinguish between these, we use the terms LISREL input and SIMPLIS input. A LISREL input is an input file written in the old LISREL command language as described in Chapter 2, with modifications and extensions given here. A SIMPLIS input is an input file written in the new command language SIMPLIS described in a separate book: *LISREL 8: Structural Equation Modeling with the SIMPLIS Command Language* (Karl G. Jöreskog & Dag Sörbom, 1993b).

One can use either the SIMPLIS language or the LISREL language in the input file but the two languages cannot be mixed in the same input file.

The SIMPLIS command language is easy to learn and use. All that is required is to name all observed and latent (if any) variables and to formulate the model to be estimated. The model can be specified either as paths or as relationships (equations) in the input file or as a path diagram at run time. Although it is still absolutely essential to understand the basic ideas and principles of latent variable modeling and structural equations, it is not necessary to be familiar with the notational system of the LISREL model or any of its submodels. No Greek or matrix notations are required. There are no complicated options to learn. Anyone who can formulate the model as a path diagram can use the SIMPLIS language immediately.

Any LISREL model can be specified in the SIMPLIS command language, including models for several groups. The models can be estimated by any of the estimation methods available in LISREL 7. While the LISREL language can only produce output in the standard LISREL form, where the model is represented in matrix form, the SIMPLIS language can produce output *either* in SIMPLIS form, where the model is represented by equations, *or* in standard LISREL form.

To distinguish between the two forms of output, we shall use the terms SIMPLIS output and LISREL output. Thus:

- ❏ SIMPLIS output means that the model is presented in the form of equations (relationships)
- ❏ LISREL output means that the model is presented in the form of matrices

With LISREL input, one will only get LISREL output. With SIMPLIS input, one can choose between SIMPLIS output (default) or LISREL output. In addition, both languages can produce high quality path diagrams on the screen and the printer, as described in Jöreskog & Sörbom (1993b).

Beginning users of LISREL and users who often make mistakes when they specify the LISREL model will benefit greatly from using the SIMPLIS language as this is much easier to learn and reduces the possibilities for mistakes to a minimum. Experienced users who seldom or never make mistakes in the model specification, may want to continue to use the LISREL command language. The advanced features *Linear and non-linear constraints*, *General covariance structures*, and *Interval restrictions* described in the sections on pages 345 through 348 can only be used with the LISREL command language.

The remaining part of this appendix describes the main new features of LISREL 8 and the differences between LISREL 7 and LISREL 8, when the LISREL language is used. The SIMPLIS command language is covered in Jöreskog & Sörbom (1993b).

A.2 Compatibility with LISREL 7

Input

Every input file for LISREL 7 should run on LISREL 8 and produce the same results. But note the following:

□ An exclamation mark (!) or the slash-asterisk combination (/*) may be used to indicate that everything that follows on this line is to be regarded as comments. Blank (empty) lines are still accepted without the ! or /*.

□ The first line for each problem may be a title line containing any information used as a heading for the problem. One may choose not to have a title line or use only a single title line. However, any number of title lines may be used to describe the model and the data. The program will read title lines until it finds

- a physical line beginning with the words Labels or Observed Variables, which is the first command in a SIMPLIS input file; or

- a physical line whose first two non-blank characters are DA, Da, dA, or da, which is the first command in a LISREL input file.

Therefore, one must not use title lines beginning with these characters. To avoid this conflict, begin every title line with !. Then, anything can appear on the title lines.

Title lines are optional but strongly recommended. Only title lines can appear before the first genuine command line.

□ The default value of AD has been changed from 10 to 20. LISREL will check the admissibility of the solution (see Jöreskog & Sörbom, 1989, p. 24 and p. 278) after AD iterations if convergence has not been obtained before that. If the solution is non-admissible after AD iterations, iterations will stop and an intermediate solution will be printed. We believe that if an admissible solution is not found in 20 iterations, it will never be found, no matter how long LISREL is allowed to iterate.

□ The default form for $\boldsymbol{\Psi}$ (PS) has been changed to diagonal (PS=DI). Previously, it was PS=SY, *i.e.*, full symmetric. All three error covariance matrices $\boldsymbol{\Psi}$, $\boldsymbol{\Theta}_\epsilon$, and $\boldsymbol{\Theta}_\delta$ are now handled in the same way, *i.e.*,

- Default means diagonal and free. Off-diagonal elements *cannot* be relaxed.

- SY means symmetric with free diagonal and fixed off-diagonal elements. Off-diagonal elements *can* be relaxed.

- SY,FR means that the whole symmetric matrix is free.

This change is most logical in the context of the new SIMPLIS command language because it means that error terms need to be mentioned in the input file only when they are supposed to be correlated with other error terms.

□ In multiple group models (NG>1), references to elements of the column vectors $\boldsymbol{\alpha}$, $\boldsymbol{\tau}_y$, $\boldsymbol{\tau}_x$, and $\boldsymbol{\kappa}$ (AL, TY, TX, KA) of the extended LISREL model (see Chapter 10) should be done with two indices (group number and row number) instead of three. The use of three indices is restricted to the parameter matrices $\boldsymbol{\Lambda}_y$, $\boldsymbol{\Lambda}_x$, $\mathbf{B}$, $\boldsymbol{\Gamma}$, $\boldsymbol{\Phi}$, $\boldsymbol{\Psi}$, $\boldsymbol{\Theta}_\epsilon$, and $\boldsymbol{\Theta}_\delta$ (LY, LX, BE, GA, PH, PS, TE, TD).

Output

□ The output has been considerably reorganized so that things appear in a more logical order. Standard errors and t-values now appear together with parameter estimates within each parameter matrix and are always printed, whenever possible (in LISREL 7 standard errors and t-values had to be requested). Therefore, the SE and TV options on the OU command are no longer needed. Also, the MI option is no longer needed because modification indices are always printed unless one puts the option XM on the OU command (note that *computation* of the modification indices cannot be suppressed when a path diagram is requested).

□ LISREL 8 uses two decimals in the output by default rather than three decimals as used in LISREL 7. If you wish to have three decimals in the output, put ND=3 on the OU command.

- Starting values or initial estimates are not printed at all unless requested with PT on the OU command, *i.e.*, starting values are only printed with the technical output.

- The meaning of the FI (Fixed-x) option has been slightly changed, see the section *Unconstrained x* on page 341.

- Some outputs may differ between LISREL 7 and LISREL 8 because the latent variables are on a different scale. LISREL 8 will standardize all latent variables, *even the η-variables*, unless otherwise specified. This is a new unique feature in LISREL 8, see the section *Scaling the latent variables* on page 339.

LISREL 8 has many extensions and new features as described in the following sections.

A.3   An extension of the LISREL model

The full LISREL model assumes that δ and ϵ, the measurement errors in x and y, respectively, are uncorrelated, see p. 4 of Jöreskog & Sörbom (1989). This is not a serious restriction, because any full LISREL model can be transformed into the form of a Submodel 3B as described on p. 158 of Jöreskog & Sörbom (1989). A Submodel 3B involves only the variables y, η, and ϵ and the parameter matrices Λ_y, $\mathbf{B}$, $\mathbf{\Psi}$, and Θ_ϵ. A covariance between an ϵ and a δ in the original model, will then appear as a covariance between two ϵ's in the transformed model. However, this transformation is often inconvenient and the parameter matrices in the transformed model are often much larger than the parameter matrices in the original model. A further problem is that it is a difficult pedagogical task to explain why the first η-variable is equal to its own disturbance term ζ as is the case in Examples 6.5 and 7.2 of Jöreskog & Sörbom (1989). See files EX65B.LS7 and EX72.LS7. For these reasons, we have extended the full LISREL model slightly, by adding a parameter matrix $\Theta_{\delta\epsilon}$ of order $q \times p$ representing the covariance matrix between δ and ϵ. The LISREL name for this matrix is TH. This matrix is a fixed zero matrix by default. It *cannot* be declared free on the MO command. However, any of its elements can be declared free on a FR command.

Example: Panel model for political efficacy

Aish & Jöreskog (1990) analyze data on political attitudes. Their data consist of 16 ordinal variables measured on the same people at two occasions. Six of the 16 variables were considered to be indicators of Political Efficacy and System Responsiveness. The attitude questions corresponding to these six variables are:

NOSAY   *People like me have no say in what the government does.*

VOTING   *Voting is the only way that people like me can have any say about how the government runs things.*

COMPLEX   *Sometimes politics and government seem so complicated that a person like me cannot really understand what is going on.*

NOCARE   *I don't think that public officials care much about what people like me think.*

TOUCH   *Generally speaking, those we elect to Parliament lose touch with the people pretty quickly.*

INTEREST   *Parties are only interested in people's votes but not in their opinions.*

Responses to these questions were scored:

1 = agree strongly, 2 = agree, 3 = disagree, and 4 = disagree strongly

Aish & Jöreskog (1990) considered many different models. One of them will be used here. This is shown in Figure 1.

The following command file illustrates the simplicity in setting up the input using the TH extension of the model. The PANELUSA.PML and PANELUSA.ACP files were obtained with PRELIS 2 (Jöreskog & Sörbom, 1993a). For further discussion of analysis of ordinal variables with PRELIS 2 and LISREL 8, see Jöreskog & Aish (1996).

```
!TWO-WAVE PANEL MODEL FOR POLITICAL EFFICACY AND RESPONSIVENESS
!See Aish and Joreskog, Quality and Quantity (1990)
!PME and ACP matrices computed by PRELIS 2
DA NI=12 NO=410 MA=PM
LA FI=PANEL.LAB
PM FI=PANELUSA.PME
```

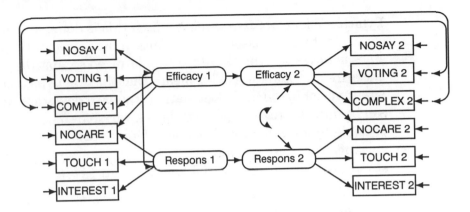

Figure A.1   Panel Model for Political Efficacy

```
AC FI=PANELUSA.ACP
MO NY=6 NX=6 NE=2 NK=2 GA=DI PS=SY,FR      !Note that PS=SY,FR
LE; EFFICAC2 RESPONS2
LK; EFFICAC1 RESPONS1
FR LY 2 1 LY 3 1 LY 4 1 LY 4 2 LY 5 2
FR LX 2 1 LX 3 1 LX 4 1 LX 4 2 LX 5 2
VA 1 LY 1 1 LY 6 2 LX 1 1 LX 6 2
FR TH 2 2 TH 3 3
OU MI RS SC
```

This is an example of a full LISREL model with correlated ϵ and δ. All nine parameter matrices are involved, but all are default except Γ, which is diagonal, and Ψ, which is a full symmetric matrix. The correlated measurement errors are specified on the FR command.

A.4 Scaling the latent variables

Latent variables are unobservable and have no definite scale. The origin and the unit of measurement in each latent variable are arbitrary. To define the model properly, the origin and the unit of measurement of each latent variable must be defined. For single-sample problems, the origin is usually fixed by assuming that each latent variable has zero mean. In order to interpret the elements of all the parameter matrices, units of measurements of the latent variables must also be defined.

Typically, there are two ways in which this is done. The most useful and convenient way of assigning the units of measurement of the latent variables is to assume that they are standardized so that they have unit variances in the population. This means that the unit of measurement in each latent variable equals its population standard deviation. In LISREL 7, this can be done for the independent latent variables (ξ-variables) but it is impossible to do so for the dependent latent variables (η-variables), as the variances of these depend on other parameters of the model. LISREL 8 standardizes *all* latent variables by default, *even* the dependent latent variables (η-variables).

Another way to assign a unit of measurement for a latent variable, is to fix a non-zero coefficient (usually 1) in the relationship for one of its observed indicators. This defines the unit for each latent variable in relation to one of the observed variables, a so called reference variable. In practice, one chooses as a reference variable the observed variable, which, in some sense, best represents the latent variable. This is the way units of measurement are assigned to the dependent latent variables in LISREL 7.

LISREL 8 defines the units of latent variables as follows.

- If a reference variable is assigned to a latent variable by the specification of a fixed non-zero coefficient in the relationship between the reference variable and the latent variable, then this defines the scale for that latent variable. This holds regardless of whether this latent variable is a dependent latent variable (an η-variable) or an independent latent variable (a ξ-variable).
- If no reference variable is specified for a latent variable, by assigning a fixed non-zero coefficient for an observed variable, the program will standardize this latent variable. This holds regardless of whether this latent variable is a dependent latent variable (an η-variable) or an independent latent variable (a ξ-variable).

In the previous input file, the units of the latent variables Efficacy and Response were defined by using the observed variables NOSAY and INTEREST as reference variables. This is somewhat meaningless, since these observed variables themselves are ordinal and do not have any units of measurements. To obtain a solution with standardized latent variables, just replace the three commands

```
FR LY 2 1 LY 3 1 LY 4 1 LY 4 2 LY 5 2
FR LX 2 1 LX 3 1 LX 4 1 LX 4 2 LX 5 2
VA 1 LY 1 1 LY 6 2 LX 1 1 LX 6 2
```

with the two commands

```
FR LY 1 1 LY 2 1 LY 3 1 LY 4 1 LY 4 2 LY 5 2 LY 6 2
FR LX 1 1 LX 2 1 LX 3 1 LX 4 1 LX 4 2 LX 5 2 LX 6 2
```

A.5 Unconstrained x

A common class of LISREL models (Submodel 3C) is one in which $\boldsymbol{\xi} \equiv \mathbf{x}$ so that the x-variables themselves influence the η-variables directly. The x-variables are background variables, covariates or other explanatory variables which are either random variables with an unconstrained covariance matrix or a set of fixed variables. For the estimation of such a model, it is sufficient to consider only the *conditional distribution* of y for given x. Examples of such models are given in Chapters 4 and 5 of Jöreskog & Sörbom (1989).

In this kind of a model we have $\boldsymbol{\Lambda}_x = \mathbf{I}$, $\boldsymbol{\Theta}_\delta = \mathbf{0}$, and $\boldsymbol{\Phi}$ is the covariance matrix of x which is unconstrained. LISREL regards x as random but x can have any distribution assumed not to contain any parameters of interest. LISREL 8 automatically recognizes this kind of model if NK is default or NK=0 on the MO command. It is no longer necessary to use the FI option to specify such models. In LISREL 8, FI means that $\boldsymbol{\Phi}$ is to be considered fixed and equal to $\mathbf{S}_{xx}$. Thus,

- Without FI, $\boldsymbol{\Phi}$ will be estimated as a free parameter matrix along with the standard errors of $\hat{\boldsymbol{\Phi}}$.
- With FI, $\boldsymbol{\Phi} = \mathbf{S}_{xx}$ is fixed and no standard errors of $\hat{\boldsymbol{\Phi}}$ are computed.

A.6 Goodness-of-fit statistics

The standard LISREL 8 output now includes all the goodness-of-fit measures that have been discussed in the literature. In particular, it gives some new and useful measures developed by Steiger (1990) and by Browne & Cudeck (1993). These measures take particular account of the error of approximation in the population and the precision of the fit measure itself. The AIC and CAIC statistics discussed by Bozdogan (1987), the Browne & Cudeck (1989) single sample cross-validation index, all measures discussed in Bollen (1989, pp. 256–282), and all those included in EQS (Bentler, 1989) are included as well. All the goodness-of-fit measures are defined and discussed in Chapter 4 of Jöreskog & Sörbom (1993b). An additional feature is that the goodness-of-fit measures may be saved in a file by putting GF=*filename* on the OU command. This is particularly useful in bootstrap and Monte Carlo studies (see Jöreskog & Sörbom, 1994).

For the hypothetical model (Jöreskog & Sörbom, 1989, pp. 6–9, 74, and Jöreskog & Sörbom, 1993b, Chapter 5) the goodness-of-fit statistics are as follows:

```
                 GOODNESS OF FIT STATISTICS

      CHI-SQUARE WITH 33 DEGREES OF FREEDOM = 29.10 (P = 0.66)
            ESTIMATED NON-CENTRALITY PARAMETER (NCP) = 0.0
       90 PERCENT CONFIDENCE INTERVAL FOR NCP = (0.0 ; 12.26)


               MINIMUM FIT FUNCTION VALUE = 0.29
        POPULATION DISCREPANCY FUNCTION VALUE (F0) = 0.0
        90 PERCENT CONFIDENCE INTERVAL FOR F0 = (0.0 ; 0.12)
      ROOT MEAN SQUARE ERROR OF APPROXIMATION (RMSEA) = 0.0
     90 PERCENT CONFIDENCE INTERVAL FOR RMSEA = (0.0 ; 0.061)
        P-VALUE FOR TEST OF CLOSE FIT (RMSEA < 0.05) = 0.89


          EXPECTED CROSS-VALIDATION INDEX (ECVI) = 0.96
      90 PERCENT CONFIDENCE INTERVAL FOR ECVI = (1.00 ; 1.12)
                ECVI FOR SATURATED MODEL = 1.33

CHI-SQUARE FOR INDEPENDENCE MODEL WITH 55 DEGREES OF FREEDOM = 1441.95
                  INDEPENDENCE AIC = 1463.95
                       MODEL AIC = 95.10
                     SATURATED AIC = 132.00
                 INDEPENDENCE CAIC = 1503.61
                      MODEL CAIC = 214.07
                    SATURATED CAIC = 369.94


            ROOT MEAN SQUARE RESIDUAL (RMR) = 0.065
                    STANDARDIZED RMR = 0.026
              GOODNESS OF FIT INDEX (GFI) = 0.95
         ADJUSTED GOODNESS OF FIT INDEX (AGFI) = 0.90
        PARSIMONY GOODNESS OF FIT INDEX (PGFI) = 0.47
```

```
              NORMED FIT INDEX (NFI) = 0.98
          NON-NORMED FIT INDEX (NNFI) = 1.00
    PARSIMONY NORMED FIT INDEX (PNFI) = 0.58
          COMPARATIVE FIT INDEX (CFI) = 1.00
          INCREMENTAL FIT INDEX (IFI) = 1.00
            RELATIVE FIT INDEX (RFI) = 0.96

                 CRITICAL N (CN) = 187.35
```

A.7   Simplified pattern matrices for equality constraints

When there are many equality constraints in the model, the writing of all EQ commands is often tedious and it is easy to make mistakes. It is now much easier to specify equality constraints directly in pattern matrices.

The general rule is: use any integer greater than 1 as a label for a parameter and then refer to this parameter in any pattern matrix using the same label. For example,

```
PA LY
0 0 2 3 0
0 0 0 3 2
```

will replace

```
PA LY
0 0 1 1 0
0 0 0 1 1
EQ LY(1,3) LY(2,5)
EQ LY(1,4) LY(2,4)
```

The actual value of the integer is irrelevant as long as it refers to the same parameter each time it is used. LISREL keeps track of all the different parameters and uses its own ordering of them. Therefore, the parameters will not, in general, have the same numbers attached to them in the parameter specification in the output as those assigned by the user. Note that, as before, a 1 in a pattern matrix refers to a free parameter, *i.e.*, one which is not equal to any other parameter, although this parameter can still be constrained on EQ or CO commands (see the section *Linear and non-linear constraints* on page 345).

The same technique can be used in multiple groups as well. For example,

```
PA LY
0 0 2 3 0
0 0 0 3 2
```

in group 1 and

```
PA LY
0 0 2 3 0
0 0 2 3 0
```

in group 2, sets

$$\mathbf{\Lambda}_y^{(1)} = \begin{pmatrix} 0 & 0 & \alpha & \beta & 0 \\ 0 & 0 & 0 & \beta & \alpha \end{pmatrix} \ \mathbf{\Lambda}_y^{(2)} = \begin{pmatrix} 0 & 0 & \alpha & \beta & 0 \\ 0 & 0 & \alpha & \beta & 0 \end{pmatrix} ,$$

where α and β are two free parameters.

A.8   Standardized effects

LISREL 7 gives indirect and total effects for the solution in which the observed and latent variables are in the units specified in the input. In addition, LISREL 8 will give indirect and total effects for the standardized solutions SS and SC, see pp. 38–40 in Jöreskog & Sörbom (1989).

If both EF and SS appear on the OU command, LISREL 8 will give the standardized effects for the SS solution, *i.e.*, the solution in which the latent variables are standardized but not the observed.

If both EF and SC appear on the OU command, LISREL 8 will give the standardized effects for the SC solution, *i.e.*, the solution in which both the latent and the observed variables are standardized.

With multiple groups, the standardized effects are based on the within group standardized solutions.

A.9 Linear and non-linear constraints

General linear and non-linear constraints can now be imposed on LISREL parameters. Let $\theta_1, \theta_2, \cdots, \theta_t$ be the free parameters in the LISREL model before the constraints are imposed. Then, the general form of these constraints is

$$\theta_i = \sum_m a_{im} \prod_{j=1}^{u} \theta_j^{b_{ij}}, \qquad i = u+1, u+2, \ldots, t,$$

where a_{im} is any positive or negative constant and b_{ij} is any constant including zero. This equation expresses $\theta_{u+1}, \theta_{u+2}, \ldots, \theta_t$ as functions of $\theta_1, \theta_2, \ldots, \theta_u$. Note that $b_{ij} = 0$ means that θ_i does not depend on θ_j. If $b_{ij} = 1$, it may be omitted.

The constraints are specified on a CO command in the input file. The equation defining the constraint is written in a straightforward way. Multiplication is specified by * and exponentiation by ** or ^. Exponents need not be integers. Parentheses are not permitted except in matrix elements. Division is not permitted although exponents may be negative. Constants are written as usual. If they are written without a decimal point, they are taken to be integers.

Examples:

```
CO TD(1,1)=1-LX(1,1)**2-LX(1,2)**2
CO LX(1,4)=LX(1,5)-LX(1,6)**4
CO BE(1,2)=-BE(2,1)
CO BE(3,2)=1.5634*GA(1,2)*GA(1,3)*GA(4,2)**1.37
CO LY(3,3)=TE(3,3)**-1
CO LY(1,1)=3.27*BE(1,2)*GA(1,1)*PH(2,2)*1.7*PS(1,1)+TD(1,1)*TE(1,1)**-1
```

There should be one constraint defined on each CO command. If the constraint is so complex that it does not fit on a line of 127 characters, just enter a C for Continue and continue on the next line.

Let v be the number of CO commands in the input file and let $\boldsymbol{\theta}_2$ be the vector of order v containing the parameters on the left sides of the constraints. Let $\boldsymbol{\theta}_1$ be the vector of order u containing all the remaining free parameters of the model. Then, $u + v = t$, and it is convenient to refer to the elements of θ_2 as the *constrained parameters* and to the elements of θ_1 as the *unconstrained or free parameters*.

The fit function is minimized with respect to θ_1 taking into account that θ_2 is a function of θ_1. From the form of the constraints, LISREL 8 deduces analytic expressions for the first-order derivatives of each constrained parameter with respect to each free parameter and the elements of the information matrix of order $u \times u$. An estimate of the $t \times t$ asymptotic covariance matrix of *all* estimated parameters may be obtained by putting EC=*filename* on the OU command. The corresponding correlation matrix may be obtained in the list output by putting PC on the OU command. In these matrices, the asymptotic covariance matrix of the free parameters appear in the upper left $u \times u$ part.

Constraints like this must be used with the utmost care. The constraints must make sense both from a substantive and a mathematical point of view. Make sure the constraints are written correctly and correspond to the constraints intended. To be safe, follow these rules:

- ❑ Find out exactly which parameters are free. This may involve choosing a particular set so that the constraints can be expressed in a form that LISREL can handle.
- ❑ All the non-fixed elements in all the parameter matrices and in all the groups must be expressed as functions of the free parameters. Only free parameters should appear on the right-hand side on CO commands. Thus,

    - Implicit equations, in which the parameter on the left also appears on the right side are not permitted.
    - Parameters that are constrained on previous CO commands, *i.e.*, that are on the left side, should not appear on the right side on any CO command. Constraints cannot be used recursively.
    - Parameters which are equal to one of the free parameters, can be specified either by CO commands or by EQ commands, but in the latter case, the free parameter must be listed first.

Non-linear constraints may be useful in the estimation of models with non-linear and interaction effects of the form proposed by Kenny & Judd

(1984). They are also useful in models for twin data, see, for example, Neale & Cardon (1992). For a complex example illustrating the generality, flexibility, and powerfulness of constraints, see Cardon, Fulker, & Jöreskog (1991).

A.10 General covariance structures

LISREL 8 has an extension which makes it possible to fit and test almost any covariance structure, *even those that cannot be specified as a* LISREL *model*. This is achieved by the introduction of additional parameters, which are not elements of the parameter matrices in LISREL but the LISREL parameters may be specified to be functions of these additional parameters.

To use this new option, specify any LISREL model in the usual way and add AP=k on the MO command, where k is the number of new parameters to be added. In the LISREL language these new parameters are labeled:

```
PAR(1), PAR(2), ..., PAR(k)
```

PAR may also be written PA. These parameters are supposed to be independent free parameters. They can be given starting values on a ST command as usual. Any parameter in the LISREL model can be specified to be a function of these and other LISREL parameters using linear and non-linear constraints as described in the previous section.

A typical prototype for a general covariance structure will be to specify a Submodel 1 with $\Lambda_x = I$ and $\Theta_\delta = 0$ and Φ default (free). Then, $\Sigma = \Phi$, and we can specify almost any covariance structure by expressing the elements of Φ as functions of new parameters.

Fictitious example

Suppose we want to fit the following covariance structure

$$\Sigma = \begin{pmatrix} \alpha & & & \\ \beta\gamma & 1+\alpha^2 & & \\ \delta & \delta^2 & \delta^3 & \\ \epsilon & \epsilon+\delta & \epsilon+\delta^2 & 1+\epsilon^2 \end{pmatrix}$$

where the parameters are $\alpha, \beta, \gamma, \delta, \epsilon$. Obviously, β and γ are not identified but LISREL will detect that. Let the parameters correspond to PAR(1), PAR(2), PAR(3), PAR(4), PAR(5). This model can be specified as follows:

```
MO NX=4 NK=4 LX=ID TD=ZE AP=5
CO PH(1,1)=PAR(1)
CO PH(2,1)=PAR(2)*PAR(3)
CO PH(2,2)=1+PAR(1)**2
CO PH(3,1)=PAR(4)
CO PH(3,2)=PAR(4)**2
CO PH(3,3)=PAR(4)**3
CO PH(4,1)=PAR(5)
CO PH(4,2)=PAR(5)+PAR(4)
CO PH(4,3)=PAR(5)+PAR(4)**2
CO PH(4,4)=1+PAR(5)**2
```

Suppose, we want to add the identification condition $\alpha = \beta$. This can be done by adding the command:

```
EQ PAR(1) PAR(2)
```

A.11   Interval restrictions

Interval restrictions of the forms $\theta \geq a$, $\theta \leq b$ and $a \leq \theta \leq b$ may be placed on any LISREL parameter θ, where a and b are specified constants.

Examples:

```
IR TD(2,2) >0
IR GA(2,4) <1
IR PH(2,1) >-1 <1
```

correspond to $\theta_{22}^{(\delta)} \geq 0$, $\gamma_{24} \leq 1$, and $-1 \leq \phi_{21} \leq 1$.

The general syntax is

```
IR parlist condition
```

where *parlist* is a list of parameters of the form MN(i,j), *condition* is $>a$, $<b$, or $>a <b$, and MN is any LISREL matrix name, *i.e.*, LY, LX, BE, GA, PH, PS, TE, TD, TH, TY, TX, AL, or KA.

It is recommended to run the problem without the interval restrictions first and then apply only those interval restrictions which are needed. Chisquare and standard errors will be affected if parameter estimates are on the boundary of the interval and standard errors may not be valid.

B   Syntax overview

This appendix provides a convenient reference to LISREL 8. The commands are arranged in logical order. The diagram is constructed according to the following conventions:

- Square brackets [] enclose optional specifications. The brackets themselves should not be coded.
- Boxes enclose alternative specifications. Only one element of the list may be entered. A **boldface** element indicates the default specification.
- Parentheses () must be entered exactly as shown.
- Equals signs = are required.
- Uppercase elements are commands, keywords, keyword values, or options. They must be entered as they appear, or they may be lengthened (LABELS instead of LA, for example). Thus, except for the ALL option on the VA and ST commands and the PATH DIAGRAM command (though PD may be used instead), everything has *two* significant characters.
- Lowercase elements describe information to be filled in by the user.
- Use blanks to separate command names, keywords, and options.
- An exclamation mark (!) or the slash-asterisk combination (/*) may be used to indicate that everything that follows on this line is to be regarded as comments. Blank (empty) lines are accepted without the ! or /*.
- Command order is important, see the section *Order of commands* on page 43.

- For format statements, see the section *FORTRAN format statements in the command file* on page 38. No format statement means free format: the data are separated by a space, comma, and/or return character.

- A parameter matrix element should be written as a parameter matrix name (LY, LX, BE, GA, PH, PS, TE, TD, TH, TY, TX, AL, or KA), followed by row and column indexes (or linear indexes) of the specific element. Row and column indexes may be separated by a comma and enclosed in parentheses, like LY(3,2), LX(4,1), or separated from the matrix name and each other by spaces, like LY 3 2 LX 4 1.

- The order of the form and mode values for the parameter matrices on the MO command line is optional, but if both are given, a comma in between is required.

- An *italic* element indicates a new feature of LISREL 8

The maximum line length in a command file is 127 columns. Commands may be continued over several lines by adding a space followed by a C (for 'continue') on the current line. A keyword and its specified value should appear on the same line: start a keyword on a new line if its specified value would extend past column 127. Note that this requirement has not been followed in the syntax diagram below.

B.1 LISREL syntax diagram

["title line"]
[...]

Input specification commands

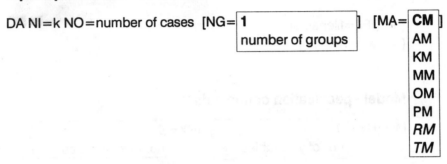

DA NI=k NO=number of cases [NG=| 1 / number of groups |] [MA=| CM / AM / KM / MM / OM / PM / *RM* / *TM* |]

[XM=global missing value] [*RP*=no. of repetitions]

[LA [[FI]=filename [FO] [RE]]]
[(character variable format statement)]
[y and x labels]

[RA [[FI]=filename [FO] [RE]]]
[(variable format statement)]
[data records]

[| CM / KM / MM / OM / PM / *RM* / *TM* | [[FI]=filename [FO] [RE] [| **SY** / FU |]]]
[(variable format statement)]
[data records]

[ME [[FI]=filename [FO] [RE]]]
[(variable format statement)]
[data records]

```
[SD [[FI]=filename [FO] [RE]]]
[(variable format statement)]
[ data records ]
[ AC   [FI]=filename]
  WM
[ AV   [FI]=filename]
  DM
[SE [[FI]=filename]]
[ variable names ]
```

Model specification commands

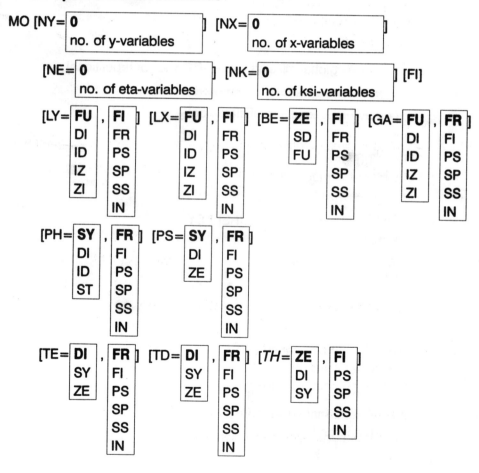

$$[TY = \boxed{\begin{array}{l}\mathbf{FI} \\ FR \\ IN \\ PS \\ SP \\ SS\end{array}}] \quad [TX = \boxed{\begin{array}{l}\mathbf{FI} \\ FR \\ IN \\ PS \\ SP \\ SS\end{array}}] \quad [AL = \boxed{\begin{array}{l}\mathbf{FI} \\ FR \\ IN \\ PS \\ SP \\ SS\end{array}}] \quad [KA = \boxed{\begin{array}{l}\mathbf{FI} \\ FR \\ IN \\ PS \\ SP \\ SS\end{array}}]$$

$$[AP = \boxed{\begin{array}{l}\mathbf{0} \\ \text{number of additional independent free parameters}\end{array}}]$$

[LK [[FI]=filename [FO] [RE]]]
[(character variable format statement)]
[ksi labels]

[LE [[FI]=filename [FO] [RE]]]
[(character variable format statement)]
[eta labels]

[FR list of parameter matrix elements]

[FI list of parameter matrix elements]

[EQ list of parameter matrix elements]

[*CO* parameter matrix element=expression with other parameters]

[*IR* list of parameter matrix elements [>number] [<number]]

[PA [[FI]=filename [FO] [RE]] matrix name]
[(integer format statement)]
[pattern records]

$$[VA \text{ numerical value} \boxed{\begin{array}{l}\text{list of parameter matrix elements} \\ \text{ALL}\end{array}}]$$

$$[ST \text{ numerical value} \boxed{\begin{array}{l}\text{list of parameter matrix elements} \\ \text{ALL}\end{array}}]$$

[MA [[FI]=filename [FO] [RE]] matrix name]
[(variable format statement)]
[records of matrix values]

[PL list of parameter matrix elements [FROM a TO b]]

[NF list of parameter matrix elements]

Output specification commands

[PD
PATH DIAGRAM]

OU [ME= ML] [RC= 0.001] [SL= 1] [NS] [RO] [AM] [SO]
         DW   value   integer
         GL
         IV
         TS
         UL
         WL

[SE] [TV] [PC] [PT] [RS] [EF] [MR] [MI] [FS] [SS] [SC] [ALL]

[XM] [XI] [TO] [ND= 2]
          WP   number of decimals

[BE=filename] [GA=filename] [LX=filename] [LY=filename]

[PH=filename] [PS=filename] [TD=filename] [TE=filename]

[EC=filename] [MA=filename] [RM=filename] [SI=filename]

[AL=filename] [KA=filename] [TX=filename] [TY=filename]

[TH=filename]

[GF=filename] [PV=filename] [SV=filename] [TV=filename]

[TM= 172800] [IT= three times all free parameters]
     maximum seconds   maximum iterations

[AD= 20] [EP= 0.000001]
     integer   convergence criterion
     OFF

B.2 Notation

The Greek Alphabet		
α	A	alpha
β	B	beta
γ	Γ	gamma
δ	Δ	delta
ϵ	E	epsilon
ζ	Z	zeta
η	H	eta
θ	Θ	theta
ι	I	iota
κ	K	kappa
λ	Λ	lambda
μ	M	mu
ν	N	nu
ξ	Ξ	xi, ksi
o	O	omicron
π	Π	pi
ρ	P	rho
σ	Σ	sigma
τ	T	tau
υ	Υ	upsilon
ϕ	Φ	phi
χ	X	chi
ψ	Ψ	psi
ω	Ω	omega

Typical LISREL Notation

x, y	observed variables
ξ, η	latent variables
ζ, δ, ϵ	error variables
Λ_x, Λ_y	factor loadings
$\mathbf{B}, \Gamma$	structural parameters
Φ, Ψ	covariance matrices
$\Theta_\delta, \Theta_\epsilon, \Theta_{\delta\epsilon}$	error covariance matrices
$\hat{\Lambda}_x$	estimate of Λ_x

Other Notation

$\mathbf{x}$	column vector
$\mathbf{x}'$	row vector
$\mathbf{X}$	matrix
$\mathbf{X}'$	matrix transpose
$\mathbf{X}^{-1}$	matrix inverse
$[x_{ij}]$	matrix element
$\|\mathbf{X}\|$	determinant of a square matrix $\mathbf{X}$
$\mathrm{tr}(\mathbf{X})$	trace of $\mathbf{X}$ (sum of diagonal elements of a square matrix)
Greek letters	population parameters, latent random variables
Roman letters	observed random variables

References

Aish, A.M., & Jöreskog, K.G. (1990)
A panel model for political efficacy and responsiveness: An application of LISREL 7 with weighted least squares.
Quality and Quantity, 24, 405–426.

Allison, P.D. (1987)
Estimation of linear models with incomplete data.
Pp. 71–103 in C. Clogg (Ed.): *Sociological Methodology 1987.*
San Francisco: Jossey Bass.

Anderson, S.B., & Maier, M.H. (1963)
34000 pupils and how they grew.
Journal of Teacher Education, **14**, 212–216.

Bagozzi, R.P. (1980)
Performance and satisfaction in an industrial sales force: An examination of their antecedents and simultaneity.
Journal of Marketing, **44**, 65–77.

Bentler, P. M. (1989)
Structural equations program manual.
Los Angeles: BMDP Statistical Software, Inc.

Bielby, W.T., Hauser, R.M., & Featherman, D.L. (1977)
Response errors of black and nonblack males in models of the intergenerational transmission of socioeconomic status.
American Journal of Sociology, **82**, 1242–1288.

Bock, R.D. (1960)
Components of variance analysis as a structural and discriminal analysis for psychological tests.
British Journal of Statistical Psychology, **13**, 151–163.

359

Bock, R.D., & Lieberman, M. (1970)
Fitting a response model for n dichotomously scored items.
Psychometrika, **35**, 179–197.

Bollen, K. A. (1989)
Structural equations with latent variables.
New York: Wiley.

Bozdogan, H. (1987)
Model selection and Akaike's information criteria (AIC).
Psychometrika, 52, 345–370.

Browne, M.W. (1970)
Analysis of covariance structures.
Paper presented at the annual conference of the South African Statistical Association.

Browne, M.W. (1974)
Generalized least squares estimators in the analysis of covariance structures.
South African Statistical Journal, **8**, 1–24.
(Reprinted in D. J. Aigner & A. S. Goldberger (eds.),
Latent variables in socioeconomic models.
Amsterdam: North Holland Publishing Co., 1977.)

Browne, M.W. (1982)
Covariance structures.
In D.M. Hawkins (Ed.): *Topics in applied multivariate analysis* (pp. 72–141).
Cambridge: Cambridge University Press.

Browne, M.W. (1984)
Asymptotically distribution-free methods for the analysis of covariance structures.
British Journal of Mathematical and Statistical Psychology, **37**, 62–83.

Browne, M. W., & Cudeck, R. (1989)
Single sample cross-validation indices for covariance structures.
Multivariate Behavioral Research, 24, 445–455.

Browne, M. W., & Cudeck, R. (1993)
  Alternative ways of assessing model fit.
  In K. A. Bollen & J. S. Long (Editors): *Testing Structural Equation Models.*
  Sage Publications.

Calsyn, J.R., & Kenny, D.A. (1977)
  Self-concept of ability and perceived evaluation of others: Cause or effect of academic achievement?
  Journal of Educational Psychology, **69**, 136–145.

Cardon, L.R., Fulker, D.W., & Jöreskog, K.G. (1991)
  A LISREL 8 model with constrained parameters for twin and adoptive families.
  Behavior Genetics , 21, 327–350.

Christoffersson, A. (1975)
  Factor analysis of dichotomized variables.
  Psychometrika, **40**, 5–32.

Dixon, W.J. (1981)
  BMDP statistical software.
  Berkeley: University of California Press.

Duncan, O.D., Haller, A.O., & Portes, A. (1968)
  Peer influence on aspiration: A reinterpretation.
  American Journal of Sociology, **74**, 119–137.

Finn, J.D. (1974)
  A general model for multivariate analysis.
  New York: Holt, Reinhart & Winston.

Goldberger, A.S. (1964)
  Econometric theory.
  New York: Wiley.

Guttman, L.A. (1954)
  A new approach to factor analysis: The radex.
  In P.F. Lazarsfeld (Ed.): *Mathematical thinking in the social sciences.*
  New York: Columbia University Press.

Hägglund, G. (1982)
  Factor analysis by instrumental variable methods.
  Psychometrika, **47**, 209–222.

Härnqvist, K. (1962)
Manual till DBA (Manual for DBA).
Stockholm: Skandinaviska Testförlaget (In Swedish).

Hasselrot, T., & Lernberg, L.O., (Eds.) (1980)
Tonåringen och livet.
Vällingby, Sweden: Liber förlag (in Swedish).

Hilton, T.L. (1969)
Growth study annotated bibliography. Progress Report 69–11.
Princeton, NJ: Educational Testing Service.

Hodge, R.W., & Treiman, D.J. (1968)
Social participation and social status.
American Sociological Review, **33**, 723–740.

Holzinger, K., & Swineford, F. (1939)
A study in factor analysis: The stability of a bifactor solution. Supplementary Educational Monograph No. 48.
Chicago: University of Chicago Press.

Huitema, B.H. (1980)
The analysis of covariance and alternatives.
New York: Wiley.

Humphreys, L.G. (1968)
The fleeting nature of college academic success.
Journal of Educational Psychology, **59**, 375–380.

Jöreskog, K.G. (1970a)
Estimation and testing of simplex models.
British Journal of Mathematical and Statistical Psychology, **23**, 121–145.

Jöreskog, K.G. (1970b)
Factoring the multitest-multioccasion correlation matrix.
In C. E. Lunneborg (Ed.): *Current problems and techniques in multivariate psychology*. Proceedings of a conference honoring Professor Paul Horst.
Seattle: University of Washington.

Jöreskog, K.G. (1971a)
Simultaneous factor analysis in several populations.
Psychometrika, **57**, 409–426.

Jöreskog, K.G. (1971b)
Statistical analysis of sets of congeneric tests.
Psychometrika, **36**, 109–133.

Jöreskog, K.G. (1973)
Analysis of covariance structures.
In P.R. Krishnaiah (Ed.): *Multivariate Analysis–III*.
New York: Academic Press, 263–285.

Jöreskog, K.G. (1977)
Structural equation models in the social sciences: Specification, estimation and testing.
In P.R. Krishnaiah (Ed.): *Applications of statistics*.
Amsterdam: North-Holland Publishing Co., 265–287.

Jöreskog, K.G. (1981a)
Analysis of covariance structures.
Scandinavian Journal of Statistics, **8**, 65–92.

Jöreskog, K.G. (1981b)
Basic issues in the application of LISREL.
Data, **1:1**, 1–6.

Jöreskog, K.G., & Aish, A.M. (1996)
Structural equation modeling with ordinal variables.
Book Manuscript in Preparation.

Jöreskog, K.G., & Sörbom, D. (1982)
Recent developments in structural equation modeling.
Journal of Marketing Research, **19**, 404–416.

Jöreskog, K.G., & Sörbom, D. (1985)
Simultaneous analysis of longitudinal data from several cohorts.
Pp. 323–341 in W.M. Mason & S.E. Fienberg (Eds.): *Cohort analysis in social research: Beyond the identification problem*.
New York: Springer-Verlag.

Jöreskog, K.G., & Sörbom, D. (1996; third edition)
PRELIS 2 User's Reference Guide
Chicago: Scientific Software International.

Jöreskog, K.G., & Sörbom, D. (1989; second edition)
LISREL 7 – A guide to the program and applications.
Chicago: SPSS Publications.

Jöreskog, K.G., & Sörbom, D. (1993a)
New features in PRELIS 2.
In: K.G. Jöreskog & D. Sörbom: *PRELIS 2 User's Reference Guide* 1996,
3rd edition
Chicago: Scientific Software International.

Jöreskog, K.G., & Sörbom, D. (1993b)
LISREL 8: Structural Equation Modeling with the SIMPLIS Command Language.
Chicago: Scientific Software International.

Jöreskog, K.G., & Sörbom, D. (1994)
Simulation with PRELIS 2 and LISREL 8.
In: K.G. Jöreskog & D. Sörbom: *PRELIS 2 User's Reference Guide* 1996,
3rd edition
Chicago: Scientific Software International.

Kenny, D.A. (1979)
Correlation and causality.
New York: Wiley.

Kenny, D.A., & Judd, C.M. (1984)
Estimating the nonlinear and interactive effects of latent variables.
Psychological Bulletin, 96, 201–210.

Kerchoff, A.C. (1974)
Ambition and attainment.
Rose Monograph Series.

Klein, L.R. (1950)
Economic fluctuations in the United States 1921–1941. Cowles Commission Monograph No. 11.
New York: Wiley.

Kristof, W. (1971)
On the theory of a set of tests which differ in length.
Psychometrika, **36**, 207–255.

Lord, F.M. (1957)
A significance test for the hypothesis that two variables measure the same trait except for errors of measurement.
Psychometrika, **22**, 207–220.

REFERENCES

Magidson, J. (1977)
   Toward a causal model approach for adjusting for pre-existing differences in the non-equivalent control group situation.
   Evaluation Quarterly, **1**, 399–420.

Mare, R.D., & Mason, W.M. (1981)
   Children's report of parental socioeconomic status.
   In G.W. Bohrnstedt & E.F. Borgatta (Eds.): *Social Measurement: Current Issues*.
   Beverly Hills: Sage Publications.

Neale, M.C., & Cardon, L.R. (1992)
   Methodology for genetic studies of twins and families.
   Dordrecht: Kluwer Academic Publishers.

Rindskopf, D.M. (1983a)
   Parameterizing inequality constraints on unique variances in linear structural equation models.
   Psychometrika, **48**, 73–83.

Rindskopf, D.M. (1983b)
   Using inequality constraints to prevent Heywood cases: the LISREL parameterization.
   Data Analyst, **1**, 1–3.

Rindskopf, D.M. (1984)
   Using phantom and imaginary latent variables to parameterize constraints in linear structural models.
   Psychometrika, **49**, 37–47.

Rock, D.A., Werts, C.E., Linn, R.L., & Jöreskog, K.G. (1977)
   A maximum likelihood solution to the errors in variables and errors in equation models.
   Journal ofMultivariate Behavioral Research, **12**, 187–197.

Sewell, W.H., Haller, A.O., & Ohlendorf, G.W. (1970)
   The educational and early occupational status attainment process: revisions and replications.
   American Sociological Review, **35**, 1014–1027.

Sörbom, D. (1974)
A general method for studying differences in factor means and factor structures between groups.
British Journal of Mathematical and Statistical Psychology, **27**, 229–239.

Sörbom, D. (1976)
A statistical model for the measurement of change in true scores.
In D.N.M. de Gruijter & J.L.Th. van der Kamp (Eds.): *Advances in psychological and educational measurement.*
New York: Wiley. 159–169.

Sörbom, D. (1981)
Structural equation models with structured means.
In K.G. Jöreskog & H. Wold (Eds): *Systems under indirect observation: Causality, structure and prediction.*
Amsterdam: North-Holland Publishing Co.

Sörbom, D., & Jöreskog, K.G. (1981)
The use of LISREL in sociological model building.
In E. Borgatta & D.J. Jackson (Eds.) *Factor analysis and measurement in sociological research: A multidimensional perspective.*
Beverly Hills: Sage.

Steiger, J.H. (1990)
Structural model evaluation and modification: An interval estimation approach.
Multivariate Behavioral Research, 25, 173–180.

Tanaka, J.S., & Huba, G.J. (1984)
Confirmatory hierarchical factor analyses of psychological distress measures.
Journal of Personality and Social Psychology, **46**, 621–635.

Theil, H. (1971)
Principles of econometrics.
New York: Wiley.

Tuddenham, R.D., & Snyder, M.M. (1954)
Physical growth of California boys and girls from birth to eighteen years.
Berkeley: University of California Press.

Warren, R.D., White, J.K., & Fuller, W.A. (1974)
  An errors-in-variables analysis of managerial role performance.
  Journal of the American Statistical Association, **69**, 886–893.

Werts, C.E., Rock, D.A., Linn, R.L., & Jöreskog, K.G. (1976)
  Testing the equality of partial correlations.
  American Scientist, **30**, 101–102.

Wheaton, B., Muthén, B., Alwin, D., & Summers, G. (1977)
  Assessing reliability and stability in panel models.
  In D.R. Heise (Ed.): *Sociological Methodology 1977*.
  San Francisco: Jossey-Bass.

Wiley, D.E. (1973)
  The identification problem for structural equation models with unmeasured variables.
  In A.S. Goldberger & O.D. Duncan (Eds.): *Structural equation models in the social sciences*.
  New York: Seminar Press, 69–83.

Wright, S. (1934)
  The method of path coefficients.
  Annals of Mathematical Statistics, **5**, 161–215.

Author index

AUTHOR INDEX

Subject index